22.50/N

23-48

TURBULENT JETS OF AIR, PLASMA, AND REAL GAS

ISSLEDOVANIE TURBULENTNYKH STRUI VOZDUKHA, PLAZMY I REAL'NOGO GAZA

ИССЛЕДОВАНИЕ ТУРБУЛЕНТНЫХ СТРУЙ ВОЗДУХА, ПЛАЗМЫ И РЕАЛЬНОГО ГАЗА

# TURBULENT JETS OF AIR, PLASMA, AND REAL GAS

Edited by G. N. Abramovich
Moscow Aviation Institute

*Translated from Russian*

CONSULTANTS BUREAU · NEW YORK · 1969

Library of Congress Catalog Card Number 69-12508

The original Russian text was published by
Mashinostroenie in Moscow in 1967


Printed in the United States of America

# PREFACE

The operation of many industrial devices, especially aircraft engines, is based on the laws governing the development of turbulent jets.

The use of high-velocity and high-temperature gas flows for aerodynamic research into flow around bodies makes it possible for us to arrive at recommendations for the choice of heat-insulating materials to be used in aircraft. Therefore, the solution of jet problems is of great scientific and practical importance.

The present collection contains the results of work in the area of turbulent-jet gas dynamics. These results have been obtained by the authors of the papers that follow after the appearance of G. N. Abramovich's monograph [2].

The theory of free turbulent jets is extended by V. A. Golubev to the initial region of a very-high-temperature jet (with temperatures as high as $20 \cdot 10^3$ °K). Since physicochemical transformations – dissociation and ionization – occur at these temperatures, theoretical investigations must be based on special forms of the equation of state in which changes in specific heat with temperature are taken into account.

In the solution of this problem, a modification of the Prandtl theory of turbulence is made, since Taylor's theory leads to disagreement with the boundary conditions. The author gives results of measurements of the outer boundary and the temperature field in a plasma jet which are in satisfactory agreement with the theory.

V. I. Bakulev considers a jet of real gas at supercritical pressures, describing the state of the gas by equations of the van der Waals type, and solves the resulting problem for an arbitrary value of the turbulent Prandtl number. The equations describing the propagation of the jet are obtained for both the initial and main regions.

The theory of jets is applied in O. V. Yakovlevskii's paper to the calculation of mixing processes occurring in closed channels, as well as to the determination of the shape of an isobaric chamber.

A. N. Sekundov investigates the propagation of jets in an opposing stream in both a closed channel and in the absence of walls and compares experimental results with theory.

The paper by Chiang Chê-haing is devoted to the study of supersonic jets with underexpansion. A method for the calculation of the gas-dynamic and main regions of the jet is proposed and extensive experimental material is presented for a wide range of variation of the degree of nonsimilarity and Mach numbers, which confirms the suitability of this method.

Integral relations are used in the theoretical work described in the last three papers.

Finally, the papers of the present collection devoted to the study of jets of real gases are supplemented by an appendix written by G. N. Abramovich, V. I. Bakulev, I. S. Makarov, and

B. G. Khudenko in which results of experiments on submerged jets of real gas are given and compared with theory.

G. N. Abramovich

# CONTENTS

High-Temperature Turbulent Jets . . . . . . . . . . 1
by V. A. Golubev

The Calculation of Turbulent Jets of Real Gases . . . . . . . . . . 36
by V. I. Bakulev

The Calculation of the Shape of on Isobaric Mixing Chamber . . . . . . . . . . 87
by O. V. Yakovlevskii

The Propagation of a Turbulent Jet in an Opposing Stream . . . . . . . . . . 99
by A. N. Sekundov

Axially Symmetric Supersonic Turbulent Jets Discharged from a Nozzle with Underexpansion . . . . . . . . . . 111
by Chiang Chê-haing

Turbulent Submerged Jets of Real Gases . . . . . . . . . . 139
by G. N. Abramovich, V. I. Bakulev, I. S. Makarov, and B. G. Khudenko

# HIGH-TEMPERATURE TURBULENT JETS

V. A. Golubev

The continuing progress of aviation technology has created the necessity for a wide range of investigations into high-velocity and high-temperature gas flows. Of particular interest is the study of the propagation of a free plasma jet.

A large number of papers by Soviet and foreign authors has been devoted to problems associated with the study of jets of incompressible liquids, as well as of gas jets at moderate temperatures [1-8, 10-16, 18-20, 24, 26, 30-33]. The general formulation of the problem of the investigation of high-temperature jets was given in [2] and further developed by other authors [13, 14, 16, 21, 35]. In some of these papers [13, 14, 36], instead of the usual equation of state for isobaric flow, the authors have used an approximate equation connecting the density and enthalpy, namely, $\rho = A/i^n$, which considerably simplifies the calculations and at the same time makes it possible to include physico-chemical transformations (dissociation and ionization) that take place in high-temperature gas. In this case, the gas cannot be treated as a one-component fluid having a constant specific heat because the reactions occurring in it produce a change in the molecular weight and gas constant [28, 29]. Therefore, temperature can no longer be used as a characteristic of the gas determining its energy level. Enthalpy which includes both the thermal energy and the energy of formation of the products of a reaction (dissociation or ionization) should now be used as a characteristic of this type.

The enthalpy, density, and other parameters of the working substance at high temperatures were determined by means of a thermodynamic calculation. It was assumed in this that the processes of dissociation, ionization, recombination, etc. taking place in the gas proceed at thermodynamic equilibrium. The composition of the water-vapor plasma was calculated with the corrections for the Coulomb interaction between the ionized particles and electrons taken into account (i.e., the Debye-Hückel correction was introduced).

The thermodynamic calculations were used, in particular, to obtain the variations of enthalpy and density with temperature [23], so that it was possible to determine the connection between density and enthalpy. This relation for water plasma and air plasma was approximated by the analytical expression $\rho = A/i^n$ (where A and n are coefficients which depend on the type of working fluid and which are constant within the temperature interval 300 to $2 \cdot 10^4$°K). The graphs of the function $\log \rho = f(\log i)$ are shown in Fig. 1.

The maximum deviation of the approximate relation from the data of the thermodynamic calculation for water plasma occurs at a temperature of 4000° and is less than 30%, while there is an appreciable deviation from the approximating curve in the interval 2000 to 6000°K. Above 6000°K, the agreement between the approximate relation and the thermodynamic calculation is

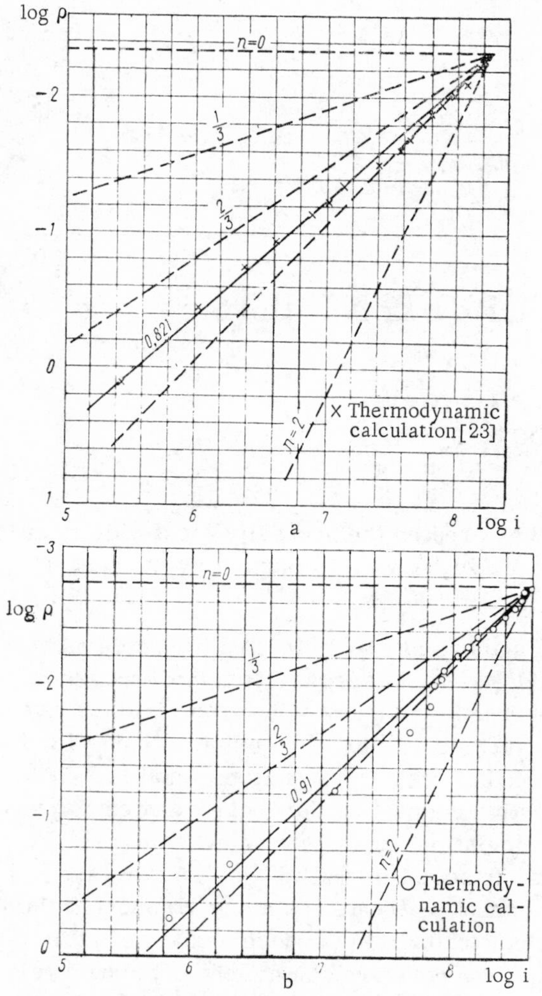


Fig. 1. The variation of density with enthalpy: a) air $\rho = 10^{4.56}/i^{0.821}$; b) water vapor $\rho = 10^{5.13}/i^{0.91}$.

satisfactory. In the case of air plasma, this error is considerably smaller than that for water plasma over the whole range of temperature under consideration.

## 1. Formulation of the Problem and Basic Assumptions

In addition to being of practical interest, the study of very-high-temperature jets is also of theoretical value since an attempt is made here to study the behavior of free turbulence in an ionized gas. As a rule, the theoretical investigation is based on the solution of the usual equations of the mechanics of a continuous medium consisting of a one-component gas. However, as the result of dissociation and ionization processes, the gas becomes a multicomponent medium. Therefore, strictly speaking, we should also consider the equations of self- and thermal diffusion since the existence of concentration and temperature gradients leads to the occurrence of mass and heat diffusion fluxes.

The variations in the composition of the working fluid with temperature are taken into account by means of a new equation of state. On the basis of this, the problem of a jet of ionized gas can be solved with the use of the usual equations for a boundary layer neglecting the equations of diffusion and thermal diffusion, provided the following assumptions are valid:

1. The processes of dissociation and ionization are taken into account through the use of a new equation of state ($\rho = A/i^n$);

2. It is assumed that the jet has the same physical properties as the surrounding medium. The justification for this assumption is the fact that the working fluid (water-vapor plasma) and the surrounding medium (air) have almost the same values of the exponent n characterizing their physical properties (see Fig. 1).

3. Assuming that the jet is completely turbulent, we neglect in the energy equation terms that describe the energy of radiation and in the equations of motion and energy terms that describe molecular viscosity and heat conduction because the latter terms are small by comparison with the turbulence terms.

## 2. The Derivation of the Basic Equations

The case under consideration is of a planar high-temperature gas stream which moves parallel to the x-axis. Figure 2 gives a schematic diagram of the jet. At the point 0, the gas begins to mix with the surrounding medium. Let us suppose that the parameters of the emerging gas (subscript 0) and the parameters of the surrounding medium (subscript H) are given.

Then, the following equations can be written down for the plane-parallel jet of the nonstationary gas stream [2]:

equation of motion

$$\rho\frac{\partial u}{\partial t}+\rho u\frac{\partial u}{\partial x}+\rho v\frac{\partial u}{\partial y}=-\frac{\partial p}{\partial x}+\frac{\partial\tau_{xx}}{\partial x}+\frac{\partial\tau_{xy}}{\partial y}; \tag{1}$$

equation of continuity

$$\frac{\partial\rho}{\partial t}+\frac{\partial}{\partial x}(\rho u)+\frac{\partial}{\partial y}(\rho v)=0; \tag{2}$$

energy equation

$$\rho\frac{\partial}{\partial t}\left(i+\frac{u^2+v^2}{2}\right)+\rho u\frac{\partial}{\partial x}\left(i+\frac{u^2+v^2}{2}\right)+\rho v\frac{\partial}{\partial y}\left(i+\frac{u^2+v^2}{2}\right)=$$

$$=\frac{\partial p}{\partial t}+\frac{\partial}{\partial x}(u\tau_{xx}+v\tau_{xy})+\frac{\partial}{\partial y}(u\tau_{xy}+v\tau_{yy})+\frac{\partial q_x}{\partial x}+\frac{\partial q_y}{\partial y}. \tag{3}$$

When fully turbulent flow is being considered, molecular transport terms can be neglected for an isobaric jet of compressible gas and Eqs. (1)-(3) for the instantaneous quantities can be rewritten as follows:

$$\rho\frac{\partial u}{\partial t}+\rho u\frac{\partial u}{\partial x}+\rho v\frac{\partial u}{\partial y}=0; \tag{4}$$

$$\frac{\partial\rho}{\partial t}+\frac{\partial}{\partial x}(\rho u)+\frac{\partial}{\partial y}(\rho v)=0; \tag{5}$$

$$\rho\frac{\partial}{\partial t}\left(i+\frac{u^2}{2}\right)+\rho u\frac{\partial}{\partial x}\left(i+\frac{u^2}{2}\right)+\rho v\frac{\partial}{\partial y}\left(i+\frac{u^2}{2}\right)=0. \tag{6}$$

In addition, in Eq. (6) we have neglected terms describing the kinetic energy of the transverse-velocity component since it is considerably smaller than the longitudinal component. On the basis of the equation of continuity, Eqs. (5) and (6) can be written as

$$\frac{\partial}{\partial t}(\rho u)+\frac{\partial}{\partial x}(\rho u\cdot u)+\frac{\partial}{\partial y}(\rho v\cdot u)=0; \tag{7}$$

$$\frac{\partial}{\partial t}\left(\rho\frac{u^2}{2}\right)+\frac{\partial}{\partial t}(i\cdot\rho)+\frac{\partial}{\partial x}(i\cdot\rho u)+\frac{\partial}{\partial y}(i\cdot\rho v)+\frac{\partial}{\partial x}\left(\rho u\frac{u^2}{2}\right)+\frac{\partial}{\partial y}\left(\rho v\frac{u^2}{2}\right)=0. \tag{8}$$

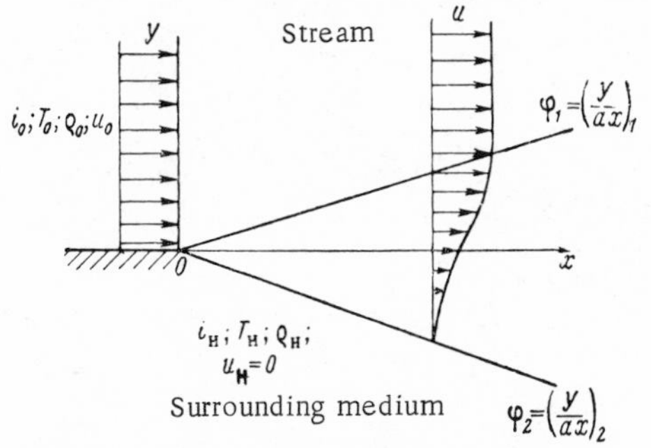


Fig. 2. Schematic diagram of the initial section of the jet.

The solution of the jet problem can be obtained with the help of either the Taylor model of a turbulence or the Prandtl model.

The choice of the Taylor model can be justified by the fact that the velocity and temperature profiles for an incompressible liquid obtained from it are in good agreement with experiment. On the other hand, when the Prandtl model was used to calculate such a jet, the theoretical temperature profile did not agree with experiment. However, as has been shown in [13], the Taylor theory leads to contradictory results when it is applied to compressible fluids. The turbulent friction stress on one boundary of the jet is not equal to zero.

On the basis of this result, we can conclude that the use of the Taylor theory of turbulence becomes incorrect for the description of jets of compressible gases. On the other hand, the Prandtl theory for incompressible fluids can be modified in such a manner that it leads to the same theoretical results as the Taylor theory; moreover, as will be shown below, in the case of jets of compressible gases the modified Prandtl theory [14] does not have the drawbacks that are associated with the use of the Taylor model.

Indeed, if we use the Prandtl turbulence model for an incompressible-fluid jet, we obtain the following formulas for the turbulent friction stress $\tau_T$ and the heat transfer $w_T$:

$$\tau_T = \varepsilon \frac{\partial u}{\partial y} = \rho l_u^2 \left(\frac{\partial u}{\partial y}\right)^2, \tag{9}$$

$$w_T = \lambda_T \frac{\partial T}{\partial y} = c_p \rho l_u l_T \frac{\partial u}{\partial y} \frac{\partial T}{\partial y}, \tag{10}$$

whereas if we use the Taylor model, the expressions for $\tau_T$ and $w_T$ are

$$\tau_T = \frac{1}{2} \rho l_1^2 \left(\frac{\partial u}{\partial y}\right)^2, \tag{11}$$

$$w_T = c_p \rho l_1 l_T \frac{\partial u}{\partial y} \frac{\partial T}{\partial y}, \tag{12}$$

where $l_u$, $l_T$, and $l_1$ are the mixing lengths for momentum, heat, and vorticity transfer, respectively, while $\varepsilon$ and $\lambda_T$ are the coefficients of turbulent exchange and turbulent heat conduction, respectively.

It has been shown in [20] that whenever the Prandtl model has been used in investigation devoted to the study of this problem, the mechanisms of heat and momentum transport were identified, i.e., it was assumed that $l_T = l_u$, and whenever the Taylor model has been used, the mechanisms of vorticity and heat transport were identified, i.e., it was assumed that $l_T = l_1$.

Moreover, in order that the values of the experimental constants be the same in both models of turbulence, it is usually assumed that $l_1 = \sqrt{2} l_u$. Then , formulas (9) and (11) give identical values for the friction stress, whereas formulas (10) and (12) give different values for the heat flux. Because of this, the velocity profiles obtained on the basis of the two models coincide, whereas the temperature profiles are different. As was pointed out above, the temperature profiles calculated on the basis of the Prandtl theory contradict experimental data, while those calculated on the basis of the Taylor theory are in good agreement with experiment. For this reason, the Taylor theory has always been favored. In fact, any attempt at a solution of the problem should be based on the following considerations:

1) it follows from formulas (9) and (10) that the turbulent Prandtl number is

$$\mathrm{Pr}_T = \frac{\varepsilon c_p}{\lambda_T} = \frac{l_u}{l_T}; \tag{13}$$

2) from formulas (12), (9), and (10) with $l_1 = \sqrt{2} l_u$ we find that

$$\lambda_T = 2 c_p \varepsilon \frac{l_T}{l_1},$$

from which we have

$$\frac{l_1}{l_T} = \frac{2 c_p \varepsilon}{\lambda_T} = 2\, \mathrm{Pr}_T; \tag{14}$$

3) it has been found on the basis of Reichardt's experiments that $l_u/l_T = 0.5$, from which we have $Pr_T = 0.5$.

Therefore, if we take the above value of the Prandtl number, formulas (13) and (14) confirm the hypothesis that the mechanisms of heat and vorticity transport are the same, i.e., that $l_T = l_1$, whereas the hypothesis that the mechanisms of heat and momentum transport are the same are not confirmed since in this case $l_T = 2l_u$.

From what has been said above, it follows that the solution of the problem significantly depends on the value adopted for the turbulent Prandtl number. If, in solving the problem according to the Prandtl model we take $Pr_T = 1$ and, consequently, $l_u = l_T$, then the u and T profiles coincide,which is correct for the assumptions used in solving the problem.

The same result is obtained if in using the Taylor model, we take according to (14) $l_1/l_T = 2$ corresponding to $Pr_T = 1$ and not $l_1/l_T = 1$ as has been done by all previous authors. Consequently, we can obtain a correct solution of the problem of an incompressible-fluid jet on the basis of both models of turbulence if we take $Pr_T = 0.5$. For consistency, when solving the problem according to the Prandtl model we must take the mixing length for heat transport to be twice as large as that for momentum transport, whereas when we use the Taylor model, we must take the mixing length for heat transport to be equal to that for vorticity transport.

Proceeding to the case of a compressible gas, we should apply the Prandtl theory because calculations carried out for a compressible gas on the basis of the Taylor model have shown that the solutions so obtained do not satisfy the boundary conditions: The turbulent friction stress must be zero on one of the boundaries of the jet, but this cannot be realized.

Further, if in using the Taylor model of turbulence we assume that the turbulent friction stress is zero on both boundaries, the problem cannot be solved at all.

A modification of the Prandtl theory will be made below. Using this model, we will solve the problem on the basis of the same assumptions that are used in conjuction with the Taylor model. In order to do this, we follow Reynolds and replace the instantaneous values of all quantities in Eqs. (5), (7), and (8) by the sums of the time-averaged and fluctuating components. Here, in addition to introducing the fluctuations of velocity and density, we use van Dreist's assumption [9] that the current density ($\rho u$ and $\rho v$) and enthalpy (i) fluctuate as a single quantity.

After performing the averaging, we obtain the following system of equations:

$$\frac{\partial}{\partial t}(\bar{\rho}\bar{u}+\overline{\rho' u'})+\frac{\partial}{\partial x}(\overline{\rho u}\cdot\bar{u}+\overline{(\rho u)' u'})+\frac{\partial}{\partial y}(\overline{\rho v}\cdot\bar{u}+\overline{(\rho v)' u'})=0, \tag{15}$$

$$\frac{\partial\bar{\rho}}{\partial t}+\frac{\partial}{\partial x}(\overline{\rho u})+\frac{\partial}{\partial y}(\overline{\rho v})=0, \tag{16}$$

$$\frac{\partial}{\partial t}(\bar{\rho}\bar{i}+\overline{\rho' i'})+\frac{\partial}{\partial x}(\overline{\rho u}\cdot\bar{i}+\overline{(\rho u)' i'})+\frac{\partial}{\partial y}(\overline{\rho v}\cdot\bar{i}+\overline{(\rho v)' i'})+\frac{1}{2}\frac{\partial}{\partial t}(\bar{\rho}\bar{u}^2+\bar{\rho}\overline{u'^2}+2\bar{u}\overline{\rho' u'}+\overline{\rho' u'^2})+$$
$$+\frac{1}{2}\frac{\partial}{\partial x}(\overline{\rho u}\cdot\bar{u}^2+\overline{\rho u}\cdot\overline{u'^2}+2\bar{u}\,\overline{(\rho u)' u'}+\overline{(\rho u)' u'^2})+\frac{1}{2}\frac{\partial}{\partial y}(\overline{\rho v}\cdot\bar{u}^2+\overline{\rho v}\cdot\overline{u'^2}+2u\,\overline{(\rho v)' u'}+\overline{(\rho v)' u'^2})=0. \tag{17}$$

Differentiating Eq. (15) and making use of the equation of continuity, we can reduce it to the following form:

$$\bar{\rho}\frac{\partial\bar{u}}{\partial t}+\overline{\rho u}\frac{\partial\bar{u}}{\partial x}+\overline{\rho v}\frac{\partial\bar{u}}{\partial y}=-\frac{\partial}{\partial t}(\overline{\rho' u'})-\frac{\partial}{\partial y}\overline{(\rho v)' u'}. \tag{18}$$

Differentiating expression (17) and transforming it with the help of the equations of continuity (16) and motion (15), we obtain†

$$\bar{\rho}\frac{\partial \bar{i}}{\partial t}+\overline{\rho u}\frac{\partial \bar{i}}{\partial x}+\overline{\rho v}\frac{\partial \bar{i}}{\partial y}=-\frac{\partial}{\partial t}(\overline{\rho' i'})-\overline{\rho' u'}\frac{\partial \bar{u}}{\partial t}-\frac{\partial}{\partial y}\overline{(\rho v)' i'}-\overline{(\rho v)' u'}\frac{\partial \bar{u}}{\partial y}. \tag{19}$$

In Eqs. (18) and (19) we have neglected the partial derivatives of the fluctuation terms since these are small by comparison with the derivatives of the fluctuations with respect to y and we have also neglected derivatives of $\overline{u'^2}/2$ as being small by comparison with $\bar{u}^2/2$ and i. As a result of these transformations, Eqs. (18), (16), and (19) for the averaged stationary motion become

$$\overline{\rho u}\frac{\partial \bar{u}}{\partial x}+\overline{\rho v}\frac{\partial \bar{u}}{\partial y}=-\frac{\partial}{\partial y}\overline{(\rho v)' u'}, \tag{20}$$

$$\frac{\partial}{\partial x}(\overline{\rho u})+\frac{\partial}{\partial y}(\overline{\rho v})=0, \tag{21}$$

$$\overline{\rho u}\frac{\partial \bar{i}}{\partial x}+\overline{\rho v}\frac{\partial \bar{i}}{\partial y}=-\frac{\partial}{\partial y}\overline{(\rho v)' i'}-\overline{(\rho v)' u'}\frac{\partial \bar{u}}{\partial y}. \tag{22}$$

Transforming the right-hand sides of Eqs. (20) and (22) and taking into account that v is a small quantity, we have

$$-\frac{\partial}{\partial y}\overline{(\rho v)' u'}=\frac{\partial \tau_{T}}{\partial y}=-\frac{\partial}{\partial y}\overline{(\bar{\rho}+\rho')(\bar{v}+v')u'}=-\frac{\partial}{\partial y}(\bar{\rho}\overline{v' u'}),$$

$$-\frac{\partial}{\partial y}\overline{(\rho v)' i'}=-\frac{\partial}{\partial y}\overline{(\rho+\rho')(\bar{v}+v')i'}=-\frac{\partial}{\partial y}(\bar{\rho}\overline{v' i'}).$$

Equations (20) and (22) can now be written as

$$\overline{\rho u}\frac{\partial \bar{u}}{\partial x}+\overline{\rho v}\frac{\partial \bar{u}}{\partial y}=-\frac{\partial}{\partial y}(\bar{\rho}\cdot\overline{v' u'}), \tag{23}$$

$$\frac{\partial}{\partial x}(\overline{\rho u})+\frac{\partial}{\partial y}(\overline{\rho v})=0, \tag{24}$$

$$\overline{\rho u}\frac{\partial \bar{i}}{\partial x}+\overline{\rho v}\frac{\partial \bar{i}}{\partial y}=-\frac{\partial}{\partial y}(\bar{\rho}\cdot\overline{v' i'})-\bar{\rho}\cdot\overline{v' u'}\frac{\partial \bar{u}}{\partial y}, \tag{25}$$

where $\frac{\partial \tau_T}{\partial y}=-\frac{\partial}{\partial y}(\bar{\rho}\cdot\overline{v' u'})$ is the derivative of the turbulent friction stress,

$-\frac{\partial}{\partial y}(\bar{\rho}\cdot\overline{v' i'})$ is the derivative of the turbulent heat flux,

$-\overline{\rho v' u'}\frac{\partial \bar{u}}{\partial y}$ is the dissipative term arising from turbulent stresses.

In the same way as in the case of incompressible fluids, we assume that in Eqs. (23) and (25) we have

$$-v'\sim u'\sim l_u\frac{\partial u}{\partial y}\ \text{and}\ i\sim l_i\frac{\partial i}{\partial y},$$

where, on the basis of what has been said above, the mixing lengths $l_u$ for momentum transport and $l_i$ for heat transport have been taken as $l_u = cx$, $l_i = 2cx$ and as constant over the cross section of the jet.

† These transformations are given in greater detail in [9].

Equations (23) and (25) can now be written as

$$\overline{\rho u}\frac{\partial \overline{u}}{\partial x}+\overline{\rho v}\frac{\partial \overline{u}}{\partial y}=c^2x^2\frac{\partial}{\partial y}\left[\overline{\rho}\left(\frac{\partial \overline{u}}{\partial y}\right)^2\right], \tag{26}$$

$$\frac{\partial}{\partial x}(\overline{\rho u})+\frac{\partial}{\partial y}(\overline{\rho v})=0, \tag{27}$$

$$\overline{\rho u}\frac{\partial \overline{i}}{\partial x}+\overline{\rho v}\frac{\partial \overline{i}}{\partial y}=2c^2x^2\frac{\partial}{\partial y}\left[\overline{\rho}\frac{\partial \overline{u}}{\partial y}\frac{\partial \overline{i}}{\partial y}\right]+c^2x^2\overline{\rho}\left(\frac{\partial \overline{u}}{\partial y}\right)^3. \tag{28}$$

In order to have a closed system of equations, we use the relation connecting density and enthalpy

$$\rho=\frac{A}{i^n}. \tag{29}$$

## 3. Transformations of the Basic Equations

In order to solve the system of equations (26)-(29), we will introduce the new variables x and $\varphi=y/ax$ and dimensionless quantities of the form

$$F'(\varphi)=\frac{\overline{\rho u}}{\rho_0 u_0},\quad \vartheta(\varphi)=\frac{\overline{\rho}}{\rho_0},\ \text{and}\ \tau(\varphi)=\frac{\overline{i}}{i_0}, \tag{30}$$

where $a$ is an experimental constant.

Using the current function $\psi=\int\overline{\rho u}\cdot dy=\rho_0 u_0 axF(\varphi)$ and taking into account that

$$\frac{\partial\varphi}{\partial x}=-\frac{\varphi}{x},\quad \frac{\partial\varphi}{\partial y}=\frac{1}{ax}, \tag{31}$$

we obtain the following expressions for the current density components:

$$\left.\begin{aligned}\overline{\rho u}&=\frac{\partial\psi}{\partial y}=\rho_0 u_0 F'(\varphi),\\ \overline{\rho v}&=-\frac{\partial\psi}{\partial x}=a\rho_0 u_0[\varphi F'(\varphi)-F(\varphi)].\end{aligned}\right\} \tag{32}$$

Since

$$\frac{\partial}{\partial x}=\frac{\partial}{\partial\varphi}\frac{\partial\varphi}{\partial x},\qquad \frac{\partial}{\partial y}=\frac{\partial}{\partial\varphi}\frac{\partial\varphi}{\partial y}, \tag{33}$$

we use the equality

$$\overline{\rho u}=\overline{\rho}\,\overline{u}+\overline{\rho' u'}=\overline{\rho}\,\overline{u}+l_i l_u\frac{\partial\overline{\rho}}{\partial y}\frac{\partial\overline{u}}{\partial y}=\overline{\rho}\,\overline{u}+2c^2x^2\frac{\partial\overline{\rho}}{\partial y}\frac{\partial\overline{u}}{\partial y}, \tag{34}$$

and the relation

$$2c^2x^2=a^3x^2, \tag{35}$$

which also holds as in the case of an incompressible fluid, to obtain the longitudinal velocity component

$$\frac{\overline{u}}{u_0}=\frac{\overline{\rho u}-a^3x^2\dfrac{\partial\overline{\rho}}{\partial y}\dfrac{\partial\overline{u}}{\partial y}}{\overline{\rho}u_0}=\frac{F'}{\vartheta}-a\frac{\vartheta'}{\vartheta}\frac{d}{d\varphi}\left(\frac{\overline{u}}{u_0}\right). \tag{36}$$

Making use of the continuity equation

$$\vartheta = \frac{1}{\tau^n}, \quad (37)$$

we can obtain an approximate form for Eq. (36) valid when a ≪ 1†

$$\frac{\bar{u}}{u_0} \simeq F'\tau^n. \quad (38)$$

With relations (31), (32), (33), and (35) taken into account, Eqs. (26) and (28) become

$$\rho_0 u_0 F \frac{du}{d\varphi} + \frac{1}{2}\left[\frac{d\rho}{d\varphi}\left(\frac{du}{d\varphi}\right)^2 + 2\rho\frac{du}{d\varphi}\frac{d^2u}{d\varphi^2}\right] = 0, \quad (39)$$

$$\rho_0 u_0 F \frac{di}{d\varphi} + \frac{d\rho}{d\varphi}\frac{du}{d\varphi}\frac{di}{d\varphi} + \rho\frac{d^2u}{d\varphi^2}\frac{di}{d\varphi} + \rho\frac{du}{d\varphi}\frac{d^2i}{d\varphi^2} + \frac{1}{2}\rho\left(\frac{du}{d\varphi}\right)^3 = 0. \quad (40)$$

For formulas (38) and (30), we have

$$\left.\begin{aligned} &\frac{du}{d\varphi} = u_0\tau^n\left(F'' + nF'\frac{\tau'}{\tau}\right), \\ &\frac{d^2u}{d\varphi^2} = u_0\tau^n\left[F''' + 2nF''\frac{\tau'}{\tau} + (n^2 - n)F'\left(\frac{\tau'}{\tau}\right)^2 + nF'\frac{\tau''}{\tau}\right], \\ &\frac{d\rho}{d\varphi} = \rho_0\vartheta' = -\rho_0 n\frac{\tau'}{\tau^{n+1}}, \quad \frac{di}{d\varphi} = i_0\tau', \quad \frac{d^2i}{d\varphi^2} = i_0\tau''. \end{aligned}\right\} \quad (41)$$

Substituting these expressions into Eqs. (39) and (40), we obtain after some transformation

$$F''' + \frac{3}{2}nF''\frac{\tau'}{\tau} + \left(\frac{n^2}{2} - n\right)F'\left(\frac{\tau'}{\tau}\right)^2 + nF'\frac{\tau''}{\tau} + F = 0, \quad (42)$$

$$F''' + nF''\frac{\tau'}{\tau} + F''\frac{\tau''}{\tau'} - nF'\left(\frac{\tau'}{\tau}\right)^2 + 2nF'\frac{\tau''}{\tau} + F + \frac{u_0^2}{2i_0}\frac{1}{\tau'\tau^n}\left[\frac{d}{d\varphi}(F'\tau^n)\right]^3 = 0. \quad (43)$$

For subsonic jets with high initial preheating, i.e., jets for which $u_0^2 \ll 2i_0$, the last term in Eq. (43) can be neglected. Subtracting Eq. (43) without its last term from Eq. (42) and transforming the expression obtained, we have

$$\frac{1}{2}n\frac{\tau'}{\tau}\left(F'' + nF'\frac{\tau'}{\tau}\right) - \frac{\tau''}{\tau'}\left(F'' + nF'\frac{\tau'}{\tau}\right) = 0$$

or

$$\left(\frac{1}{2}n\frac{\tau'}{\tau} - \frac{\tau''}{\tau'}\right)\left(F'' + nF'\frac{\tau'}{\tau}\right) = 0. \quad (44)$$

An examination of Eq. (44) shows that if try to satisfy this equation by taking the second factor equal to zero, we will obtain a trivial solution which is physically meaningless. Indeed, the second factor of Eq. (44) is identical to the expression for the velocity gradient $du/d\varphi$ which cannot be equal to zero over the whole of the cross section of the jet.

---

† The exact solution is given in Section 6.

Therefore, let us equate to zero the first factor of Eq. (44), namely,

$$\frac{1}{2}n\frac{\tau'}{\tau}-\frac{\tau''}{\tau'}=0. \tag{45}$$

On the basis of the energy equation (45) and (42) or (43), we obtain the equation of motion

$$F'''+\frac{3}{2}nF''\frac{\tau'}{\tau}+(n^2-n)F'\left(\frac{\tau'}{\tau}\right)^2+F=0. \tag{46}$$

Setting $\rho=\text{const.}$ and taking the equation

$$\frac{\vartheta'}{\vartheta}=-n\frac{\tau'}{\tau}$$

into account, we will reduce Eqs. (45) and (46) to those for an incompressible fluid

$$\tau''=0, \tag{47}$$

$$F'''+F=0. \tag{48}$$

From the equation

$$\overline{\rho v}=\bar{\rho}\bar{v}+\overline{\rho' v'}=\bar{\rho}\bar{v}+2c^2x^2\frac{\partial\bar{\rho}}{\partial y}\frac{\partial\bar{u}}{\partial y}$$

we will obtain the expression for the transverse velocity component

$$\frac{\bar{v}}{u_0}=\frac{\overline{\rho v}}{\bar{\rho}u_0}-\frac{a^3x^2\frac{d\bar{\rho}}{d\varphi}\frac{d\bar{u}}{d\varphi}\frac{1}{a^2x^2}}{\bar{\rho}u_0},$$

or, after some transformations,

$$\frac{\bar{v}}{au_0}=\tau^n\left[(\varphi F'-F)+n\frac{\tau'}{\tau}\left(F''+nF'\frac{\tau'}{\tau}\right)\right]. \tag{49}$$

The turbulent friction stress across the jet cross-section can be obtained from Eq. (26),

$$\frac{\partial\bar{\tau}_T}{\partial y}=c^2x^2\frac{\partial}{\partial y}\left[\bar{\rho}\left(\frac{\partial\bar{u}}{\partial y}\right)^2\right],$$

which on the basis of Eqs. (29), (30), (31), (33), (37), and (41) becomes after an integration

$$\frac{\tau_T}{a\frac{\rho_0u_0^2}{2}}=\tau^n\left[F''(\varphi)+nF'(\varphi)\frac{\tau'}{\tau}\right]^2. \tag{50}$$

Here, the integration constant is zero if the integration is started on the boundary where $\tau_T=0$ and $\partial u/\partial y=0$.

The turbulent heat flux in the transverse direction with the frictional heat neglected is given by Eq. (28), namely,

$$\frac{\partial\overline{W}_T}{\partial y}=2c^2x^2\frac{\partial}{\partial y}\left(\bar{\rho}\frac{\partial\bar{u}}{\partial y}\frac{\partial\bar{i}}{\partial y}\right).$$

We can obtain the equation of heat transfer by performing analogous transformations and an integration,

$$\frac{W_T}{a\rho_0 u_0 i_0} = \tau' \left[ F''(\varphi) + nF'(\varphi)\frac{\tau'}{\tau} \right]. \tag{51}$$

In the case of constant density ($\vartheta = 1$), the expressions for the longitudinal and transverse velocity components and for the turbulent friction stress and heat transfer reduce to the well-known [1] expressions for an incompressible fluid,

$$\frac{u}{u_0} = F'(\varphi), \tag{52}$$

$$\frac{v}{au_0} = \varphi F'(\varphi) - F(\varphi), \tag{53}$$

$$\frac{\tau_T}{a\frac{\rho_0 u_0^2}{2}} = [F''(\varphi)]^2, \tag{54}$$

$$\frac{W_T}{a\rho_0 u_0 i_0} = \tau' F'(\varphi). \tag{55}$$

By solving Eqs. (45) and (46), we can obtain the velocity and enthalpy profiles for a plane-parallel boundary layer of a turbulent gas jet.

## 4. Solutions of the Energy Equation

Let us take

$$z = \frac{\tau'}{\tau^{\frac{n}{2}}}; \tag{56}$$

then, on the basis of Eq. (45), we have

$$z' = -\frac{\tau'}{\tau^{\frac{n}{2}}}\left(\frac{1}{2}n\frac{\tau'}{\tau} - \frac{\tau''}{\tau'}\right) = 0.$$

Consequently, taking

$$\frac{d\tau}{\tau^{\frac{n}{2}}} = c_1' d\varphi, \tag{57}$$

we find after an integration that

$$\frac{2}{2-n}\tau^{\frac{2-n}{2}} = c_1'\varphi + c_2'. \tag{58}$$

The boundary conditions for the inner boundary of the boundary layer are $i = i_0$, i.e.,

$$\tau = 1 \text{ when } \varphi = \varphi_1, \tag{59}$$

and for the outer boundary they are $i = i_H$, i.e.,

$$\tau = \tau_H \text{ when } \varphi = \varphi_2. \tag{60}$$

On the basis of conditions (59) and (60), we have

$$c_1' = \frac{2}{2-n}\,\frac{1-\tau_H^{\frac{2-n}{2}}}{\varphi_1-\varphi_2}, \tag{61}$$

$$c_2' = \frac{2}{2-n}\left(1-\frac{1-\tau_H^{\frac{2-n}{2}}}{\varphi_1-\varphi_2}\right). \tag{62}$$

Substituting these expressions into Eq. (58), we obtain the expression for the enthalpy profile

$$\tau = \left[\eta + (1-\eta)\,\tau_H^{\frac{2-n}{2}}\right]^{\frac{2}{2-n}}, \tag{63}$$

where

$$\eta = \frac{\varphi-\varphi_2}{\varphi_1-\varphi_2}.$$

With n=2 we have

$$\frac{\tau'}{\tau} = c_1', \tag{64}$$

and after an integration we obtain

$$\ln\tau = c_1'\varphi + c_2'.$$

With the help of the boundary conditions (59) and (60) we will find the integration constants

$$c_1' = -\frac{\ln\tau_H}{\varphi_1-\varphi_2}, \tag{65}$$

$$c_2' = \frac{\ln\tau_H}{\varphi_1-\varphi_2}\,\varphi_1 \tag{66}$$

and the function

$$\tau = \tau_H^{1-\eta}. \tag{67}$$

With n=0, Eq. (45) reduces to the equation for an incompressible fluid and its solution then has the form

$$\tau = \eta + (1-\eta)\,\tau_H. \tag{68}$$

## 5. Solution of the Equation of Motion

Let us study several particular solutions of the equation of motion as we were unable to find a general solution (for arbitrary n).

1. With n=2, Eq. (46) becomes

$$F'''(\varphi) + 3F''(\varphi)\frac{\tau'}{\tau} + 2F'(\varphi)\left(\frac{\tau'}{\tau}\right)^2 + F(\varphi) = 0. \tag{69}$$

Introducing the new variable

$$\eta = \frac{\varphi - \varphi_2}{\varphi_1 - \varphi_2},$$

we obtain in place of (69)

$$F'''(\eta) + 3t \cdot F''(\eta) + 2t^2 \cdot F'(\eta) + b_*^3 \cdot F(\eta) = 0, \tag{70}$$

where

$$\frac{\tau'}{\tau} = -\frac{\ln \tau_H}{\varphi_1 - \varphi_2} = \frac{\ln \frac{i_0}{i_H}}{\varphi_1 - \varphi_2} = \frac{t}{b_*} \text{ and } b_* = \varphi_1 - \varphi_2.$$

The characteristic equation of the equation of motion

$$k^3 + 3tk^2 + 2t^2k + b_*^3 = 0$$

can be reduced by the substitution $z = k + t$ to the form

$$z^3 + 3pz + 2q = 0, \tag{71}$$

where

$$2q = b_*^3, \quad 3p = -t^2.$$

The roots of Eq. (71), are

$$z_1 = \xi + \zeta, \quad z_2 = \varepsilon_1\xi + \varepsilon_2\zeta, \quad z_3 = \varepsilon_2\xi + \varepsilon_1\zeta,$$

where

$$\varepsilon_{1,2} = -\frac{1}{2} \pm i\frac{\sqrt{3}}{2}, \quad \xi = \sqrt[3]{-q + \sqrt{q^2 + p^3}},$$

$$\zeta = \sqrt[3]{-q - \sqrt{q^2 + p^3}}.$$

It should be noted that the solution of Eq. (70) is meaningful only when $D > 0$, where $D = q^2 + p^3$.

Setting

$$\alpha_1 = z_1 - t, \quad \alpha_2 = -\frac{1}{2}z_1 - t, \quad \beta = \frac{\sqrt{3}}{2}(\xi - \zeta),$$

we find that the roots of the characteristic equation are

$$k_1 = \alpha_1, \quad k_2 = \alpha_2 + i\beta, \quad k_3 = \alpha_2 - i\beta. \tag{72}$$

The solution of the differential equation (70) corresponding to the roots (72) is of the form

$$F(\eta) = c_1 e^{\alpha_1 \eta} + c_2 e^{\alpha_2 \eta} \cos \beta\eta + c_3 e^{\alpha_2 \eta} \sin \beta\eta. \tag{73}$$

The integration constants $c_1$, $c_2$, and $c_3$, as well as the inner and outer ordinates, $\varphi_1$ and $\varphi_2$, of the boundary layer of the jet are found from the same five boundary conditions as in the case of an incompressible fluid.

On the inner boundary of the jet (where $\varphi = \varphi_1$ or $\eta = 1$) we have

$$\left.\begin{aligned}
&u = u_0, \quad \rho = \rho_0, \text{ i.e., } \quad F'(\varphi_1) = 1 \text{ or } F'(1) = b_*;\\
&\frac{\partial u}{\partial y} = 0, \text{ i.e., } F''(\varphi_1) = -2\frac{t}{b_*} \text{ or } F''(1) = -2b_* t;\\
&v = 0, \text{ i.e., } F(\varphi_1) = \varphi_1 \text{ or } F(1) = \varphi_1.\\
&\text{On the outer boundary of the jet (where } \varphi = \varphi_2 \text{ or } \eta = 0\text{) we have}\\
&u = 0, \quad \rho = \rho_H, \text{ i.e., } F'(\varphi_2) = 0 \text{ or } F'(0) = 0;\\
&\frac{\partial u}{\partial y} = 0, \text{ i.e., } F''(\varphi_2) = 0 \text{ or } F''(0) = 0.
\end{aligned}\right\} \quad (74)$$

On the basis of these boundary conditions and Eq. (73), we can write

$$\begin{aligned}
&F'(1) = c_1 e^{\alpha_1}\alpha_1 + c_2 e^{\alpha_2}\gamma_1 + c_3 e^{\alpha_2}\gamma_2 = b_*,\\
&F''(1) = c_1 e^{\alpha_1}\alpha_1^2 + c_2 e^{\alpha_2}(\alpha_2\gamma_1 - \beta\gamma_2) + c_3 e^{\alpha_2}(\alpha_2\gamma_2 + \beta\gamma_1) = -2b_* t,\\
&F(1) = c_1 e^{\alpha_1} + c_2 e^{\alpha_2}\cos\beta + c_3 e^{\alpha_2}\sin\beta = \varphi_1,\\
&F'(0) = c_1\alpha_1 + c_2\alpha_2 + c_3\beta = 0,\\
&F''(0) = c_1\alpha_1^2 + c_2(\alpha_2^2 - \beta^2) + c_3 2\alpha_2\beta = 0,
\end{aligned} \qquad (75)$$

where

$$\gamma_1 = \alpha_2\cos\beta - \beta\sin\beta,$$
$$\gamma_2 = \alpha_2\sin\beta + \beta\cos\beta.$$

It should be noted that the solution of the system of transcendental equations (75) is associated with a number of difficulties since the coefficients $\alpha_1$, $\alpha_2$, $\beta$, etc. are themselves functions of the initial heating $\tau_H$ and the width $b_*$ of the jet. Therefore, we will propose the following method of solution: The fourth equation of system (75) yields

$$c_1 = -c_2\frac{\alpha_2}{\alpha_1} - c_3\frac{\beta}{\alpha_1}.$$

Substituting this expression into the fifth equation of the system, we obtain

$$c_1 = c_3\beta\frac{\alpha_1 - 2\alpha_2}{\alpha_2^2 - \alpha_1\alpha_2 - \beta^2} \quad \text{and} \quad c_2 = c_3\frac{\beta}{\alpha_1}\,\frac{\alpha_2^2 + \beta^2}{\alpha_2^2 - \alpha_1\alpha_2 - \beta^2}.$$

Next, after the substitution of the expressions for $c_1$ and $c_2$ into the second equation of system (75) and some transformations, we find that

$$c_3 = -\frac{2b_* t(\alpha_2^2 - \alpha_1\alpha_2 - \beta^2)}{(\alpha_2^2 + \beta^2)M}, \qquad (76)$$

after which we can determine $c_1$ and $c_2$

$$c_2 = -\frac{2b_* t\beta(\alpha_1 - 2\alpha_2)}{(\alpha_2^2 + \beta^2)M}, \qquad (77)$$

$$c_1 = -\frac{2b_* t\beta}{\alpha_1 M}, \qquad (78)$$

where

$$M = \alpha_1 \beta e^{\alpha_1} + e^{\alpha_2} (\alpha_2 \gamma_2 - \alpha_1 \gamma_2 - \beta \gamma_1).$$

Substituting the values of $c_1$, $c_2$, and $c_3$ into the first equation of system (75), we obtain the formula

$$-\frac{2t}{M}\left\{\beta e^{\alpha_1} + \frac{e^{\alpha_2}}{\alpha_2^2 + \beta^2}\left[(\alpha_1 - 2\alpha_2)\beta\gamma_1 + (\alpha_2^2 - \alpha_1\alpha_2 - \beta^2)\gamma_2\right]\right\} = 1, \tag{79}$$

from which we find the solution (i.e., the value of $b_*$) of this system. In general, the determination of $c_1$, $c_2$, $c_3$, $\varphi_1$, and $\varphi_2$ can be carried out in the following manner.

For a given initial heating of the jet $\tau_H$ or $t = \ln(i_0/i_H)$, we take several values of $b_* = \varphi_1 - \varphi_2$ and find the values of $\xi$, $\zeta$, $\alpha_1$, $\alpha_2$, $\beta$, $\gamma_1$, $\gamma_2$, etc. from the formulas given above for each of the values of $b_*$. Substituting these values into formula (79), we find the value of $b_*$ which satisfies Eq. (79). Next, using the value of $b_*$ found in this way we recalculate the values of $\xi$, $\zeta$, etc. and then use formulas (76), (77), and (78) to find the values of $c_1$, $c_2$, $c_3$. The inner boundary of the jet is determined from the third equation of system (75),

$$\varphi_1 = -\frac{2b_* t}{M}\left\{\frac{\beta}{\alpha_1} e^{\alpha_1} + \frac{e^{\alpha_2}}{\alpha_2^2 + \beta^2}\left[\beta(\alpha_1 - 2\alpha_2)\cos\beta + (\alpha_2^2 - \alpha_1\alpha_2 - \beta^2)\sin\beta\right]\right\}. \tag{80}$$

Substituting the values of the constants $c_1$, $c_2$, etc. into Eq. (70), we obtain an expression from which we can find the function $F(\eta)$ and its derivatives.

We can determine the profile of the longitudinal velocity component in the boundary layer of a high-temperature jet by means of formula (38),

$$\frac{u}{u_0} = F'(\varphi)\,\tau^2, \tag{81}$$

the transverse velocity component by means of Eq. (49),

$$\frac{v}{a u_0} = \tau^2\left\{[\varphi F'(\varphi) - F(\varphi)] + 2\frac{t}{b_*}\left[F''(\varphi) + 2F'(\varphi)\frac{t}{b_*}\right]\right\} \tag{82}$$

and the velocity gradient by means of formula (27),

$$\frac{1}{u_0}\frac{du}{d\varphi} = \tau^2\left[F''(\varphi) + 2F'(\varphi)\frac{t}{b_*}\right]. \tag{83}$$

In order to determine the apparent turbulent friction stress, we make use of Eq. (50) which can be written as

$$\frac{\tau_T}{a\dfrac{\rho_0 u_0^2}{2}} = \tau^2\left[F''(\varphi) + 2F'(\varphi)\frac{t}{b_*}\right]^2. \tag{84}$$

The calculations performed with the help of these formulas are given in Tables 1 and 2. These tables show that the turbulent friction stress on both boundaries of the jets is zero.

According to the Taylor model of turbulence, the apparent turbulent friction stress in the boundary layer of a jet is given by the expression

$$\frac{\partial \bar{\tau}_T}{\partial y} = 2c^2 x^2 \bar{\rho}\,\frac{\partial \bar{u}}{\partial y}\,\frac{\partial^2 \bar{u}}{\partial y^2}, \tag{85}$$

## TABLE 1

$n=2$; $b_*=5.98$; $\varphi_1=3.3$; $\tau_н=1.757\cdot10^{-3}$; $c_1=-3.425$; $c_2=-33.55$; $c_3=-40.55$

| $\eta$ | $\varphi$ | $\tau$ | $F(\varphi)$ | $F'(\varphi)$ | $F''(\varphi)$ | $F'''(\varphi)$ | $\frac{u}{u_0}$ | $\frac{1}{u_0}\frac{du}{d\varphi}$ | $\frac{v}{au_0}$ | $\frac{\tau_T}{a\frac{\varrho_0 u_0^2}{2}}$ | $\frac{W_T}{a\varrho_0 u_0 i_0}$ |
|---|---|---|---|---|---|---|---|---|---|---|---|
| 0.0 | —2.65 | $1.757\cdot10^{-3}$ | —36.98 | 0.0 | 0.0 | 36.97 | 0.0 | 0.0 | $1.143\cdot10^{-4}$ | 0.0 | 0.0 |
| 0.1 | —2,052 | $3,31\cdot10^{-3}$ | —36,09 | 3.58 | 8,58 | 0,679 | $3.93\cdot10^{-5}$ | $1.8\cdot10^{-4}$ | $6,89\cdot10^{-4}$ | $2.86\cdot10^{-3}$ | 0.0566 |
| 0.2 | —1.454 | 0.0063 | —32.52 | 8.23 | 6,33 | —6.18 | $3.28\cdot10^{-4}$ | $9.5\cdot10^{-4}$ | $2.81\cdot10^{-3}$ | 0,02246 | 0.159 |
| 0.3 | —0.856 | 0.0118 | —26.7 | 10.9 | 2,59 | —6,15 | $1,53\cdot10^{-3}$ | 0,0036 | 0.01 | 0,0922 | 0.322 |
| 0.4 | —0,258 | 0.0224 | —19,88 | 11,42 | —0.526 | —4.17 | $5,73\cdot10^{-3}$ | 0,0119 | 0.0335 | 0.283 | 0,5625 |
| 0,5 | 0.34 | 0.042 | —13.29 | 10.48 | —2,485 | —2,48 | 0,0185 | 0,0348 | 0,103 | 0,685 | 0.875 |
| 0,6 | 0.94 | 0,0794 | —7,55 | 8,66 | —3,48 | —0,912 | 0.0545 | 0,094 | 0.2965 | 1,392 | 1,25 |
| 0,7 | 1.53 | 0,1493 | —3,0 | 6,48 | —3,7 | 0,1216 | 0,1445 | 0.224 | 0,76 | 2,24 | 1,584 |
| 0,8 | 2.13 | 0.282 | 0.25 | 4,34 | —3.3 | 0,779 | 0,345 | 0.471 | 1.7 | 2,76 | 1.76 |
| 0,9 | 2.73 | 0,53 | 2.275 | 2,47 | —2.83 | 1.13 | 0,691 | 0,674 | 2,67 | 1,613 | 1.348 |
| 1.0 | 3,33 | 1.0 | 3.33 | 1.0 | —2.12 | 1,191 | 1.0 | 0.0 | 0.0 | 0.0 | 0.0 |

## TABLE 2

$n=2$; $b_*=4.986$; $\varphi_1=2.78$; $\tau_н=1.049\cdot10^{-2}$; $c_1=-1.52$; $c_2=-11.85$; $c_3=-10.77$

| $\eta$ | $\varphi$ | $\tau$ | $F(\varphi)$ | $F'(\varphi)$ | $F''(\varphi)$ | $F'''(\varphi)$ | $\frac{u}{u_0}$ | $\frac{1}{u_0}\frac{du}{d\varphi}$ | $\frac{v}{au_0}$ | $\frac{\tau_T}{a\frac{\varrho_0 u_0^2}{2}}$ | $\frac{W_T}{a\varrho_0 u_0 i_0}$ |
|---|---|---|---|---|---|---|---|---|---|---|---|
| 0,0 | —2.206 | 0.01049 | —13.37 | 0.0 | 0.0 | 13.4 | 0,0 | 0.0 | $1.475\cdot10^{-3}$ | 0.0 | 0.0 |
| 0,1 | —1.707 | 0.0166 | —13.18 | 1.057 | 3.38 | 2,14 | $2.91\cdot10^{-4}$ | 0.0015 | $5.8\cdot10^{-3}$ | $7.77\cdot10^{-3}$ | 0.0803 |
| 0.2 | —1,209 | 0,0261 | —12,21 | 2.76 | 3,34 | —1,63 | $1,885\cdot10^{-3}$ | 0,0058 | 0.0165 | 0,0478 | 0.2 |
| 0,3 | —0,71 | 0.0411 | —10.43 | 4,185 | 2.21 | —2,63 | $7.07\cdot10^{-3}$ | 0,0166 | 0,043 | 0,164 | 0.3685 |
| 0.4 | —0.211 | 0,0649 | —8.14 | 4.96 | 0.885 | —2.59 | 0,0209 | 0.0418 | 0,1062 | 0,416 | 0.588 |
| 0.5 | 0.289 | 0.1022 | —5.604 | 5.34 | —0,299 | —2.11 | 0.05575 | 0,099 | 0,254 | 0.932 | 0.879 |
| 0.6 | 0.787 | 0,1615 | —3,15 | 4.7 | —1,184 | —1.474 | 0,1228 | 0.193 | 0,53 | 1,422 | 1,087 |
| 0,7 | 1.284 | 0,255 | —0,955 | 3.92 | —1.765 | —0,824 | 0,255 | 0,351 | 1,028 | 1,884 | 1.252 |
| 0,8 | 1,784 | 0,401 | 0,767 | 3.0 | —2,02 | —0,249 | 0.482 | 0.556 | 1.75 | 1,914 | 1.258 |
| 0.9 | 2,284 | 0,634 | 2,012 | 1,99 | —2.025 | 0,213 | 0,801 | 0.647 | 2.2 | 1.034 | 0,928 |
| 1.0 | 2.78 | 1.0 | 2,77 | 1,0 | —1,83 | 0.548 | 1.0 | 0.0 | 0.0 | 0.0 | 0.0 |

which after some transformations can be written as follows for the case n = 1:

$$\frac{\tau_T}{a\frac{\rho_0 u_0^2}{2}} = -2\int_c^{\varphi} \tau F(\varphi)\left[F''(\varphi)+F'(\varphi)\frac{t}{b_*}\right]d\varphi. \tag{86}$$

Taking the lower limit of integration to be the outer boundary of the jet $\varphi_2$, where $\partial u/\partial y = 0$, $\tau_T = 0$, and introducing the variable $\eta$, we can rewrite Eq. (96) as

$$\frac{\tau_T}{a\frac{\rho_0 u_0^2}{2}} = -\frac{2}{b_*}\int_0^{\eta} \tau_H^{1-\eta} F(\eta)\left[F''(\eta)+F'(\eta)t\right]d\eta. \tag{87}$$

The expression for $\tau_H^{1-\eta}$ can be rewritten as

$$\tau_H^{1-\eta} = \tau_H\tau_H^{-\eta} = \tau_H e^{-\eta\ln\tau_H} = \tau_H e^{t\eta}.$$

Substituting this expression, as well as the equations for the function $F(\eta)$ and its derivatives into Eq. (87) [the function $F(\eta)$ with n=1 for the Taylor turbulence model is given in [13], we obtain after the necessary transformations

$$\frac{\tau_T}{a\frac{\rho_0 u_0^2}{2}} = -\frac{2\tau_H}{b_*}\left\{c_1^2 m_1\int_0^{\eta} e^{k_1\eta}d\eta + [c_2(m_1+m_2)+c_3m_3]\int_0^{\eta} e^{k_2\eta}\cos\beta\eta d\eta + \right.$$

$$+c_1[c_3(m_1+m_2)-c_2m_3]\int_0^{\eta} e^{k_2\eta}\sin\beta\eta d\eta + c_2(c_2m_2+c_3m_3)\int_0^{\eta} e^{k_3\eta}\cos^2\beta\eta d\eta + [c_3(c_2m_2+c_3m_3)+$$

$$+c_2(c_3m_2-c_2m_3)]\int_0^{\eta} e^{k_3\eta}\sin\beta\eta\cos\beta\eta d\eta + c_3(c_3m_2-c_2m_3)\int_0^{\eta} e^{k_3\eta}\sin^2\beta\eta d\eta, \tag{88}$$

where

$$m_1 = \alpha_1(\alpha_1+t), \qquad k_1 = 2\alpha_1+t,$$
$$m_2 = \alpha_2^2-\beta^2+\alpha_2 t, \qquad k_2 = \alpha_1+\alpha_2+t,$$
$$m_3 = \beta(2\alpha_2+t), \qquad k_3 = 2\alpha_2+t.$$

The expressions for $c_1$, $c_2$, $c_3$ for n=1 are given in [13]. If in Eq. (88) we perform the transformations

$$\cos^2\beta\eta = \frac{1}{2}(1+\cos 2\beta\eta),$$

$$\sin\beta\eta\cos\beta\eta = \frac{1}{2}\sin 2\beta\eta,$$

$$\sin^2\beta\eta = \frac{1}{2}(1-\cos 2\beta\eta),$$

then Eq. (88) can be integrated to give

$$\frac{\tau_T}{a\frac{\rho_0 u_0^2}{2}} = -\frac{2\tau_H}{b_*}\left\{c_1^2 m_1\left(\frac{e^{k_1\eta}}{k_1}-\frac{1}{k_1}\right) + c_1[c_2(m_1+m_2)+c_3m_3]\left[\frac{e^{k_2\eta}}{k_2^2+\beta^2}(k_2\cos\beta\eta+\beta\sin\beta\eta) - \frac{k_2}{k_2^2+\beta^2}\right]+\right.$$

$$+c_1[c_3(m_1+m_2)-c_2m_3]\left[\frac{e^{k_2\eta}}{k_2^2+\beta^2}(k_2\sin\beta\eta-\beta\cos\beta\eta)+\frac{\beta}{k_2^2+\beta^2}\right]+\frac{c_2(c_2m_2+c_3m_3)}{2}\left[\frac{e^{k_3\eta}}{k_3}-\frac{1}{k_3}+\right.$$

TABLE 3

| $\eta$ | $n=1$ | | | | | | | |
|---|---|---|---|---|---|---|---|---|
| | $\tau_H=1.757\cdot10^{-3}$ | | $\tau_H=2.84\cdot10^{-3}$ | | $\tau_H=7.23\cdot10^{-3}$ | | $\tau_H=1.049\cdot10^{-2}$ | |
| | $\frac{1}{u_0}\frac{du}{d\varphi}$ | $\frac{\tau_T}{a\frac{\varrho_0u_0^2}{2}}$ | $\frac{1}{u_0}\frac{du}{d\varphi}$ | $\frac{\tau_T}{a\frac{\varrho_0u_0^2}{2}}$ | $\frac{1}{u_0}\frac{du}{d\varphi}$ | $\frac{\tau_T}{a\frac{\varrho_0u_0^2}{2}}$ | $\frac{1}{u_0}\frac{du}{d\varphi}$ | $\frac{\tau_T}{a\frac{\varrho_0u_0^2}{2}}$ |
| 0,0 | 0.0 | 0.0 | 0.0 | 0.0 | 0,0 | 0.0 | 0.0 | 0.0 |
| 0.1 | 0.01136 | 0.0488 | 0.01415 | 0.0478 | 0,0226 | 0.0467 | 0.0249 | 0.0424 |
| 0.2 | 0.0322 | 0.2367 | 0.039 | 0.2237 | 0,059 | 0.236 | 0.063 | 0.1955 |
| 0,3 | 0.0668 | 0.626 | 0.0794 | 0,6017 | 0.1115 | 0,58 | 0.1183 | 0,4975 |
| 0.4 | 0.1223 | 1.25 | 0.1406 | 0.2067 | 0,1896 | 1,123 | 0.1935 | 0.94 |
| 0.5 | 0,201 | 2.08 | 0.2265 | 1.9697 | 0.2865 | 1,81 | 0.286 | 1.48 |
| 0.6 | 0.304 | 2.972 | 0.3306 | 2.7547 | 0.394 | 2.49 | 0.366 | 2.001 |
| 0.7 | 0.419 | 3.75 | 0,438 | 3.3697 | 0.488 | 2,99 | 0.49 | 2.36 |
| 0.8 | 0.48 | 4.12 | 0.493 | 3.6057 | 0.505 | 3.17 | 0.503 | 2.55 |
| 0.9 | 0.405 | 3.892 | 0.4035 | 3,4357 | 0.424 | 3,01 | 0.425 | 2.415 |
| 1.0 | 0.0 | 3.695 | 0,0 | 3.251 | 0,0 | 2.83 | 0.0 | 2.328 |

$$+\frac{e^{k_3\eta}}{k_3^2+4\beta^2}(k_3\cos 2\beta\eta+2\beta\sin 2\beta\eta)-\frac{k_3}{k_3^2+4\beta^2}\Big]+\frac{c_3(c_2m_2+c_3m_3)+c_2(c_3m_2-c_2m_3)}{2}\Big[\frac{e^{k_3\eta}}{k_3^2+4\beta^2}(k_3\sin 2\beta\eta-$$

$$-2\beta\cos 2\beta\eta)+\frac{2\beta}{k_3^2+4\beta^2}\Big]+\frac{c_3(c_3m_2-c_2m_3)}{2}\Big[\frac{e^{k_3\eta}}{k_3}-\frac{1}{k_3}-\frac{e^{k_3\eta}}{k_3^2+4\beta^2}(k_3\cos 2\beta\eta+2\beta\sin 2\beta\eta)+\frac{k_3}{k_3^2+4\beta^2}\Big]\Big\}. \quad (89)$$

Table 3 contains the results of the calculations of the velocity gradient and turbulent friction stress carried out according to the Taylor turbulence model. It can be seen from the table that despite the fact that the velocity gradient is zero on both boundaries of the jet, the turbulent friction stress on one of the boundaries is nonzero. Similar results have been obtained with other values of n and, in particular, with n=2/3 and n=1/3. This result contradicts the boundary conditions of the problem.

In order to obtain the solutions of the equation of motion (46) for other values of n, let us introduce a new independent variable $\tau$ and perform the necessary transformations. On the basis of Eq. (57), we have

$$\frac{d\tau}{d\varphi}=c_1'\tau^{n/2},$$

so that

$$\left.\begin{aligned} F'(\varphi)&=\frac{dF}{d\varphi}=\frac{dF}{d\tau}\,\frac{d\tau}{d\varphi}=c_1'\tau^{n/2}F'(\tau),\\ F''(\varphi)&=\frac{d}{d\varphi}\left(\frac{dF}{d\varphi}\right)=c_1'^2\left[\frac{n}{2}\,\tau^{n-1}F'(\tau)+\tau^nF''(\tau)\right],\\ F'''(\varphi)&=c_1'^3\left[\frac{n}{2}(n-1)\,\tau^{\frac{3}{2}n-2}F'(\tau)+\frac{3}{2}\,n\tau^{\frac{3}{2}n-1}F''(\tau)+\tau^{\frac{3}{2}n}F'''(\tau)\right]\end{aligned}\right\} \quad (90)$$

Substituting expression (90) into Eq. (46), we have

$$\tau^{\frac{3}{2}n} F'''(\tau)+3n\tau^{\frac{3}{2}n-1} F''(\tau)+\frac{3}{2}n\left(\frac{3}{2}n-1\right)\tau^{\frac{3}{2}n-2} F'(\tau)+cF(\tau)=0, \tag{91}$$

where

$$c=\frac{1}{c_1'^3}, \quad c_1'=\frac{2}{2-n}\,\frac{1-\tau_H^{\frac{2-n}{2}}}{b_*}.$$

We will seek a solution of Eq. (91) in the form of a generalized series

$$F(\tau)=\sum_{k=0}^{\infty} a_k\tau^{r+k}. \tag{92}$$

An analysis of Eq. (91) shows that the solution of this equation with the help of series (92) can only be obtained when n=2/3 or 1.

Let us investigate some particular cases of the solution of Eq. (91).

2. With n=2/3, Eq. (91) becomes

$$\tau F'''+2F''+cF=0. \tag{93}$$

On the basis of series (92), we have

$$\left.\begin{aligned} F'(\tau)&=\sum_{k=0}^{\infty} a_k(r+k)\tau^{r+k-1},\\ F''(\tau)&=\sum_{k=0}^{\infty} a_k(r+k)(r+k-1)\tau^{r+k-2},\\ F'''(\tau)&=\sum_{k=0}^{\infty} a_k(r+k)(r+k-1)(r+k-2)\tau^{r+k-3}.\end{aligned}\right\} \tag{94}$$

Substituting this expression, as well as series (92) into Eq. (93), we have

$$\sum_{k=0}^{\infty} a_k(r+k)^2(r+k-1)\tau^{r+k-2}+c\sum_{k=0}^{\infty} a_k\tau^{r+k}=0. \tag{95}$$

Equality (95) must be satisfied identically for any $\tau$, so that all of the coefficients of the series on the left-hand side of this equation must be equal to zero. In order to determine the constants $a_0$, $a_1$, $a_2$, etc., we will equate to zero coefficients of like powers of $\tau$,

$$\left.\begin{aligned} &\tau^{r-2} \text{ with } k=0,\ a_0r^2(r-1)=0,\\ &\tau^{r-1} \text{ with } k=1,\ a_1(r+1)^2r=0,\\ &\tau^{r} \text{ with } k=2,\ a_2(r+2)^2(r+1)+ca_0=0,\\ &\tau^{r+1} \text{ with } k=3,\ a_3(r+3)^2(r+2)+ca_1=0,\\ &\tau^{r+2} \text{ with } k=4,\ a_4(r+4)^2(r+3)+ca_2=0\end{aligned}\right\} \tag{96}$$

and so on.

From the first equation of system (96) on the assumption that $a_0 \neq 0$, we find the roots of Eq. (95),

$$r_1=0, \quad r_2=1, \quad r_3=0.$$

It can be seen from system (96) that in order for the system to have a unique solution, all of the odd coefficients ($a_1$, $a_3$, etc.) must be set equal to zero. The even coefficients of the series corresponding to these roots are determined by the recurrence relation

$$a_{2k}=-\frac{ca_{2k-2}}{(r+2k)^2(r+2k-1)}, \tag{97}$$

which is obtained from system (96). Here, we have k=1, 2, 3, ... .

Having substituted the values of the coefficients when $r_1=0$ into series (92), we obtain the first particular solution of Eq. (91) as

$$F_1(\tau)=1-0.25c\tau^2+0.00521c^2\tau^4-0.000029c^3\tau^6+0.0000000646c^3\tau^8-\ldots. \tag{98}$$

Carrying out the analogous procedure for the second root r=1, we obtain the second particular solution of Eq. (91),

$$F_2(\tau)=\tau-0.0556c\tau^3+0.000556c^2\tau^5-0.00000189c^3\tau^7+0.00000000292c^4\tau^9-\ldots. \tag{99}$$

The third particular solution of Eq. (91) cannot be obtained by means of series (92) because the first and third solutions obtained with the help of series (92) will be linearly dependent. We can obtain the third linearly independent particular solution by lowering the order of differential equation (93).

If two particular solutions of a third-order differential equation are known, then we can reduce the order of the differential equation to the first and solve the resulting equation by simple integration. To do this, we take

$$F_3(\tau)=F_1(\tau)\,Y, \tag{100}$$

where Y is the new unknown function, so that

$$\left.\begin{aligned}F_3'&=F_1'Y+F_1Y',\\ F_3''&=F_1''Y+2F_1'Y'+F_1Y'',\\ F_3'''&=F_1'''Y+3F_1''Y'+3F_1'Y''+F_1Y'''.\end{aligned}\right\} \tag{101}$$

Substituting Eq. (100) and its derivatives (101) into expression (93), we obtain

$$\tau F_1Y'''+(3\tau F_1'+2F_1)\,Y''+(3\tau F_1''+4F_1')\,Y'+(\tau F_1'''+2F_1''+cF_1)\,Y=0. \tag{102}$$

Because of Eq. (93), the term in the last set of brackets is equal to zero. Moreover, if in Eq. (102) we set

$$U=Y'=\left(\frac{F_3}{F_1}\right)', \tag{103}$$

then the order of Eq. (102) will be reduced by unity. As a result of this, we have

$$U''+\left(3\,\frac{F_1'}{F_1}+2\,\frac{1}{\tau}\right)U'+\left(3\,\frac{F_1''}{F_1}+4\,\frac{F_1'}{F_1}\,\frac{1}{\tau}\right)U=0. \tag{104}$$

Let us now set

$$\left.\begin{aligned} &U=U_1 W,\\ &U'=U_1' W+U_1 W',\\ &U''=U_1'' W+2U_1' W'+U_1 W'', \end{aligned}\right\} \tag{105}$$

where W is a new unknown function of U and

$$U_1=\left(\frac{F_2}{F_1}\right)'. \tag{106}$$

When we substitute these expressions into Eq. (104), we obtain

$$U_1 W''+\left(2U_1'+3U_1\frac{F_1'}{F_1}+2U_1\frac{1}{\tau}\right)W'+\left(U_1''+3U_1'\frac{F_1'}{F_1}+2U_1'\frac{1}{\tau}+3U_1\frac{F_1''}{F_1}+4U_1\frac{F_1'}{F_1}\frac{1}{\tau}\right)W=0. \tag{107}$$

Because of (104), the term in the last set of brackets of Eq. (107) is equal to zero.

If we now set

$$V=W'=\left(\frac{U}{U_1}\right)', \tag{108}$$

then Eq. (108) yields.

$$V'+\left(2\frac{U_1'}{U_1}+3\frac{F_1'}{F_1}+\frac{2}{\tau}\right)V=0$$

or

$$\frac{dV}{V}=-\left(2\frac{U_1'}{U_1}+3\frac{F_1'}{F_1}+\frac{2}{\tau}\right)d\tau. \tag{109}$$

Integrating this equation, we obtain

$$\ln V=-2\ln U_1-3\ln F_1-2\ln\tau,$$

which after an exponential transformation reduces to

$$V=\frac{1}{U_1^2 F_1^3\tau^2}, \tag{110}$$

where

$$U_1=\left(\frac{F_2}{F_1}\right)'=\frac{F_2'F_1-F_2F_1'}{F_1^2}.$$

Substituting this into (110), we obtain the equation

$$V=\frac{F_1}{(F_2'F_1-F_2F_1')\tau^2}. \tag{111}$$

Further, from the definitions of V and U we have

$$U = U_1 \int V$$

and

$$F_3 = F_1 \int U = F_1 \int U_1 \int V. \tag{112}$$

Omitting cumbersome transformations which are necessary for the derivation of expressions for U and V and the subsequent integrations, we obtain the following expression for the third particular solution of Eq. (91):

$$F_3(\tau) = -\ln \tau F_1 - 0.5c\tau^2 + 0.0147c^2\tau^4 + 0.0000962c^3\tau^6 + 0.00000271c^4\tau^8 - \ldots. \tag{113}$$

The result of all this is that the general solution of Eq. (93) will be the sum of the three particular solutions,

$$F(\tau) = c_1F_1(\tau) + c_2F_2(\tau) + c_3F_3(\tau). \tag{114}$$

The constants $c_1$, $c_2$, $c_3$, as well as the jet boundaries $\varphi_1$ and $\varphi_2$ are given by the same boundary conditions as thos for the case n=2.

On the inner boundary of the jet (with $\varphi = \varphi_1$ or $\tau = 1$) we have

$$u = u_0,\ \rho = \rho_0,\ \text{i.e.,}\ F'(\varphi_1) = 1 \quad \text{or} \quad F'(1) = \frac{1}{c_1'};$$

$$\frac{\partial u}{\partial y} = 0,\ \text{i.e.,}\ F''(\varphi_1) = nc_1' \quad \text{or} \quad F''(1) = -\frac{3}{2}\frac{n}{c_1'};$$

$$v = 0,\ \text{i.e.,}\ F(\varphi_1) = \varphi_1 \quad \text{or} \quad F(1) = \varphi_1. \tag{115}$$

On the outer boundary of the jet (with $\varphi = \varphi_2$ or $\tau = \tau_H$) we have

$$u = 0,\ \rho = \rho_H,\ \text{i.e.,}\ F'(\varphi_2) = 0 \quad \text{or} \quad F'(\tau_H) = 0;$$

$$\frac{\partial u}{\partial y} = 0,\ \text{i.e.,}\ F''(\varphi_2) = 0 \quad \text{or} \quad F''(\tau_H) = 0.$$

Making use of these five boundary conditions, we obtain five equations for the determination of $c_1$, $c_2$, $c_3$, $\varphi_1$, and $\varphi_2$,

$$\left.\begin{aligned} F'(1) &= c_1A_1 + c_2B_1 + c_3D_1 = \frac{1}{c_1'}, \\ F''(1) &= c_1A_2 + c_2B_2 + c_3D_2 = -\frac{3n}{2c_1'}, \\ F(1) &= c_1A_3 + c_2B_3 + c_3D_3 = \varphi_1, \\ F'(\tau_H) &= c_1A_4 + c_2B_4 + c_3D_4 = 0, \\ F''(\tau_H) &= c_1A_5 + c_2B_5 + c_3D_5 = 0. \end{aligned}\right\} \tag{116}$$

where $A_1$, $B_1$, ..., $B_3$, $D_3$, correspond to the series $F_1'$, $F_2'$, ..., $F_2$, $F_3$ with $\tau = 1$ and $A_4$, $B_4$, ..., $B_5$, $D_5$ correspond to the series $F_1'$, $F_2'$, ..., $F_2''$, $F_3''$ with $\tau = \tau_H$.

It should be noted that the solution of system (116) is associated with a number of computational difficulties since the coefficients $A_1$, $B_1$, ..., $B_5$, $D_5$ are functions of the initial heating and the jet width $b_*$. Therefore, the following procedure is proposed for the solution of system (116).

For a given initial heating of the jet $\tau_H$, we take a number of values of the jet width $b_*$ and calculate the coefficients $A_1$, $B_1$, etc. for all values of $b_*$ specified. Then, having obtained from the fourth and fifth equations of system (116) two expressions for $c_1$ and having equated them, we obtain

$$c_2=c_3\frac{\frac{D_4}{A_4}-\frac{D_5}{A_5}}{\frac{B_5}{A_5}-\frac{B_4}{A_4}}=c_3E. \tag{117}$$

Substituting this expression into the fourth equation of the system, we have

$$c_1=c_3\left(-E\frac{B_4}{A_4}-\frac{D_4}{A_4}\right)=c_3k. \tag{118}$$

As a result of the substitution of the expressions for $c_2$ and $c_1$ into the first equation of system (116), we can obtain an expression for the determination of $c_{3(1)}$,

$$c_{3(1)}=\frac{1}{c_1'}\frac{1}{A_1k+B_1E+D_1}. \tag{119}$$

If the same expressions for $c_2$ and $c_1$ are substituted into the second equation, we obtain

$$c_{3(2)}=-\frac{3}{2}\frac{n}{c_1'}\frac{1}{A_2k+B_2E+D_2}. \tag{120}$$

We can now determine $c_1$ and $c_2$:

$$\left.\begin{aligned}c_{1(1)}&=kc_{3(1)};\\ c_{1(2)}&=kc_{3(2)};\\ c_{2(1)}&=Ec_{3(1)};\\ c_{2(2)}&=Ec_{3(2)}.\end{aligned}\right\} \tag{121}$$

The points of intersection of identically labelled curves for some definite value of $b_*$ which is the same for all curves will then correspond to a unique solution of system (116). Subsituting the values of the constants obtained ($c_1$, $c_2$, etc.) into Eq. (114), we obtain an expression which can be used to determine the function $F(\tau)$ and its derivatives. The values of $F'(\varphi)$ and $F''(\varphi)$ can be obtained with the help of formulas (90). The longitudinal and transverse velocity components, as well as the turbulent friction stress and heat flux are determined from Eqs. (38), (49), (50), and (51), respectively (see Table 4).

3. When $n=1$, the equation of motion (46) can be written as

$$\tau^{\frac{3}{2}}F'''(\tau)+3\tau^{\frac{1}{2}}F''(\tau)+\frac{3}{4}\tau^{-\frac{1}{2}}F'(\tau)+cF(\tau)=0 \tag{122}$$

and solved with the help of series (92) in the same way as the equation with $n=2/3$.

Let us substitute series (92) and its derivatives (94) into Eq. (122) to obtain

$$\sum_{k=0}^{\infty}a_k(r+k)\left[(r+k-1)(r+k-2)+3(r+k)-\frac{9}{4}\right]\tau^{r+k-\frac{3}{2}}+c\sum_{k=0}^{\infty}a_k\tau^{r+k}=0. \tag{123}$$

TABLE 4

$$n=\frac{2}{3};\ b_*=3.62;\ \varphi_1=1.16;\ \tau_H=1.757\cdot10^{-3};\ c_1=-0.72;\ c_2=-1.85\cdot10^{-4};\ c_3=1.005\cdot10^{-5}$$

| $\eta$ | $\varphi$ | $\tau$ | $F(\varphi)$ | $F'(\varphi)$ | $F''(\varphi)$ | $F'''(\varphi)$ | $\frac{u}{u_0}$ | $\frac{1}{u_0}\frac{du}{d\varphi}$ | $\frac{v}{a_0u_0}$ | $\frac{\tau_T}{a\frac{\varrho_0u_0^2}{2}}$ | $\frac{W_T}{a\varrho_0u_0i_0}$ | $\frac{\varrho u^2}{\varrho_0u_0^2}$ |
|---|---|---|---|---|---|---|---|---|---|---|---|---|
| 0.0 | —2.46 | $1.757\cdot10^{-3}$ | —0.72 | 0.0 | 0.0 | 0.72 | 0.0 | 0.0 | 0.0105 | 0.00 | 0.0 | 0.0 |
| 0.1 | —2.098 | 0.0302 | —0.715 | 0.0276 | 0.133 | 0.315 | 0.0031 | 0.0225 | 0.1285 | 0.0045 | 0.0273 | $8.6\cdot10^{-5}$ |
| 0.2 | —1.736 | 0.0973 | —0.695 | 0.0956 | 0.243 | 0.2994 | 0.0202 | 0.0768 | 0.2085 | 0.028 | 0.0668 | $1.83\cdot10^{-3}$ |
| 0.3 | —1.376 | 0.173 | —0.641 | 0.2045 | 0.348 | 0.2603 | 0.0636 | 0.1644 | 0.257 | 0.0868 | 0.1206 | 0.013 |
| 0.4 | —1.012 | 0.2618 | —0.542 | 0.347 | 0.431 | 0.1882 | 0.142 | 0.2710 | 0.258 | 0.1795 | 0.173 | 0.0493 |
| 0.5 | —0.65 | 0.3618 | —0.388 | 0.513 | 0.481 | 0.0752 | 0.2605 | 0.384 | 0.233 | 0.29 | 0.2203 | 0.134 |
| 0.6 | —0.29 | 0.4715 | —0.1715 | 0.686 | 0.48 | —0.083 | 0.4155 | 0.478 | 0.1985 | 0.376 | 0.251 | 0.285 |
| 0.7 | 0.07 | 0.5909 | 0.107 | 0.855 | 0.416 | —0.284 | 0.601 | 0.525 | 0.17 | 0.393 | 0.256 | 0.513 |
| 0.8 | 0.435 | 0.7194 | 0.44 | 0.977 | 0.271 | —0.522 | 0.784 | 0.483 | 0.153 | 0.291 | 0.220 | 0.766 |
| 0.9 | 0.798 | 0.8559 | 0.806 | 1.032 | 0.032 | —0.7759 | 0.931 | 0.315 | 0.1113 | 0.1105 | 0.136 | 0.96 |
| 1.0 | 1.16 | 1.0 | 1.160 | 1.0 | —0.288 | 1.022 | 1.0 | 0.0 | 0.0 | 0.0 | 0.0 | 1.0 |

Equating to zero the coefficients of like powers of $\tau$, we obtain a system of equations

$$\left.\begin{aligned}
&\tau^{r-\frac{3}{2}} && \text{for } k=0 && a_0r\left[(r-1)(r-2)+3r-\frac{9}{4}\right]=0,\\
&\tau^{r} && \text{for } k=\frac{3}{2} && a_{3/2}\left(r+\frac{3}{2}\right)\left[\left(r+\frac{1}{2}\right)\left(r-\frac{1}{2}\right)+\right.\\
&&&&& \left.+3\left(r+\frac{3}{2}\right)-\frac{9}{4}\right]+ca_0=0,\\
&\tau^{r+\frac{3}{2}} && \text{for } k=3 && a_3(r+3)\left[(r+2)(r+1)+\right.\\
&&&&& \left.+3(r+3)-\frac{9}{4}\right]+ca_{3/2}=0,\\
&\tau^{r+k} && \text{for } k=k && a_k(r+k)\left[(r+k-1)(r+k-2)+\right.\\
&&&&& \left.+3(r+k)-\frac{9}{4}\right]+ca_{k-\frac{3}{2}}=0.
\end{aligned}\right\} \qquad (124)$$

From the first equation of system (124) we find the roots of Eq. (123) to be

$$r_1=0;\quad r_2=\frac{1}{2};\quad r_3=-\frac{1}{2}.$$

Next, from system (124) we find the values of the constants $a_{3/2}$, $a_3$, etc., for each of the roots $r_1$, $r_2$, and, $r_3$. Substituting the values of $a_{3/2}$, $a_3$, etc. found for $r_1=0$, $r_2={}^1/_2$, and $r_3=-{}^1/_2$ we obtain the three particular solutions of Eq. (122),

TABLE 5

$n=1$; $\tau_н=1.757\cdot10^{-3}$; $b_*=4.068$; $\varphi_1=1.327$; $c_1=-1.156$; $c_2=-0.03388$; $c_3=-3.45\cdot10^{-5}$

| $\eta$ | $\varphi$ | $\tau$ | $F(\varphi)$ | $F'(\varphi)$ | $F''(\varphi)$ | $F'''(\varphi)$ | $\frac{u}{u_0}$ | $\frac{1}{u_0}\frac{du}{d\varphi}$ | $\frac{u}{a_0 u_0}$ | $\frac{\tau_т}{a\frac{\varrho_0 u_0^2}{2}}$ | $\frac{W_т}{a\varrho_0 u_0 i_0}$ | $\frac{\varrho u^2}{\varrho_0 u_0^2}$ |
|---|---|---|---|---|---|---|---|---|---|---|---|---|
| 0,0 | —2,741 | $1.757\cdot10^{-3}$ | —1,158 | 0.0 | 0.0 | 1.158 | 0.0 | 0,0 | $2.04\cdot10^{-3}$ | 0,0 | 0,0 | 0,0 |
| 0,1 | —2,334 | 0,01896 | —1.15 | 0,0409 | 0.167 | 0.295 | $7.76\cdot10^{-4}$ | $5,82\cdot10^{-3}$ | 0,0399 | $1.78\cdot10^{-3}$ | 0,0199 | $3.17\cdot10^{-5}$ |
| 0,2 | —1,927 | 0,05452 | —1.117 | 0,1325 | 0,281 | 0,268 | $7.22\cdot10^{-3}$ | 0,0299 | 0.1072 | 0,0164 | 0.0603 | $9,56\cdot10^{-4}$ |
| 0,3 | —1,521 | 0.10847 | —1.038 | 0.268 | 0.381 | 0,222 | 0.0291 | 0,0829 | 0,187 | 0,0633 | 0,1186 | 0,0078 |
| 0.4 | —1.111 | 0.18075 | —0,8969 | 0,44 | 0,456 | 0.1399 | 0,0794 | 0.1702 | 0,252 | 0.1605 | 0,189 | 0,0349 |
| 0,5 | —0.706 | 0.2714 | —0,6767 | 0.632 | 0,483 | 0.0207 | 0,168 | 0,283 | 0.311 | 0.295 | 0.2565 | 0.104 |
| 0,6 | —0.301 | 0,3804 | —0.3782 | 0,829 | 0,463 | —0,1528 | 0,315 | 0.416 | 0,367 | 0,4565 | 0.318 | 0.261 |
| 0.7 | 0.109 | 0,5078 | —0.0089 | 0.9975 | 0.35 | —0,338 | 0.507 | 0.513 | 0,4 | 0.518 | 0.34 | 0.504 |
| 0.8 | 0.519 | 0,6535 | 0.4234 | 1.112 | 0,175 | —0,5764 | 0.726 | 0,538 | 0.414 | 0,4435 | 0.3135 | 0,811 |
| 0.9 | 0.919 | 0.8176 | 0.8778 | 1.122 | —0.1072 | —0.7939 | 0,918 | 0.391 | 0.329 | 0.187 | 0.203 | 1,022 |
| 1,0 | 1,327 | 1,0 | 1.327 | 0.0 | —0.472 | —1,001 | 1,0 | 0,0 | 0,0 | 0,0 | 0.0 | 1,0 |

TABLE 6

$n=1$; $\tau_н=0.01049$; $b_*=3.87$; $\varphi_1=1.314$; $c_1=-1.065$; $c_2=-0.2315$; $c_3=-0.001185$

| $\eta$ | $\varphi$ | $\tau$ | $F(\varphi)$ | $F'(\varphi)$ | $F''(\varphi)$ | $F'''(\varphi)$ | $\frac{u}{u_0}$ | $\frac{1}{u}\frac{du}{d\varphi}$ | $\frac{v}{a u_0}$ | $\frac{\tau_т}{a\frac{\varrho_0 u_0^2}{2}}$ | $\frac{W_т}{a\varrho_0 u_0 i_0}$ | $\frac{\varrho u^2}{\varrho_0 u_0^2}$ |
|---|---|---|---|---|---|---|---|---|---|---|---|---|
| 0.0 | —2,556 | 0.01049 | —1.0972 | 0,0 | 0.0 | 1,0972 | 0,0 | 0,0 | 0.0115 | 0.0 | 0.0 | 0.0 |
| 0.1 | —2.169 | 0.03706 | —1,0896 | 0,0483 | 0.2085 | 0,3396 | 0,0018 | 0,012 | 0,0651 | 0.0039 | 0.0288 | $8.65\cdot10^{-5}$ |
| 0.2 | —1.782 | 0.07964 | —1.0524 | 0,1522 | 0.32 | 0.2674 | 0,0121 | 0,0453 | 0.136 | 0,0258 | 0.0741 | $1.84\cdot10^{-3}$ |
| 0,3 | —1,396 | 0.13838 | —0,9653 | 0,293 | 0,409 | 0.2033 | 0,0405 | 0.107 | 0,21 | 0,0827 | 0.1333 | 0.0119 |
| 0.4 | —1,009 | 0.21317 | —0,8183 | 0,466 | 0,47 | 0.1113 | 0,0992 | 0.2 | 0,274 | 0,187 | 0.2045 | 0,0462 |
| 0.5 | —0,623 | 0.30404 | —0.6029 | 0,652 | 0,489 | —0.0131 | 0.198 | 0,315 | 0,324 | 0.3265 | 0.2645 | 0.129 |
| 0.6 | —0.236 | 0.41101 | —0,3109 | 0,837 | 0.452 | —0.1791 | 0,344 | 0,435 | 0,361 | 0,482 | 0.314 | 0,280 |
| 0.7 | 0.15 | 0.5341 | 0.0483 | 0,992 | 0.374 | —0,3783 | 0,529 | 0,52 | 0,384 | 0,5075 | 0.33 | 0,5245 |
| 0.8 | 0.537 | 0.6733 | 0.4531 | 1,093 | 0,16 | —0,5883 | 0.736 | 0,523 | 0,385 | 0.407 | 0.295 | 0,814 |
| 0.9 | 0,924 | 0.8286 | 0,8933 | 1,105 | —0,1096 | —0,8099 | 0,915 | 0.375 | 0,296 | 0,17 | 0,1915 | 1,01 |
| 1,0 | 1.314 | 1,1 | 1.314 | 1,0 | —0,463 | —0,989 | 1.0 | 0.0 | 0.0 | 0.0 | 0,0 | 1,00 |

$$F_1(\tau)=1-0.334c\tau^{3/2}+0.0127c^2\tau^3-0.000141c^3\tau^{9/2}+0.000000658c^4\tau^6-\ldots, \quad (125)$$

$$F_2(\tau)=\tau^{1/2}-0.133c\tau^2+0.00318c^2\tau^{7/2}-0.0000257c^3\tau^5+0.0000000841c^4\tau^{13/2}-\ldots, \quad (126)$$

$$F_3(\tau)=\tau^{-1/2}-1.333c\tau+0.089c^2\tau^{5/2}-0.00141c^3\tau^4+0.00000856c^4\tau^{11/2}-\ldots. \quad (127)$$

The general solution of Eq. (122) is thus

$$F(\tau)=c_1F_1(\tau)+c_2F_2(\tau)+c_3F_3(\tau). \quad (128)$$

The arbitrary constants $c_1$, $c_2$, $c_3$, as well as the inner and outer boundaries of the jet, $\varphi_1$ and $\varphi_2$, are found from the boundary conditions (115). Subsequent calculations involve the same considerations and equations as in the case with $n=2/3$.

The convergence of the series obtained was checked with the help of D'Alembert's principle. The results of the calculations are shown in Tables 5 and 6. The variation of the width $b_*$ and the inner boundary $\varphi_1$ of the boundary layer of a gas jet as a function of the value of n for the working medium for two values of the heating $\tau_H$ is shown in Figs. 3 and 4.

The profiles of the enthalpy $\tau$ and the velocity $u/u_0$ in the boundary layer of the jet are shown in Fig. 5 for various values of $\tau_H$ and n.

4. When $n=0$, the equation of motion (46) reduces to the equation of motion of an incompressible fluid

$$F'''(\varphi)+F(\varphi)=0,$$

whose solution is well known [1] and can be rewritten as

$$F(\varphi)=c_1e^{-\varphi}+c_2e^{\frac{\varphi}{2}}\cos\frac{\sqrt{3}}{2}\varphi+c_3e^{\frac{\varphi}{2}}\sin\frac{\sqrt{3}}{2}\varphi. \quad (129)$$

An analysis of Eq. (129) and its derivatives shows that this system can have an infinite number of solutions. Therefore, we naturally have the problem of determining which of the solutions of the systems are physically meaningful. The answer to this question can only be obtained on the basis of an investigation of these equations with boundary conditions taken into account.

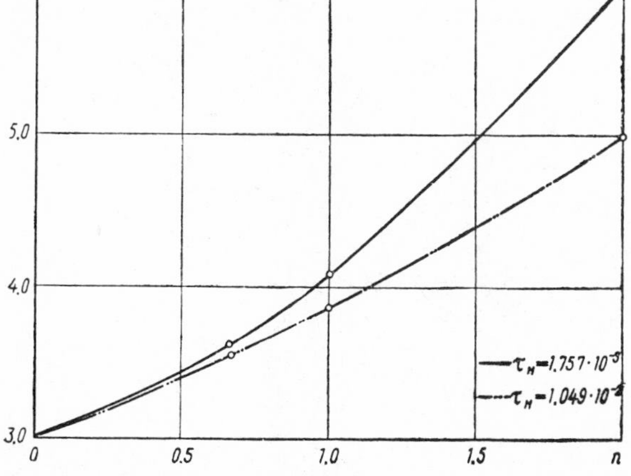


Fig. 3. Variation of the width $b_*$ of the boundary layer of a gas jet as a function of n (points ○ represent theoretical results).

On the basis of these equations and boundary conditions for an incompressible fluid, we have obtained numerically two solutions (two roots of the equation corresponding to two values of $b_*=\varphi_1-\varphi_2$) which satisfied the system of equations and the boundary conditions of the problem. The first solution corresponded to $b_*=3.02$, the second to $b_*=6.655$.

The velocity profiles shown in Fig. 6 were calculated for these two solutions. As can be seen from Fig. 6, the velocities obtained from the second solution are found to be negative in one section of the jet and this situation, of course, should not occur.

Because of this, the second and subsequent solutions must be rejected as being physically meaningless.

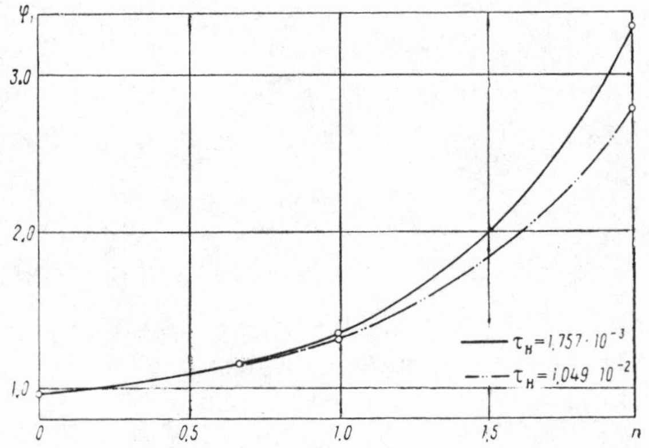


Fig. 4. Variation of the position of the inner jet boundary $\varphi_1$ as a function of n (points O represent theoretical results).

It is obvious that the same conclusions can be drawn for other values of n, in particular, for n=2.

It should be noted that with n=0, the equations for the longitudinal and transverse velocity components, as well as those for the turbulent friction stress and heat transfer reduce to the corresponding equations for an incompressible fluid.

## 6. Exact Solution of the Equations of Motion

In the solutions of the system of equations (26)-(29) presented above, we have made use of an approximate expression for the transverse velocity component $\bar{u}/u_0 \simeq F'/\vartheta$. At the same time, Eq. (36) shows that the exact expression for $\bar{u}/u_0$ should be written as

$$\frac{\bar{u}}{u_0} = \frac{F'}{\vartheta} - \frac{\alpha}{2} a \frac{\vartheta'}{\vartheta} \frac{d}{d\varphi}\left(\frac{\bar{u}}{u_0}\right), \tag{130}$$

so that the solution of the system of equations (26)-(29) can be made more accurate [6]. Moreover, we assume that the mixing length for heat transport $l_i$ is $\alpha$ times as large as that for the momentum transport $l_u$, where $a = \sqrt[3]{2c^2}$.

Let us write the equations of motion and energy as

$$F + \frac{1}{2}\vartheta' z' + \vartheta z'' = 0, \tag{131}$$

$$F + \frac{\alpha}{2}\vartheta' z' + \frac{\alpha}{2}\vartheta z'' + \frac{\alpha}{2}\vartheta z' \frac{\tau''}{\tau'} + \frac{u_0^2}{2 i_0}\frac{\vartheta}{\tau'}(z')^3 = 0, \tag{132}$$

where $z = \frac{u}{u_0}$.

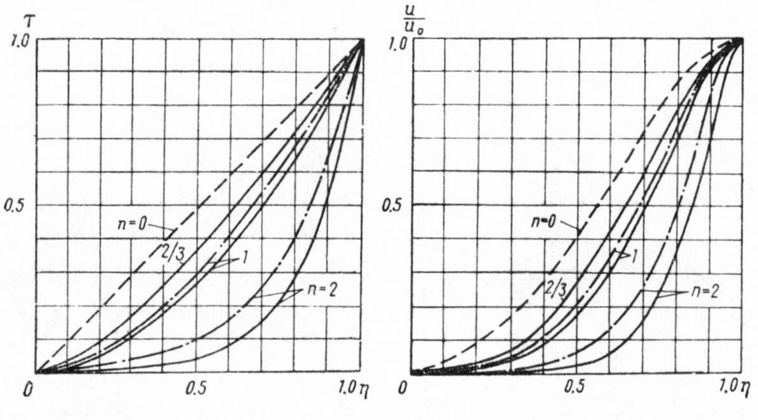


Fig. 5. Profiles of the enthalpy $\tau$ and the velocity $u/u_0$ in the boundary layer of the jet for several values of $\tau_H$ and n: —— $\tau_H = 1.757\ 10^{-3}$; — · — $\tau_H = 1.049\ 10^{-2}$.

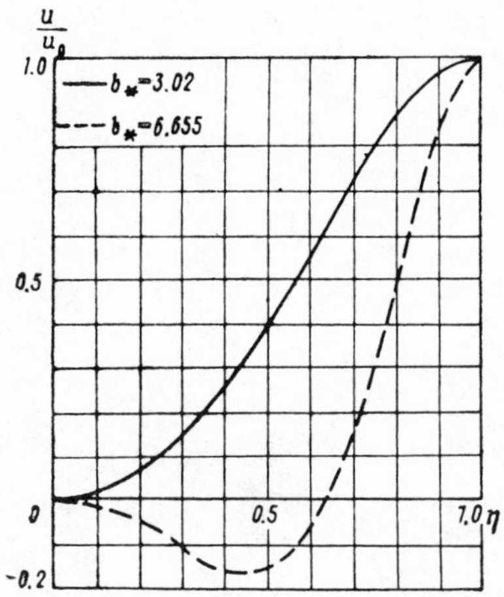


Fig. 6. Velocity profiles in a jet of incompressible fluid.

The evaluation of the last term of Eq. (132) carried out with the help of the approximate expression for $\bar{u}/u_0$ has shown that for any value of the heating and any n, the value of $(\vartheta/\tau')(z')^3$ is less than unity. In the case of a subsonic high-temperature jet, the ratio $u_0^2/2i_0$ is much less than unity. Because of this, the last term in Eq. (132) can be neglected.

Differentiating the equation of motion (131) and dividing it by $\vartheta$, we obtain

$$\frac{F'}{\vartheta}+\frac{1}{2}\frac{\vartheta''}{\vartheta}z'+\frac{3}{2}\frac{\vartheta'}{\vartheta}z''+z'''=0. \tag{133}$$

Substituting into this equation the expression for the transverse velocity component (130), we obtain the equation of motion in the form

$$z'''+\frac{3}{2}\frac{\vartheta'}{\vartheta}z''+\left(\frac{1}{2}\frac{\vartheta''}{\vartheta}+\frac{\alpha}{2}a\frac{\vartheta'}{\vartheta}\right)z'+z=0. \tag{134}$$

If we subtract (132) from Eq. (131), we obtain the following expression:

$$\left(\frac{1}{2}-\frac{\alpha}{2}\right)\vartheta'z'+\left(1-\frac{\alpha}{2}\right)\vartheta z''-\frac{\alpha}{2}\vartheta z'\frac{\tau''}{\tau'}=0. \tag{135}$$

We will not give the solution of these equations in their general form, i.e., for arbitrary values of n.

When $\alpha=2$, Eqs. (134) and (135) coincide with the equations derived on the basis of the modified Prandtl model and can be written as

$$z'''+\frac{3}{2}\frac{\vartheta'}{\vartheta}z''+\left(\frac{1}{2}\frac{\vartheta''}{\vartheta}+a\frac{\vartheta'}{\vartheta}\right)z'+z=0, \tag{136}$$

$$\left(\frac{1}{2}\frac{\vartheta'}{\vartheta}+\frac{\tau''}{\tau'}\right)z'=0. \tag{137}$$

An analysis of Eq. (137) shows that it is meaningless when $z'=0$ because in this case the velocity gradient in the jet is everywhere zero. Therefore, we must equate the bracketed terms to zero. The equation of motion (136) and the energy equation (137) can now be integrated.

Transforming Eqs. (136) and (137) with the help of expression (37), we obtain

$$z'''-\frac{3}{2}n\frac{\tau'}{\tau}z''+\left[\frac{n}{2}\left(1+\frac{n}{2}\right)\left(\frac{\tau'}{\tau}\right)^2-an\frac{\tau'}{\tau}\right]z'+z=0, \tag{138}$$

$$\frac{n}{2}\frac{\tau'}{\tau}-\frac{\tau''}{\tau'}=0. \tag{139}$$

With n=2, the solution of the energy equation is

$$\tau=\tau_H^{1-\eta},$$

where

$$\frac{\tau'}{\tau}=\frac{t}{b_*}.$$

On the basis of this, the equation of motion (138) can be written as

$$z'''(\varphi)-3\frac{t}{b_*}z''(\varphi)+2\frac{t}{b_*}\left(\frac{t}{b_*}-a\right)z'(\varphi)+z(\varphi)=0. \tag{140}$$

Transforming to the variable $\eta$, we obtain

$$z'''(\eta)-3tz''(\eta)+2t(t-ab_*)z'(\eta)+b_*^3z(\eta)=0. \tag{141}$$

Its characteristic equation is

$$k^3-3tk^2+2t(t-ab_*)k+b_*^3=0 \tag{142}$$

and after the substitution of $z=k-t$, it can be put into the form

$$z^3+3pz+2q=0,$$

where

$$2q=-2ab_*t+b_*^3,\quad 3p=-t^2-2ab_*t.$$

The roots of the characteristic equation (142) can be found analogously to those of (72), while the solution of Eq. (141) is

$$z(\eta)=\frac{u}{u_0}(\eta)=c_1e^{\alpha_1\eta}+c_2e^{\alpha_2\eta}\cos\beta\eta+c_3e^{\alpha_2\eta}\sin\beta\eta. \tag{143}$$

In order to determine $c_1$, $c_2$, and $c_3$, as well as the inner and outer jet boundaries, $\varphi_1$ and $\varphi_2$, we make use of the same five boundary conditions as in the case of the incompressible fluid.

On the basis of the boundary conditions, we can write down the following system of equations:

$$\left.\begin{aligned}
&z(1)=c_1e^{\alpha_1}+c_2e^{\alpha_2}\cos\beta+c_3e^{\alpha_2}\sin\beta=1,\\
&z'(1)=c_1e^{\alpha_1}\alpha_1+c_2e^{\alpha_2}\gamma_1+c_3e^{\alpha_2}\gamma_2=0,\\
&z''(1)=c_1e^{\alpha_1}\alpha_1^2+c_2e^{\alpha_2}(\alpha_2\gamma_1-\beta\gamma_2)+c_3e^{\alpha_2}(\alpha_2\gamma_2+\beta\gamma_1)=-\varphi_1b_*^2.\\
&z(0)=c_1+c_2=0,\\
&z'(0)=c_1\alpha_1+c_2\alpha_2+c_3\beta=0.
\end{aligned}\right\} \tag{144}$$

From the first, fourth, and fifth equations of this system we find that

$$c_1=\frac{1}{H};\quad c_2=-\frac{1}{H};\quad c_3=-\frac{\alpha_1-\alpha_2}{\beta}\frac{1}{H},$$

where

$$H=e^{\alpha_1}-e^{\alpha_2}\left(\cos\beta+\frac{\alpha_1-\alpha_2}{\beta}\sin\beta\right),$$

while $\varphi_1$ and $\varphi_2$ can be found from the second and third equations.

The calculations carried out with the help of the improved theory indicate a greater width of the jet than the value obtained on the basis of the approximate theory. Thus, with $a = 0.08$, $n=2$, and heating $\tau_H=1.757$ the value for the width of the jet increases by 9%. For $n< 2$, the percentage increase in the width value obtained from the improved theory is less. This can be

TABLE 7

| $\eta$ | $\tau_H=1.757\cdot10^{-3}$ | | | $\tau_H=1.049\cdot10^{-2}$ | |
|---|---|---|---|---|---|
| | $n=2$ | $n=1$ | $n=\frac{2}{3}$ | $n=2$ | $n=1$ |
| | $n\frac{\tau'}{\tau}z'$ | $n\frac{\tau'}{\tau}z'$ | $n\frac{\tau'}{\tau}z'$ | $n\frac{\tau'}{\tau}z'$ | $n\frac{\tau'}{\tau}z'$ |
| 0.0 | 0.0 | 0.0 | 0.0 | 0.0 | 0.0 |
| 0.1 | 0.1136 | 0.01985 | 0.01825 | 0.161 | 0.0288 |
| 0.2 | 0.3183 | 0.06045 | 0.04465 | 0.4 | 0.074 |
| 0.3 | 0.645 | 0.1186 | 0.0803 | 0.74 | 0.133 |
| 0.4 | 1.128 | 0.1885 | 0.1158 | 1.18 | 0.2 |
| 0.5 | 1.76 | 0.256 | 0.147 | 1.76 | 0.265 |
| 0.6 | 2.505 | 0.318 | 0.167 | 2.18 | 0.314 |
| 0.7 | 3.183 | 0.339 | 0.1704 | 2.51 | 0.33 |
| 0.8 | 3.52 | 0.314 | 0.1467 | 2.53 | 0.295 |
| 0.9 | 2.7 | 0.2032 | 0.0903 | 1.86 | 0.191 |
| 1.0 | 0.0 | 0.0 | 0.0 | 0.0 | 0.0 |

demonstrated in the following manner: It can be seen from formula (130) that the improvement of the solution depends on the magnitude of the second term which can be written as follows:

$$an\frac{\tau'}{\tau}z'.$$

Table 7 contains the values of $n(\tau'/\tau)z'$ along the width of the jet and it can be seen that this quantity decreases with decreasing n, whereas the magnitude of $F'/\vartheta = F'\tau^n$, or $u/u_0$, increases with decreasing n. As a result of this, the importance of the second term in Eq. (130) decreases with decreasing n. An increase in a leads to a somewhat greater increase in the width of the jet. However, the velocity profile in the boundary layer of the jet is practically independent of the theory used. An analysis of Eq. (136) shows that the latter quantity becomes of the form

$$\frac{\tau''}{\tau'}=\frac{z''}{z'},$$

i.e., the velocity and enthalpy profiles will be the same (solution of the problem according to Prandtl's theory).

In the case of an incompressible fluid, Eq. (134) coincides with Tolmin's equation and can be written as

$$z'''+z=0.$$

The energy equation (135) for an incompressible fluid with $\alpha=1$ coincides with Prandtl's equation obtained on the basis of his "old" theory, $\tau''/\tau'=z''/z'$ while with $\alpha=2$, it coincides with Tolmin's equation $\tau''/\tau'=0$.

In the second case, the enthalpy (temperature) profile in the boundary layer of the jet is a straight line.

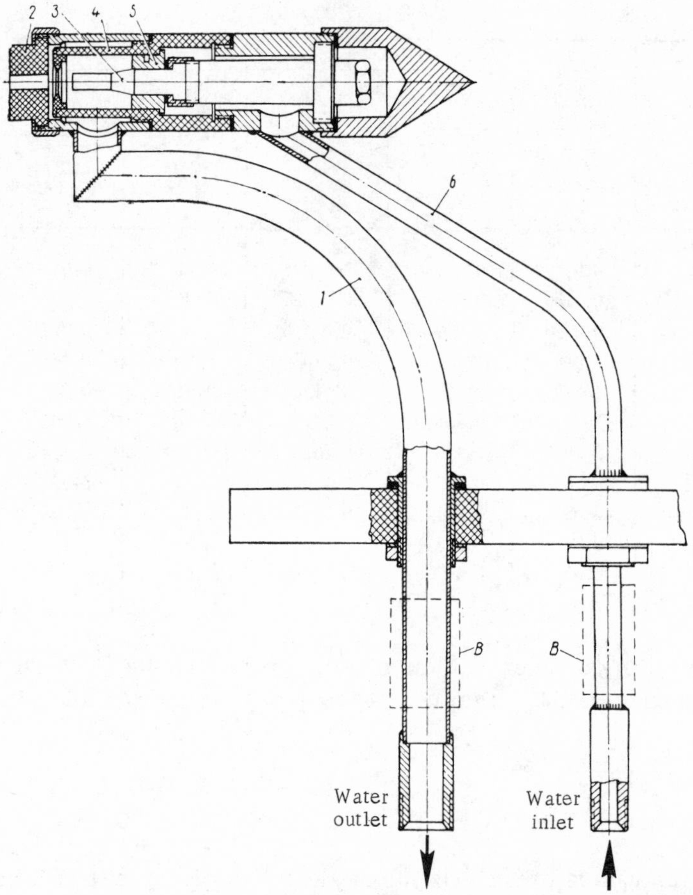


Fig. 7. Plasma generator: 1), 6) current and water feed pipes, 3) rear electrode, 4) intermediate housing, 5) cooling coil, B) places of busbar attachment.

## 7. Analysis of Experimental Data and Comparison with Theory

Experimental investigations of high-temperature plasma jets were carried out by means of a plasma generator (plasmotron) with graphite electrodes 2 and 3 (see Fig. 7). Arc stabilization was achieved by means of cooling-water which was supplied along tube 6, fed through the helical channel 5, and extracted by means of pipe 1. Brass pipes 1 and 6 also served as busbars for the supply of electric current to the electrodes 2 and 3. The device was put into operation by means of graphite rods 2 mm in diameter. The power supply consisted of a d.c. generator with a power output of 300 kW. The stability of the plasma-jet parameters was achieved through the stability of the electric and geometric parameters of the source. The temperature along transverse cross sections and along the length of the plasma jet was determined spectroscopically with an ISP-28 spectrograph by the method based on the measurement of the relative intensities of the Balmer-series line $H_\beta$ of atomic hydrogen [17, 22, 25, 27, 34, 37, 38, 39]. A modification of this method of temperature determination was also used in which the whole jet was photographed in the light of only the $H_\beta$ line. Light filters were used to isolate this line from the total spectrum.

A shadow instrument IAB-451 was used for the determination of the outer boundary of the zone in which the plasma jet intermixed with the surrounding medium. Figure 8 shows shadow

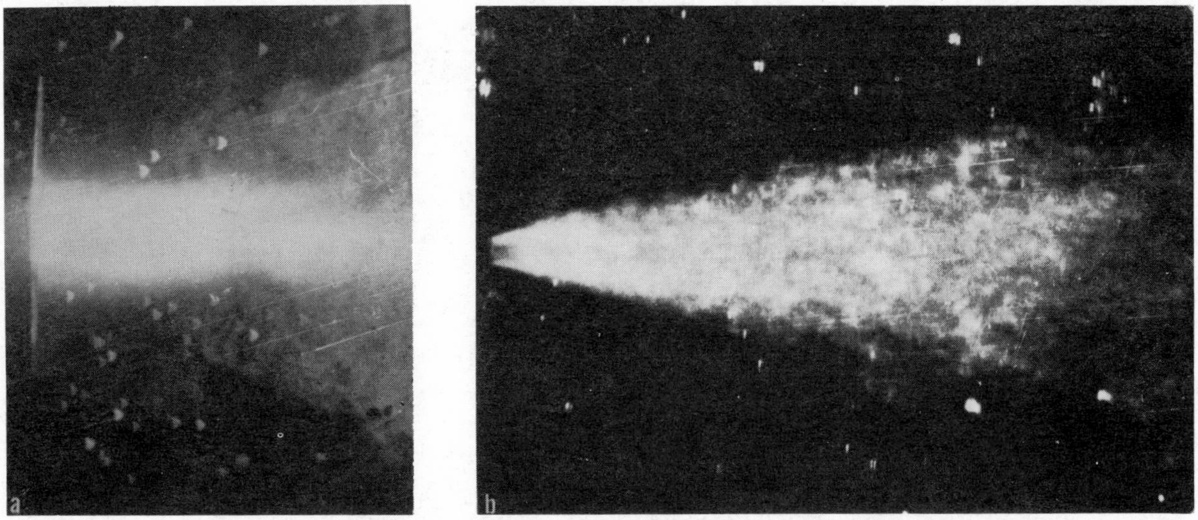


Fig. 8. Shadow photographs: a) plasma jet, b) "cold" jet.

photographs of a plasma jet with nozzle-exit temperature of $17.5 \cdot 10^3$°K and a "cold" jet with an exit temperature of 340°K. A comparison of these photographs shows that the aperture angle and, consequently, the width of the plasma jet is greater than those of a jet of incompressible fluid. The increase of the jet width with increasing initial heating is also confirmed by direct measurements of temperature and velocity head. Thus, a comparison of the dimensionless enthalpy profiles obtained in the initial section of the plasma jet with the temperature profiles of the "cold" jet shows that the width of the plasma jet is greater than that of the "cold" jet (Fig. 9). Analogous results are obtained from a comparison of the dimensionless velocity-head profiles in the initial section of a jet heated to a temperature of 4000°K with those of an isothermal jet (Fig. 10). A proof of the correctness of such an assertion is also provided by experiments carried out in the main section of the jet. This can be seen from from a comparison of the velocity-head profiles of a "cold" and a hot (T = 4000°K) jet (Fig. 11). As can be seen from Fig. 12, an increase in the initial heating leads to an increase in the width of the jet.

The increase in the jet width with increasing initial heating is in agreement with the results of the theoretical calculations reported in this paper.

An increase in the intermixing zone with increasing initial heating leads to a decrease in the length of the initial section (Figs. 13, 14). It can also be seen from Fig. 14 that even on the

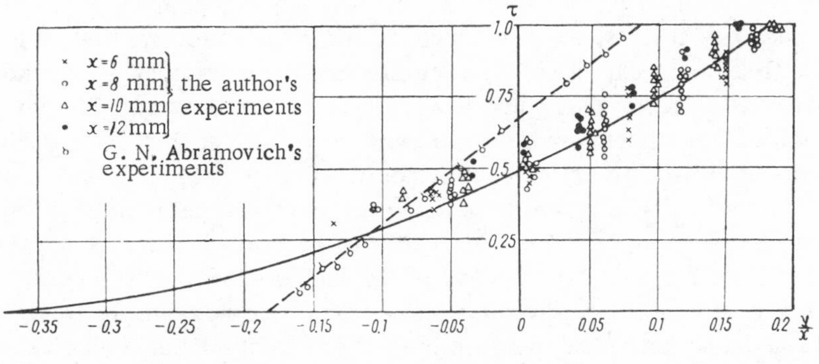


Fig. 9. Comparison of the enthalpy profiles in the boundary layer of a jet: —— theory (plasma jet $\rho_H/\rho_0 = 245$, $a = 0.143$), – – – theory (incompressible fluid, $a = 0.09$).

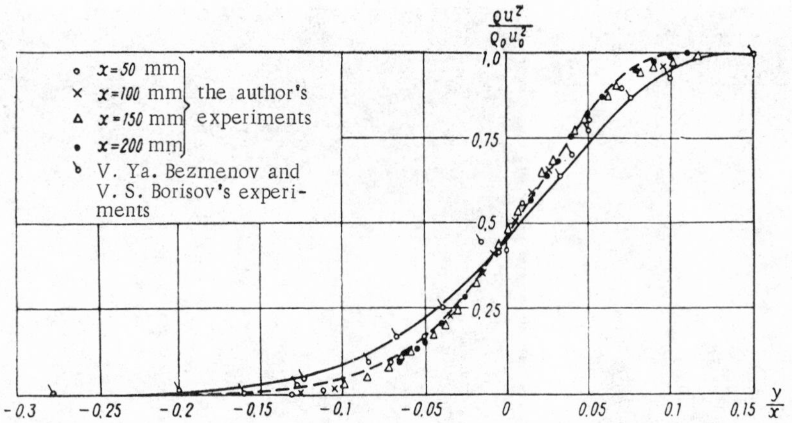


Fig. 10. Comparison of velocity-head profiles in the boundary layer of a jet: —— theory (isothermal jet $\rho_H/\rho_0 = 15$, $a = 0.127$), – – – theory (incompressible fluid, $a = 0.1$).

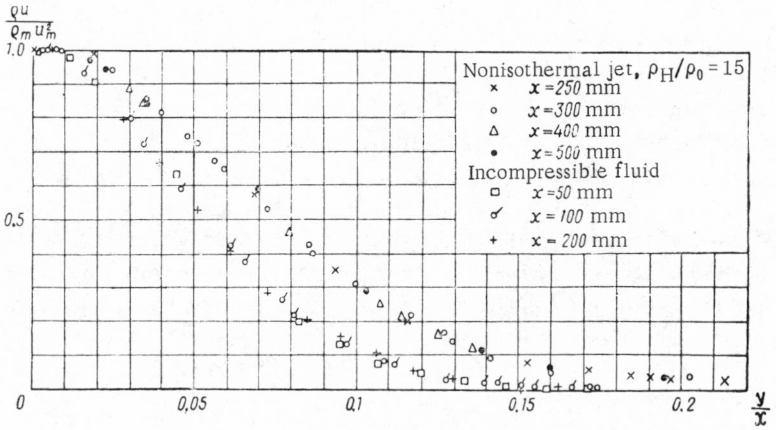


Fig. 11. Velocity-head profiles in the main section of a jet: Data for the nonisothermal jet are from V. Ya. Bezmenov and V. S. Borisov's experiments, those for the incompressible-fluid jet are from the author's experiments.

axis of the initial section of the jet, the temperature and, consequently, the enthalpy do not remain constant, but fall to some extent. This temperature decrease can apparently be explained by noting that a part of the energy contained in the jet is radiated away. The small temperature decrease at such high values of temperature can only be explained if it is assumed that the blackness of such a plasma jet is very low and is only 0.001-0.002. This value of the blackness was determined as the ratio of the radiant energy (measured experimentally with the help of a "Tera-50" radiometer) to the amount of energy radiated by a black body whose temperature is equal to that on the axis of the jet. The shadow photographs show that the outer boundary of the plasma jet remains rectilinear, as is the case for a jet of incompressible fluid. In the case of strongly heated jets and, in particular, plasma jets, the velocity-head, velocity, and enthalpy (temperature) profiles remain affine as can be seen from Figs. 9, 10, 11, 12. The linearity of the jet boundaries and the affineness of the parameters verify the assumption, adopted for the calculation, that the mixing length increases linearly along the jet.

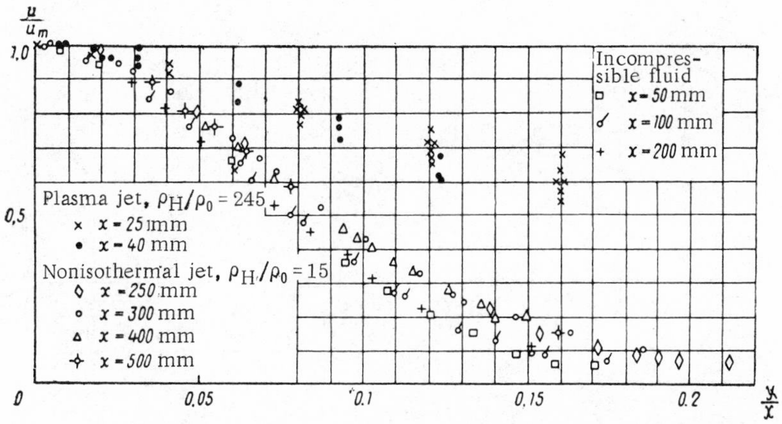


Fig. 12. Velocity profiles in the main section of a jet: Data for the plasma jet are from G. G. Smolin's experiments, those for the nonisothermal jet are from V. Ya. Bezmenov and V. S. Borisov's experiments, and those for the incompressible-fluid jet are from the author's experiments.

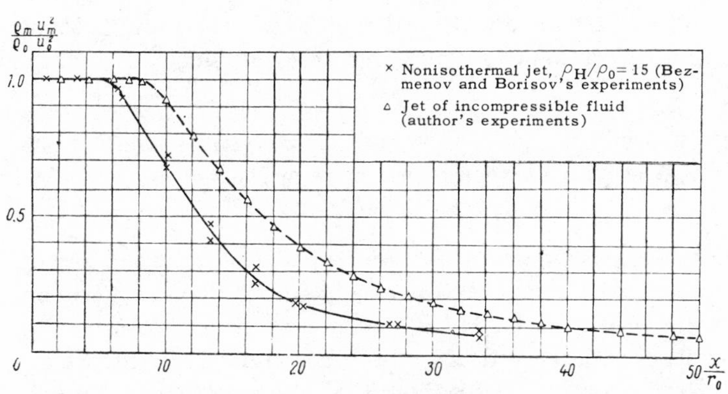


Fig. 13. Variation of the velocity head along the jet axis.

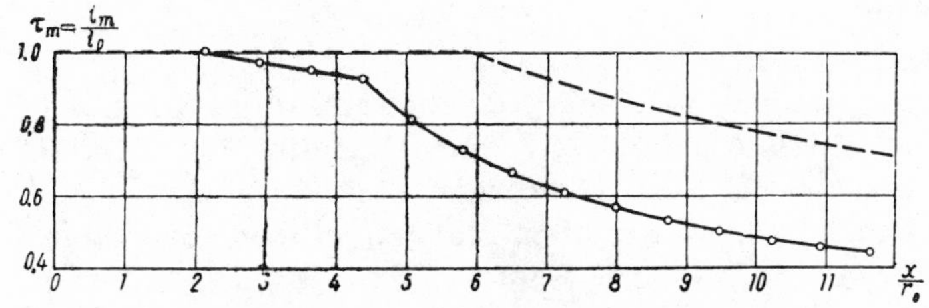


Fig. 14. Variation of the enthalpy along the jet axis; ○ plasma jet, $\rho_H/\rho_0 = 245$, author's experiments; – – – jet of incompressible fluid.

Figure 15 shows the dimensionless velocity and temperature profiles obtained in experiments with a jet heated to 4000°K, and it can be seen from the figure that the temperature profile lies above the velocity profile. This result is in agreement with the assumption used in the calculations that the mixing length for heat transport is greater than that for momentum transport. Figure 9 shows comparisons of the experimental enthalpy profiles in the initial section of the plasma jet and the temperature profiles in a "cold" jet with theoretical data. A comparison of these results show that the experimental data are in good agreement with theoretical

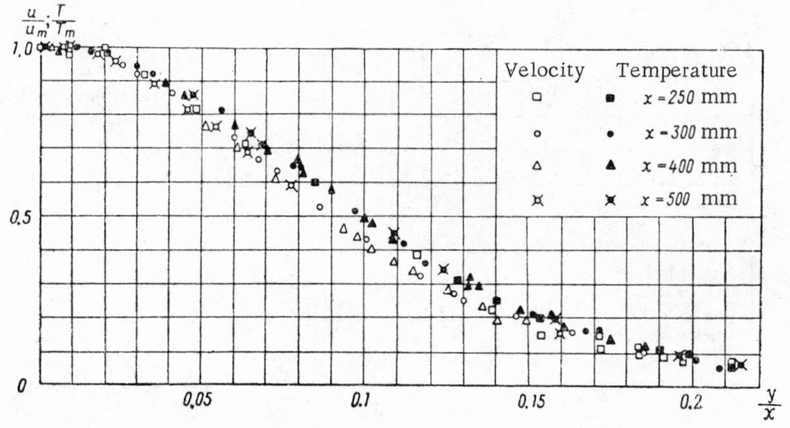


Fig. 15. Velocity and temperature profiles in the initial section of a nonisothermal jet, $\rho_H/\rho_0 = 15$, according to V. Ya. Bezmenov and V. S. Borisov's experiments.

calculations and that the enthalpy profiles are not universal but depend on the initial heating. Figure 10 gives the experimental data on the dimensionless velocity-head profiles obtained in the initial section of both an isothermal jet and a jet heated to 4000°K, together with the theoretical results; it can be seen from the figure that there is satisfactory agreement between theory and experiment.

The results obtained in this paper show that it is possible to calculate the parameters of a very-high-temperature jet with an accuracy that is sufficient for practical purposes.

## Literature Cited

1. G. N. Abramovich, Free Turbulent Jets of Liquids and Gases, Gosenergoizdat (1948).
2. G. N. Abramovich, Theory of Turbulent Jets, Fizmatgiz (1960).
3. G. N. Abramovich, "Turbulent mixing on the boundary between two plane-parallel streams of fluid (parallel and counterflow motion)," in: Theoretical Hydrodynamics, No. 19, edited by L. I. Sedov, Oborongiz (1956).
4. G. N. Abramovich, "Turbulent free jets of liquids and gases," Tr. Tsentr. Aerogidrodinam. Inst., No. 512 (1940).
5. Pai Shih-yi, Theory of Jets, Fizmatgiz (1960).
6. V. I. Bakulev, "Calculation of a submerged jet of a real gas", Inz. Zh. 1, No. 3 (1961).
7. V. Ya. Borodachev, The Propagation of a Plane-Parallel Turbulent Jet of Incompressible Fluid in the Case of Parallel Flow, Oborongiz, 1957.
8. L. A. Vulis, "The calculation of turbulent free jets of a compressible gas," Izv. Akad. Nauk Kaz. SSR, Ser. Energ., No. 10 (1956).
9. E. van Dreist, "The turbulent boundary layer in compressible fluids," in: Mechanics [Russian translation] No. 1/11 (1952), pp. 27–55.
10. L. A. Vulis and N. N. Terekhina, "The propagation of a turbulent gas jet in a medium of another density," Zh. Tekhn. Fiz., Vol. 26, No. 6 (1956).
11. M. A. Velikanov, Dyanamics of Channeled Streams, Gostekhteoretizdat (1954).
12. L. A. Vulis and I. B. Palatnik, "The mechanism of turbulent mixing in gas streams," Inzh.-Fiz. Zh. Vol. 4, No. 9 (1961).
13. V. A. Golubev, "Theoretical investigations into turbulent plane-parallel high-temperature jets with dissociation and ionization taken into account," Inzh.-Fiz. Zh., Vol. 4, No. 6 (1961).

14. V. A. Golubev, "The calculation of turbulent very-high-temperature jets," Inzh. Zh., Vol. 1, No. 4 (1961).
15. Sh. A. Ershin and Z. B. Sakipov, "A study of the initial section of a turbulent jet of compressible gas," Zh. Tekhn. Fiz., Vol. 29, No. 1 (1959).
16. P. P. Koryavov, "Numerical calculations of high-temperature laminar jets," Vychisl. Mat. i Mat. Fiz., Vol. 1, No. 5 (1961).
17. V. Lochte-Holtgreven, "Ionization measurements at high temperatures," in: Temperature and Its Measurement [Russian translation], IL (1960).
18. L. G. Loitsyanskii, Mechanics of Liquids and Gases, Gostekhteoretizdat (1957).
19. A. I. Mikhailov, "Investigations of the flow in combustion chambers of gas-turbine engines," Tr. Lab. Dvigatelei Akad. Nauk SSSR, No. 3 (1957), 43–62.
20. I. I. Mezhirov and E. E. Solodkin, "The dynamic and turbulent boundary layer in a compressible gas," Tr. Tsentr. aerogidrodinam. Inst. No. 1 (1951)..
21. L. Moore, "The solution of the equations of a laminar boundary layer with dissociation for a compressible fluid with varying physical properties," in Mechanics [Russian translation], No. 5 (1953).
22. Optical Pyrometry of Plasma, Collection of Russian Translations, edited by Prof. N. N. Sobolev, IL (1960).
23. A. S. Predvoditelev, Tables of the Thermodynamic Properties of Air, Izd. Akad. Nauk SSSR, 1957.
24. N. N. Terekhina, "The propagation of a free turbulent gas jet," in: The Investigation of the Physical Bases of Burner and Furnace Operation, edited by L. A. Vulis, Alma-Ata (1957), pp. 125–147.
25. V. B. Tikhonov and E. A. Yakovlev, "Stabilized high-temperature electric arcs of high power (electric-arc plasmotrons)," in: Transactions of the MAI, No. 119, Oborongiz (1960).
26. A. A. Townsend, Structure of Turbulent Shear Flow, Cambridge Univ. Press (1956).
27. A. Unsold, The Physics of Stellar Atmospheres [Russian translation], IL (1949).
28. Physical Gas Dynamics, edited by A. S. Predvoditelev, Izd. Akad. Nauk (1959).
29. G. G. Chernyi, Gas Flow at High Supersonic Velocities, Fizmatgiz (1959).
30. H. Schlichting, Boundary Layer Theory, McGraw-Hill.
31. Yu. A. Shcherbina, "The influence of initial turbulence on the boundaries and range of a submerged jet," in: Investigations in Mechanics and Applied Mathematics, Transactions of MFTI, No. 7, Oborongiz, 1961.
32. O. V. Yakovlevskii, "On the thickness of the turbulent mixing zone on the boundary between two flows of different velocity and density," Izv. Akad. Nauk SSSR, Otd. Tekhn. Nauk, No. 10. (1958).
33. O. V. Yakovlevskii, "The hypothesis of the universality of the ejection properties of turbulent gas jets and its applications," Akad. Nauk SSSR, Otd. Tekhn. Nauk, No. 3 (1961).
34. E. Burhorn, H. Maecher, and F. Peters, "Temperaturemessungen an wasserstabilisierten Hochleistungsbögen," Z. Phys., Vol. 131 (1951), pp. 28–40.
35. R. Weiss, "Untersuchung des Plasmastrahles, der aus einem Hochleistungsbögen austritt," Z. Phys., Vol. 138 (1954), pp. 176–182.
36. W. L. Bade, "Simple analytical approximation to the equation of state of dissociated air," Am. Rocket Soc. J., Vol. 29, No. 4 (1959), pp. 298–299.
37. R. W. Larenz, "Über ein Verfahren zur Messung sehr hoher Temperaturen in nahezu durchlässigen Bogensäulen," Z. Phys., Vol. 129 (1951), pp. 327–342.
38. R. W. Larenz, "Temperaturmessungen in der Säule eines Gerdien-Bogens, Z. Phys., Vol. 129 (1951), pp. 343–364.
39. G. Jürgens, "Temperatur und Elektronendichte in einem Wasserstabilisierten Lichtbogen," Z. Phys., Vol. 134 (1952), pp. 21–41.

40. V. A. Golubev, Yu. V. Moskvin, and S. I. Khovrin, "Theoretical and experimental investigations of water plasmas," Teplofiz. Vysok. Temp., Vol. 3, No. 5 (1965).
41. V. A. Golubev and Yu. N. Ivanov, "The emissivity of argon at high temperatures and pressures," Teplofiz. Vysok. Temp., Vol. 4, No. 5 (1966).

# THE CALCULATION OF TURBULENT JETS OF REAL GASES

V. I. Bakulev

Much attention is being devoted at the present time to problems of propagation of turbulent jets of incompressible and compressible gases, supersonic jets, as well as to problems of the propagation of very-high-temperature jets.

One of the interesting problems in this area concerns the propagation of turbulent jets of real gases.

By a real gas (see Fig. 1) we mean a substance situated at a pressure above the critical pressure, as well as to the right of the upper boundary curve 2, i.e., a one-phase working substance.

For processes taking place at constant pressure, we give an approximate equation of state for a real gas, or, more accurately, the equation connecting the enthalpy with specific volume.

In the following, we consider three problems of the propagation of jets of real gases:

1) The boundary layer of an infinite plane-parallel jet (initial region of the jet);

2) A plane-parallel jet emerging from a very narrow slit (main region of a flat jet);

3) An axially symmetric jet emerging from a very small aperture (main region of an axially symmetric jet).

The calculations are based on the Prandtl theory of turbulence and the assumption that the mixing length for vector quantities is 1/n times as large as those of scalar quantities: $nl_u = l_i$, where $n = 1/Pr_T$ ($Pr_T$ is the turbulent Prandtl number). In solving these problems, we assume that the thicknesses of the dynamic and thermal boundary layers are equal and that $l_u = cx$ for both submerged jets and jets in a parallel stream.

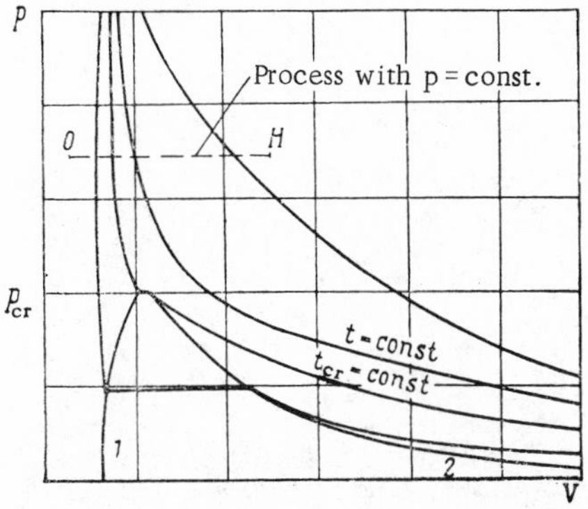


Fig. 1. pV diagram of a real gas.

## 1. Thermodynamic Processes in Free Turbulent Jets of Real Gases

The discharge of the working fluid through the jet nozzle into a chamber and the subsequent intermixing of it with the surrounding medium occurs at approximately constant static pressure p = const. if the jet does not interact with the chamber wall or other jets.

If the working pressure in the chamber is above

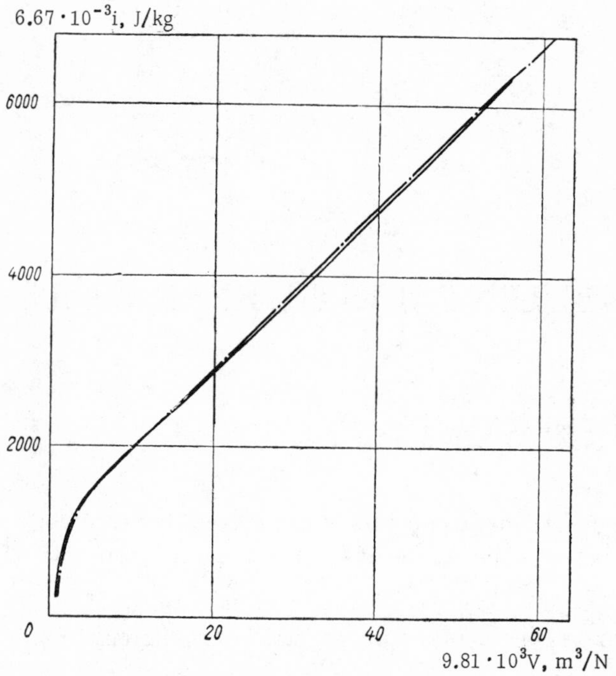


Fig. 2. Variation of the enthalpy of carbon dioxide with specific volume at $p=981 \cdot 10^4$ N/m$^2$: ——— tabulated data, – · – · – approximating curve.

the critical pressure for the given substance, then the thermodynamic process of nonisothermal jet mixing will be represented on a pV diagram by a straight line which will lie above the liquid-vapor phase of the substance (see Fig. 1).

In this process, the working substances will have no heat of vaporization, i.e., the parameters in the boundary layer of the jet will vary continuously without the formation of droplets and their gradual evaporation. In other words, at supercritical pressures the substance will have only a single phase [1-4].

An analytical expression describing the state of a real gas is necessary for jet calculations. Qualitatively, a real gas can be described by van der Waals' equation [5, 6, 7], but there is no single quantitative equation of state valid for all substances. The literature [8, 9] contains equations of state for real gases, but these are different for different substances. In addition, these equations are very complex.

We will attempt to select an approximating function to describe the variation of the enthalpy of a real gas with specific volume $i=f(V)$.

The function giving the variation of enthalpy at pressures above the critical pressure [10-15] for processes that take place at p=const. is of the form of a cubic parabola for all substances (see Figs. 2, 3). Let us take the approximating function to be also a cubic parabola, namely,

$$i=AV+B+\frac{C}{V}+\frac{D}{V^2}, \tag{1.1}$$

where the coefficients A, B, C, and D for any given substance are functions only of the pressure.

This equation describes with sufficient accuracy the behavior of the enthalpy of various real gases (see Figs. 2, 3) at temperatures up to 2500-3500°K.

If the accuracy of Eq. (1.1) is insufficient, we can replace this equation by a sum of functions involving any noncomplex powers of the specific volume,

$$i=\sum_{j=-k}^{j=n} A_j V^j, \tag{1.2}$$

where k and n are any real positive numbers forming a sequence j.

With the help of Eq. (1.2), we can approximate with high accuracy the real behavior of the enthalpy of a real gas in any temperature range. However, the values of the coefficients $A_j$ in this equation cannot be easily determined since for this we require the solution of a system of

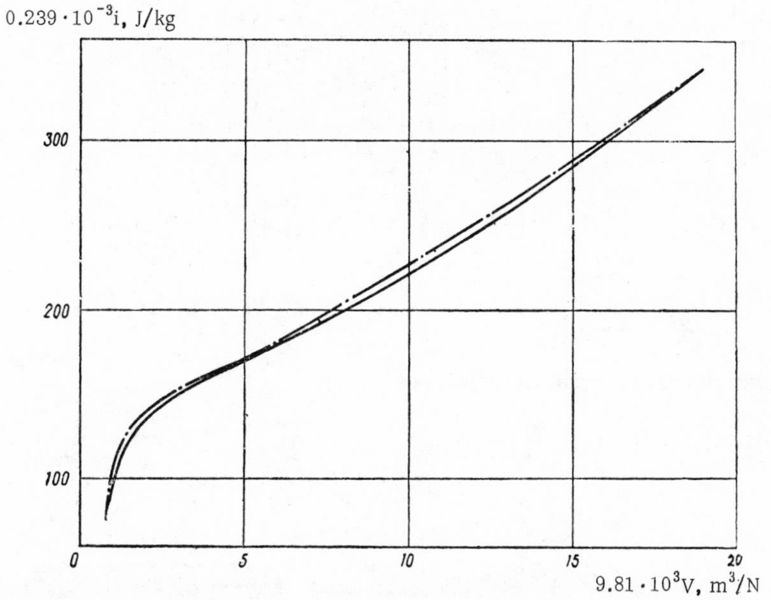


Fig. 3. Variation of the enthalpy of nitrogen with specific volume at $p = 393 \cdot 10^4$ N/m$^2$: —— tabulated data, – · – approximating curve.

(n + k) linear algebraic equations. For further calculations of jets of real gases we can use any of the equations given above. The simple Eq. (1.1) is fully adequate for the study of jet flows at pressures above the critical pressure and at moderate temperatures, so that in the following we will only make use of this equation.

In order to calculate the temperature field in the boundary layer of a jet of real gas, it is also necessary to know the variation of the specific volume with temperature $V = f(T)$ for the given working substance at p = const. (Figs. 4, 5). It is not necessary for us to have an analytical expression for this dependence, since the temperature field in the boundary layer of a jet can be obtained graphically.

Equation (1.1) should be fitted as closely as possible to the graphical dependence $i = f(V)$. We will therefore use the least-squares method [16] for the determination of the coefficients A, B, C, and D.

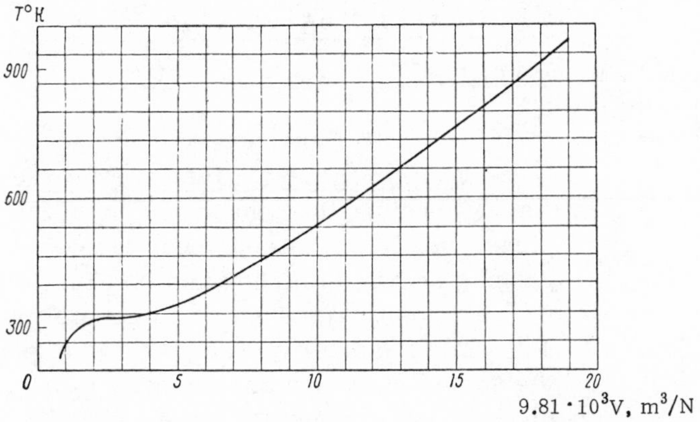


Fig. 4. Variation of the specific volume of carbon dioxide with temperature at $p = 981 \cdot 10^4$ N/m$^2$.

The sum of squares of the deviations between the approximating curve and the actual points (see Fig. 2) should be reduced to a minimum:

$$\sum_{j=1}^{n}\left[i_j - \left(AV_j + B + \frac{C}{V_j} + \frac{D}{V_j^2}\right)\right]^2 = \min,$$

where n is the number of points selected from the actual curve.

Differentiating this equation with respect to A, B, C, and D, we obtain the system of equations

$$\left.\begin{aligned}
&\sum_{j=1}^{n}\left[i_j-\left(AV_j+B+\frac{C}{V_j}+\frac{D}{V_j^2}\right)\right]V_j=0,\\
&\sum_{j=1}^{n}\left[i_j-\left(AV_j+B+\frac{C}{V_j}+\frac{D}{V_j^2}\right)\right]\cdot 1=0,\\
&\sum_{j=1}^{n}\left[i_j-\left(AV_j+B+\frac{C}{V_j}+\frac{D}{V_j^2}\right)\right]\cdot\frac{1}{V_j}=0,\\
&\sum_{j=1}^{n}\left[i_j-\left(AV_j+B+\frac{C}{V_j}+\frac{D}{V_j^2}\right)\right]\cdot\frac{1}{V_j^2}=0,
\end{aligned}\right\} \tag{1.3}$$

from which we can determine the coefficients

$$\overset{*}{a}_{1,1}=\frac{\sum_{j=1}^{n} i_jV_j}{n};\quad \overset{*}{a}_2=\frac{\sum_{j=1}^{n} V_j^2}{n};\quad \overset{*}{a}_1=\frac{\sum_{j=1}^{n} V_j}{n};\quad 1;\quad \overset{*}{a}_{-1}=\frac{\sum_{j=1}^{n} V_j^{-1}}{n};$$

$$\overset{*}{a}_{0,1}=\frac{\sum_{j=1}^{n} i_j}{n};\quad \overset{*}{a}_1;\quad 1;\quad \overset{*}{a}_{-1};\quad \overset{*}{a}_{-2}=\frac{\sum_{j=1}^{n} V_j^{-2}}{n};$$

$$\overset{*}{a}_{-1,1}=\frac{\sum_{j=1}^{n} i_jV_j^{-1}}{n};\quad 1;\quad \overset{*}{a}_{-1};\quad \overset{*}{a}_{-2};\quad \overset{*}{a}_{-3}=\frac{\sum_{j=1}^{n} V_j^{-3}}{n};$$

$$\overset{*}{a}_{-2,1}=\frac{\sum_{j=1}^{n} i_jV_j^{-2}}{n};\quad \overset{*}{a}_{-1};\quad \overset{*}{a}_{-2};\quad \overset{*}{a}_{-3};\quad \overset{*}{a}_{-4}=\frac{\sum_{j=1}^{n} V_j^{-4}}{n}.$$

Substituting these coefficients into system (1.3), we obtain four linear algebraic equations for the determination of A, B, C, and D.

$$\left.\begin{aligned}
&\overset{*}{a}_{1,1}=\overset{*}{a}_2A+\overset{*}{a}_1B+C+\overset{*}{a}_{-1}D,\\
&\overset{*}{a}_{0,1}=\overset{*}{a}_1A+B+\overset{*}{a}_{-1}C+\overset{*}{a}_{-2}D,\\
&\overset{*}{a}_{-1,1}=A+\overset{*}{a}_{-1}B+\overset{*}{a}_{-2}C+\overset{*}{a}_{-3}D,\\
&\overset{*}{a}_{-2,1}=\overset{*}{a}_{-1}A+\overset{*}{a}_{-2}B+\overset{*}{a}_{-3}C+\overset{*}{a}_{-4}D.
\end{aligned}\right\} \tag{1.4}$$

It should be emphasized that the values of the coefficients A, B, C, and D obtained in this way will be valid only for a given working substance and a process which takes place at constant pressure. A change in the pressure or another working substance give other values of the coefficients.

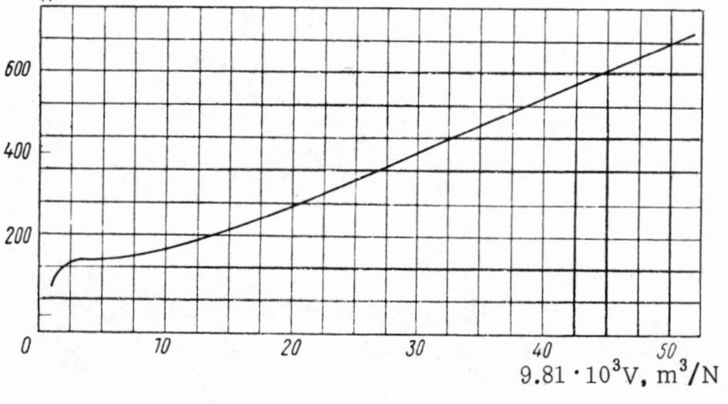


Fig. 5. Variation of the specific volume of nitrogen with temperature at $p=393\cdot 10^4$ N/m$^2$.

## 2. Initial Region of a Plane-Parallel Turbulent Jet of a Real Gas

Formulation of the Problem. Let us consider the case of mixing of two plane-parallel infinite streams of real gases (see Fig. 6). The main stream flows with a velocity $u_0$ (density $\rho_0$, temperature $T_0$), while the other stream is flowing in the same direction with a velocity $u_H$, (density, $\rho_H$, temperature $T_H$). We will place the coordinate origin at the point at which the intermixing starts.

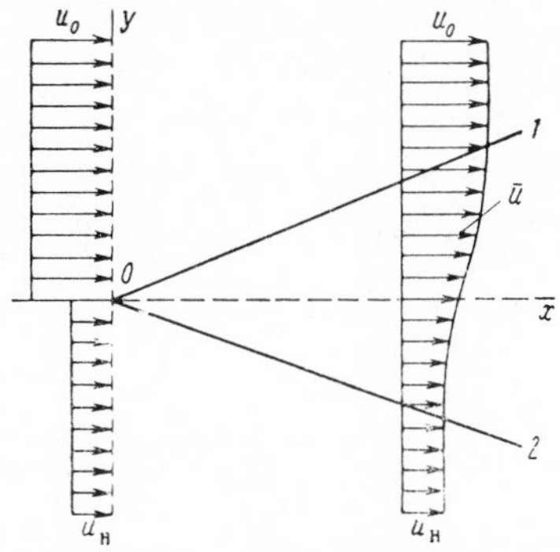


Fig. 6. Boundary layer of a jet.

Starting at the point of joining of the two streams, a free turbulent boundary layer is formed which gradually widens in the direction of motion. The inner boundary of the boundary layer will be denoted by line 1, the outer boundary by line 2.

In the boundary layer, the velocity, density, and temperature change smoothly from their values on the inner boundary ($u_0$, $\rho_0$, $T_0$) to the values on the outer boundary ($u_H$, $\rho_H$, $T_H$).

In order to determine the profiles of the velocity, density, and other parameters in the boundary layer, we will make use of the equations of motion, continuity, energy, and the equation of state [17-26].

The averaging of the equations of motion, continuity, and energy is carried out according to Reynolds's method [24, 25], while the Prandtl theory [17, 24, 26] will be used for the description of turbulent friction.

Equations of Motion and Continuity. The equation for a plane-parallel nonstationary motion of a viscous gas in the direction of the axis of abscissas is of the form [17]

$$\rho \frac{\partial u}{\partial t} + \rho u \frac{\partial u}{\partial x} + \rho v \frac{\partial u}{\partial y} = -\frac{\partial p}{\partial x} + \frac{\partial \tau_{xx}}{\partial x} + \frac{\partial \tau_{xy}}{\partial y}, \tag{2.1}$$

where u and v are the instantaneous velocity components, $\rho$ and p are the instantaneous values of the density and pressure, $\tau_{xx}$ and $\tau_{xy}$ are the components of the normal and tangential stress.

Let us also write down the equation of continuity for the instantaneous values of the velocity and density of a viscous gas in the nonstationary plane-parallel flow,

$$\frac{\partial \rho}{\partial t} + \frac{\partial}{\partial x}(\rho u) + \frac{\partial}{\partial y}(\rho v) = 0. \tag{2.2}$$

We will replace the instantaneous values of all quantities by the sums of their averaged values and their fluctuations. In doing this, we will make use of van Dreist's hypothesis that in addition to velocity, density, and pressure fluctuations, there are fluctuations of the current densities $\rho u$ and $\rho v$ as single entities [17, 27, 28].

In this case, the equations of continuity for the averaged quasi-stationary motion ($\partial\bar{\rho}/\partial t = 0$) will be

$$\frac{\partial}{\partial x}(\overline{\rho u}) + \frac{\partial}{\partial y}(\overline{\rho v}) = 0. \tag{2.3}$$

Making use of the equation of continuity (2.2), we can write Eq. (2.1) as follows:

$$\frac{\partial}{\partial t}(\rho \cdot u) + \frac{\partial}{\partial x}(\rho u \cdot u) + \frac{\partial}{\partial y}(\rho v \cdot u) = -\frac{\partial p}{\partial x} + \frac{\partial \tau_{xx}}{\partial x} + \frac{\partial \tau_{xy}}{\partial y}.$$

In this equation we now replace all instantaneous values of various quantities by their averaged values and obtain the equation of motion for a plane-parallel quasi-stationary motion,

$$\frac{\partial}{\partial t}(\bar{\rho} \cdot \bar{u}) + \frac{\partial}{\partial t}(\overline{\rho' u'}) + \frac{\partial}{\partial x}(\overline{\rho u} \cdot \bar{u}) + \frac{\partial}{\partial x}[\overline{(\rho u)' u'}] + \frac{\partial}{\partial y}(\overline{\rho v} \cdot \bar{u}) + \frac{\partial}{\partial y}[\overline{(\rho v)' u'}] = -\frac{\partial \bar{p}}{\partial x} + \frac{\partial \bar{\tau}_{xx}}{\partial x} + \frac{\partial \bar{\tau}_{xy}}{\partial y}.$$

Assuming that in turbulent jet flow the normal and tangential viscous stresses are small by comparison with the turbulent friction stress, that the pressure is constant, that the derivative of the correlation of fluctuation quantities with respect to x is small by comparison with the derivative with respect to y, and that the motion expressed in terms of the average quantities is a quasi-stationary one $\left[\frac{\partial}{\partial t}(\overline{\rho u})=0;\ \frac{\partial}{\partial t}(\overline{\rho' u'})=0\right]$, we obtain the equation of motion of an averaged two-dimensional turbulent stream

$$\frac{\partial}{\partial x}(\overline{\rho u}\cdot\overline{u})+\frac{\partial}{\partial y}(\overline{\rho v}\cdot\overline{u})=-\frac{\partial}{\partial y}[\overline{(\rho v)' u'}].$$

Using the continuity equation (2.3), we can rewrite this equation as

$$\overline{\rho u}\frac{\partial\overline{u}}{\partial x}+\overline{\rho v}\frac{\partial\overline{u}}{\partial y}=-\frac{\partial}{\partial y}[\overline{(\rho v)' u'}], \tag{2.4}$$

where $\overline{(\rho v)' u'}=\tau_T$ is the turbulent friction stress.

The expression for the turbulent friction stress can be put into the following form [17]:

$$\tau_T=-\overline{(\overline{\rho}+\rho')(\overline{v}+v')u'}\approx-\overline{\rho}\cdot\overline{v'u'},$$

since here $\overline{\rho}\overline{v'}=0$ and the terms $\overline{\rho' v' u'}$ and $\overline{v}\overline{\rho' u'}$ are negligibly small.

In the case of an incompressible-fluid jet, we will assume as in the Prandtl theory that

$$\tau_T=\pm l_u^2\rho\frac{\partial\overline{u}}{\partial y}\left|\frac{\partial\overline{u}}{\partial y}\right|.$$

According to dimension theory, we find that the so-called mixing length $l_u$ has the dimensions of length. In view of the absence of walls [$l_u(y)$ = const.], we take $l_u = cx$ for both a submerged jet and a jet in a stream moving in the same direction [17, 18, 28].

The formula for the turbulent friction stress is

$$\tau_T=\pm c^2x^2\overline{\rho}\frac{\partial\overline{u}}{\partial y}\left|\frac{\partial\overline{u}}{\partial y}\right|.$$

Here, the plus sign is taken when $\partial\overline{u}/\partial y > 0$.

Substituting into Eq. (2.4) the expression for turbulent friction, we obtain the equation of motion for a plane-parallel quasi-stationary jet flow,

$$\overline{\rho v}\frac{\partial\overline{u}}{\partial y}+\overline{\rho u}\frac{\partial\overline{u}}{\partial x}=\pm c^2x^2\frac{\partial}{\partial y}\left[\overline{\rho}\left(\frac{\partial\overline{u}}{\partial y}\right)^2\right]. \tag{2.5}$$

The energy equation for nonstationary plane-parallel flow is of the form [17, 26]

$$\rho\frac{d}{dt}\left(i+\frac{u^2+v^2}{2}\right)=\frac{\partial p}{\partial t}+\frac{\partial}{\partial x}(u\tau_{xx}+v\tau_{xy})+\frac{\partial}{\partial y}(u\tau_{yx}+v\tau_{yy})+\left(\frac{\partial q_x}{\partial x}+\frac{\partial q_y}{\partial y}\right), \tag{2.6}$$

where $\tau_{xy}=\tau_{yx}$ are the components of tangential stress, $\tau_{xx}$, $\tau_{yy}$ are the components of normal stress, $i=c_pT$ is the enthalpy of the gas, and $q_x$ and $q_y$ are terms characterizing the amount of heat being transferred per unit time through a unit area.

Let us transform the energy equation with the help of the continuity equation (2.2),

$$\frac{\partial}{\partial t}(\rho i)+\frac{\partial}{\partial x}(\rho u i)+\frac{\partial}{\partial y}(\rho v i)+\rho\frac{\partial}{\partial t}\left(\frac{u^2}{2}+\frac{v^2}{2}\right)+\rho u\frac{\partial}{\partial x}\left(\frac{u^2}{2}+\frac{v^2}{2}\right)+$$

$$+\rho v\frac{\partial}{\partial y}\left(\frac{u^2}{2}+\frac{v^2}{2}\right)=\frac{\partial p}{\partial t}+\frac{\partial}{\partial x}(u\tau_{xx}+v\tau_{xy})+\frac{\partial}{\partial y}(u\tau_{yx}+v\tau_{yy})+\left(\frac{\partial q_x}{\partial x}+\frac{\partial q_y}{\partial y}\right).$$

Let us replace the instantaneous values of quantities appearing in the energy equation by the sums of their average values and fluctuations. We will also assume that there exist fluctuations of enthalpy as a single quantity [28].

Assuming that the effects due to molecular viscosity and molecular heat conduction are small by comparison with turbulent-mixing effects, that the molecular friction stresses are small by comparison with turbulent friction stress, that pressure is constant, that the transverse velocities are considerably smaller than the longitudinal velocities and that the motion is quasi-stationary [17], we obtain the following approximate energy equation for an averaged two-dimensional turbulent jet:

$$\frac{\partial}{\partial x}(\overline{\rho u}\bar{i})+\frac{\partial}{\partial y}(\overline{\rho v}\bar{i})+\frac{\partial}{\partial y}[\overline{(\rho v)'i'}]+\overline{(\rho v)'u'}\frac{\partial\bar{u}}{\partial y}=0.$$

In this equation we have neglected derivatives of fluctuations with respect to x as being small by comparison with the derivatives with respect to y, we have neglected the terms $\overline{\rho v}\cdot\bar{v}\cdot\partial\bar{v}/\partial y$ and $(\bar{v}^2/2)\cdot\partial(\bar{e}v)/\partial y$ (since $\bar{v}$ is small by comparison with $\bar{u}$), and we have also subtracted the equation of motion and the continuity equation (2.3) from it.

Taking into account the smallness of the quantity $\bar{v}$, we can write

$$\overline{(\rho v)'i'}\approx\bar{\rho}\overline{v'i'}.$$

Then, making use of this relation and the transformations made above for the equation of motion, we will obtain the energy equation

$$\overline{\rho u}\frac{\partial}{\partial x}\bar{i}+\overline{\rho v}\frac{\partial}{\partial y}\bar{i}=-\frac{\partial}{\partial y}[\bar{\rho}\overline{v'i'}]-\bar{\rho}\overline{v'u'}\frac{\partial\bar{u}}{\partial y}. \quad (2.7)$$

The heat flux $W_T$ in a two-dimensional turbulent stream is governed by the correlation between the transverse component of the velocity fluctuations and the enthalpy fluctuations

$$W_T=-\bar{\rho}\overline{v'i'}.$$

Making use of the Prandtl turbulence model, we can obtain the following expression for the heat flux:

$$W_T=\pm\bar{\rho}l_i l_u\left|\frac{\partial\bar{u}}{\partial y}\right|\frac{\partial\bar{i}}{\partial y}, \quad (2.8)$$

where $l_i$ is the so-called mixing length for heat transfer.

The plus sign corresponds to $\partial\bar{u}/\partial y > 0$.

Let us express the turbulent Prandtl number in terms of the mixing lengths: $Pr_T = l_u/l_i$ [28, 29].

Let us express $l_i$ in terms of $l_u$ and $Pr_T$ and substitute it into expression (2.8) after setting $n=1/Pr_T$.

We obtain an expression for the heat flux in turbulent flow

$$W_{\text{т}}=\pm nl_u^2\bar{\rho}\left|\frac{\partial\bar{u}}{\partial y}\right|\frac{\partial\bar{i}}{\partial y}.$$

Substituting into Eq. (2.7) the expression for the heat flux, turbulent friction, and $l_u$, we obtain the energy equation for turbulent plane-parallel quasistationary jet flow,

$$\overline{\rho u}\frac{\partial}{\partial x}\bar{i}+\overline{\rho v}\frac{\partial}{\partial y}\bar{i}=\pm nc^2x^2\frac{\partial}{\partial y}\left[\bar{\rho}\frac{\partial\bar{u}}{\partial y}\frac{\partial\bar{i}}{\partial y}\right]+c^2x^2\bar{\rho}\left(\frac{\partial\bar{u}}{\partial y}\right)^3. \tag{2.9}$$

Transformation of the Equations for the Turbulent Boundary Layer of a Jet of Real Gas. In order to solve the equations of motion and energy we will introduce the new variables

$$x;\quad \varphi=y/ax,$$

where $a=\sqrt[3]{2c^2}$ is an experimental constant.

In this coordinate system, the velocity, current density, gas density, specific volume, and enthalpy will be functions only of $\varphi$

$$\frac{\bar{u}-u_{\text{н}}}{u_0-u_{\text{н}}}=Z(\varphi);\quad \frac{\overline{\rho u}}{\rho_0 u_0}=F'(\varphi);\quad \frac{\bar{\rho}}{\rho_0}=\vartheta(\varphi);\quad \frac{\bar{V}}{V_0}=\theta(\varphi);\quad \frac{\bar{i}}{i_0}=\tau(\varphi).$$

Here, $V_0$ and $i_0$ are the values of the specific volume and enthalpy on the inner boundary of the jet and $V_H$ and $i_H$ are the values of these quantities on the outer boundary; $F'(\varphi)=dF(\varphi)/d\varphi$ is the derivative of a dimensionless function of one independent variable $\varphi$.

In this case, the current function is

$$\psi=\int\overline{\rho u}\,dy=\rho_0 u_0 axF(\varphi).$$

From this, it is easy to obtain the transverse component of the current density

$$\overline{\rho v}=-\frac{\partial\psi}{\partial x}=-\rho_0 u_0 a\left[F(\varphi)+x\frac{dF(\varphi)}{d\varphi}\frac{\partial\varphi}{\partial x}\right]$$

or, in final form,

$$\overline{\rho v}=a\rho_0 u_0(\varphi F'-F).$$

Substituting into the equation of motion the relations given above, and taking into account the relations

$$\frac{\partial\bar{u}}{\partial x}=\frac{d\bar{u}}{d\varphi}\frac{\partial\varphi}{\partial x}=-\frac{\varphi}{x}\frac{d\bar{u}}{d\varphi},\quad \frac{\partial\bar{u}}{\partial y}=\frac{d\bar{u}}{d\varphi}\frac{\partial\varphi}{\partial y}=\frac{1}{ax}\frac{d\bar{u}}{d\varphi},$$

$$\frac{\bar{u}}{u_0}=m+(1-m)Z(\varphi);\quad m=\frac{u_{\text{н}}}{u_0},$$

we obtain

$$-F=\frac{1}{2}(1-m)[\vartheta'Z'+2\vartheta Z''].\tag{2.10}$$

Let us write down the relationship between the main velocity component $\bar{u}$ and the current density $\overline{\rho u}$

$$\overline{\rho u}=\bar{\rho}\bar{u}+\overline{\rho' u'}.$$

Following the Prandtl model of turbulence, we assume that the correlation $\overline{\rho' u'}$ can be expressed in terms of the derivatives of these quantities with respect to y, while the coefficient of proportionality $l_e$ for the density can be taken equal to $l_i$. We can then write

$$\overline{\rho u}=\bar{\rho}\bar{u}+l_i l_u \frac{\partial\bar{\rho}}{\partial y}\frac{\partial\bar{u}}{\partial y}.$$

Substituting into this equation the relations obtained earlier, we finally find

$$F'=\vartheta\left[m+(1-m)Z\right]+a\frac{n}{2}(1-m)\vartheta' Z'. \tag{2.11}$$

Differentiating the equation of motion (2.10) with respect to $\varphi$ and replacing F' by its value from expressions (2.11), we obtain the equation of motion in the following form:

$$Z'''+\frac{3}{2}\frac{\vartheta'}{\vartheta}Z''+\left[a\frac{n}{2}\frac{\vartheta'}{\vartheta}+\frac{1}{2}\frac{\vartheta''}{\vartheta}\right]Z'+Z+\frac{m}{1-m}=0. \tag{2.12}$$

Let us now replace the density function $\vartheta$ in Eq. (2.12) by the specific volume function $\theta(\vartheta=1/\theta)$ and transform to the new independent variable $\eta=(\varphi-\varphi_2)/(\varphi_1-\varphi_2)$, where $\varphi_1-\varphi_2=b_*$ is the dimensionless width of the boundary layer. We will then obtain the equation of motion for a boundary layer of a plane-parallel turbulent jet of a real gas

$$L(Z)=Z'''(\eta)-\frac{3}{2}\frac{\theta'}{\theta}Z''(\eta)-\left\{a\frac{n}{2}b_*\frac{\theta'}{\theta}+\left[\frac{1}{2}\frac{\theta''}{\theta}-\left(\frac{\theta'}{\theta}\right)^2\right]\right\}Z'(\eta)+b_*^3Z(\eta)+\frac{m}{1-m}b_*^3=0. \tag{2.13}$$

In solving the equation of motion (2.13), we make use of the following five boundary conditions.

On the inner boundary of the boundary layer we have $[\eta=1,\ (\varphi=\varphi_1)]$:

1. $\bar{u}=u_0,\ Z(1)=1;$
2. $\frac{\partial\bar{u}}{\partial y}=0,\quad Z'(1)=0;$
3. $\overline{\rho v}=0,\quad Z''(1)=-\varphi_1 b_*^2\frac{1}{1-m}.$

On the outer boundary of the boundary layer we have $[\eta=0,\ (\varphi=\varphi_2)]$:

4. $\bar{u}=u_{\text{н}};\quad Z(0)=0;$
5. $\frac{\partial\bar{u}}{\partial y}=0;\quad Z'(0)=0.$

(2.13a)

Let us transform the energy equation (2.9) using the same relations as were used in the equation of motion. As the result of such a transformation we will obtain the energy equation in terms of the independent variable $\varphi$,

$$-F\tau'=(1-m)\frac{n}{2}[\vartheta'Z'\tau'+\vartheta Z''\tau'+\vartheta Z'\tau'']+(1-m)^3\frac{u_0^2}{2i_0}\vartheta(Z')^3. \tag{2.14}$$

In the case of appreciably subsonic flow, the last term in this equation can be neglected since $u_0^2 \ll 2i_0$ and, consequently, this term will be small by comparison with the others.

Multiplying Eq. (2.10) by $\tau'$ and subtracting it from Eq. (2.14), we obtain

$$k_1\vartheta'Z'\tau'+k_2\vartheta Z''\tau'+\vartheta Z'\tau''=0, \tag{2.15}$$

where $k_1=1-1/n$, $k_2=1-2/n$.

If we now divide Eq. (2.15) by $\vartheta Z'\tau'$, we will obtain the energy equation for a boundary layer of a plane-parallel turbulent jet in the form

$$k_1\frac{\vartheta'}{\vartheta}+k_2\frac{Z''}{Z'}+\frac{\tau''}{\tau'}=0. \tag{2.16}$$

We will make use of the following boundary conditions for the solution of Eq. (2.16).

$$\left.\begin{array}{l}\text{On the inner boundary of the boundary layer we}\\ \text{have } \varphi=\varphi_1,\ i=i_0,\ \bar{\rho}=\rho_0,\ \bar{u}=u_0 \text{ and, consequently,}\\ \tau(\varphi_1)=1,\ \vartheta(\varphi_1)=1,\ Z(\varphi_1)=1;\\ \text{On the outer boundary of the boundary layer we}\\ \text{have } \varphi=\varphi_2,\ i=i_{\text{H}},\ \bar{\rho}=\rho_{\text{H}},\ \bar{u}=u_{\text{H}}, \text{ and, consequently,}\\ \tau(\varphi_2)=\dfrac{i_{\text{H}}}{i_0}=\tau_{\text{H}},\ \vartheta(\varphi_2)=\dfrac{\rho_{\text{H}}}{\rho_0}=\vartheta_{\text{H}},\ Z(\varphi_2)=0.\end{array}\right\} \tag{2.16a}$$

Solution of the Equations of Motion and Energy. Let us rewrite the equation of motion (2.13) as follows:

$$L(Z)=Z'''-\frac{3}{2}\frac{\theta'}{\theta}Z''-\left[a\frac{n}{2}b_*\frac{\theta'}{\theta}+\sigma(\eta)\right]Z'+b_*^3Z+\frac{m}{1-m}b_*^3=0, \tag{2.17}$$

where $\theta'/\theta$ and $\frac{1}{2}\theta''/\theta-(\theta'/\theta)^2=\sigma(\eta)$ are unknown functions of $\eta$, to be determined during the solution of the energy equation.

We will seek the general solution of this equation with the help of Galerkin's method [30, 31],

$$Z_k=\sum_{j=1}^{j=k}\tilde{a}_j\tilde{\varphi}_j,\quad (j=1,2,3.\,.\,.\,.\,.k).$$

For this purpose, we will consider the system of functions

$$\tilde{\varphi}_1=2\eta^3-3\eta^2;\quad \tilde{\varphi}_2=(1-\eta)^2\eta^2;\quad \tilde{\varphi}_3=(1-\eta)^2\eta^3;\quad .\,.\,.\,.\,.\,\tilde{\varphi}_j=(1-\eta)^2\eta^j. \tag{2.18}$$

For any $\tilde{\alpha}_j$, this system will automatically satisfy three of the boundary conditions (2.13a): $Z'(1)=0$, $Z(0)=0$, $Z'(0)=0$.

If we take $\tilde{\alpha}_1=-1$, then system (2.18) will also satisfy the fourth boundary condition $Z(1)=1$.

We will seek the solution of the equation of motion in the second approximation, namely,

$$Z_2 = -(2\eta^3 - 3\eta^2) + \tilde{a}_2 (1-\eta)^2 \eta^2. \tag{2.19}$$

The unknowns in the second approximation are $\tilde{\alpha}_2$, $b_*$, and $\varphi_1$.

Let us write down three equations for the determination of these unknowns

$$\int_0^1 L(Z_2)\tilde{\varphi}_1 d\eta = 0; \quad \int_0^1 L(Z_2)\tilde{\varphi}_2 d\eta = 0; \quad Z_2''(1) = -\varphi_1 b_*^2 \frac{1}{1-m}.$$

Integrating the first two equations, we obtain

$$\left.\begin{aligned} \tilde{a}_2 &= \frac{6 + A_1 + a\frac{n}{2} b_* A_3 + B_1 - 0.372 b_*^3 - 0.5\frac{m}{1-m} b_*^3}{2.4 + A_2 + a\frac{n}{2} b_* A_4 + B_2 + 0.0167 b_*^3}, \\ \tilde{a}_2 &= \frac{-0.4 + A_5 + a\frac{n}{2} b_* A_7 + B_3 + 0.0167 b_*^3 + 0.0333\frac{m}{1-m} b_*^3}{A_6 + a\frac{n}{2} b_* A_8 + B_4 - 0.00159 b_*^3} \end{aligned}\right\} \tag{2.20}$$

In these equations we have

$$\left.\begin{aligned} A_1 &= 36J_4 - 72J_3 + 27J_2, \\ A_2 &= 36J_5 - 90J_4 + 60J_3 - 9J_2, \\ A_3 &= 12J_5 - 30J_4 + 18J_3, \\ A_4 &= 8J_6 - 24J_5 + 22J_4 - 6J_3, \\ A_5 &= 18J_5 - 45J_4 + 36J_3 - 9J_2, \\ A_6 &= 18J_6 - 54J_5 + 57J_4 - 24J_3 + 3J_2, \\ A_7 &= 6J_6 - 18J_5 + 18J_4 - 6J_3, \\ A_8 &= 4J_7 - 14J_6 + 18J_5 - 10J_4 + 2J_3. \\ B_1 &= 12j_5 - 30j_4 + 18j_3, \\ B_2 &= 8j_6 - 24j_5 + 22j_4 - 6j_3, \\ B_3 &= 6j_6 - 18j_5 + 18j_4 - 6j_3, \\ B_4 &= 4j_7 - 14j_6 + 18j_5 - 10j_4 + 2j_3, \end{aligned}\right\} \tag{2.21}$$

where

$$J_k = \int_0^1 \frac{\theta'}{\theta} \eta^k d\eta, \quad j_k = \int_0^1 \sigma(\eta) \eta^k d\eta \quad (k = 2, 3, 4 \ldots).$$

The integrals $J_k$ and $j_k$ can be evaluated analytically or they may be obtained graphically after the energy equation has been solved.

Solving system (2.20) graphically, we find the coefficient $\tilde{\alpha}_2$ and the dimensionless width of the boundary layer $b_*$.

In order to find the third unknown $\varphi_1$, we substitute the value of $Z''_2$ at $\eta = 1$ into the fifth of the boundary conditions (2.13a). As a result of this, we obtain

$$\varphi_1 = (6 - 2\tilde{a}_2)\frac{1}{b_*^2}(1-m). \tag{2.22}$$

In order to determine the convergence of the method, we use analogous procedures to find the solution of Eq. (2.17) in the third approximation,

$$Z_3 = -(2\eta^3 - 3\eta^2) + \tilde{a}_2(1-\eta)^2\eta^2 + \tilde{a}_3(1-\eta)^2\eta^3.$$

Let us write down four equations for the determination of the unknowns $\tilde{\alpha}_2$, $\tilde{\alpha}_3$, $b_*$, and $\varphi_1$.

$$1.\ \int_0^1 L(Z_3)\tilde{\varphi}_1 d\eta = 0; \qquad 2.\ \int_0^1 L(Z_3)\tilde{\varphi}_2 d\eta = 0;$$

$$3.\ \int_0^1 L(Z_3)\tilde{\varphi}_3 d\eta = 0; \qquad 4.\ Z_3''(1) = -\varphi_1 b_*^2 \frac{1}{1-m}.$$

Substituting into these equations the values of $Z_3$, $Z_3'$, $Z_3''$, $Z_3'''$, $\tilde{\varphi}_1$, $\tilde{\varphi}_2$, $\tilde{\varphi}_3$, we obtain after some transformations the following system of equations:

$$\left.\begin{aligned}
&1.\ -\left(6 + A_1 + a\frac{n}{2}b_*A_3 + B_1 - 0.372b_*^3 - 0.5\frac{m}{1-m}b_*^3\right) + \\
&\quad + \tilde{a}_2\left(2.4 + A_2 + a\frac{n}{2}b_*A_4 + B_2 + 0.0167b_*^3\right) + \\
&\quad + \tilde{a}_3\left(2.2 + A_9 + a\frac{n}{2}b_*A_{10} + B_5 + 0.00992b_*^3\right) = 0; \\
&2.\ -\left(-0.4 + A_5 + a\frac{n}{2}b_*A_7 + B_3 + 0.0167b_* + \right. \\
&\quad \left. + 0.0333\frac{m}{1-m}b_*^3\right) + \tilde{a}_2\left(A_6 + a\frac{n}{2}b_*A_8 + B_4 - 0.00159b_*^3\right) + \\
&\quad + \tilde{a}_3\left(0.02857 + A_{11} + a\frac{n}{2}b_*A_{12} + B_6 - 0.0008b_*^3\right) = 0; \\
&3.\ -\left(0.2 - A_{13} - a\frac{n}{2}b_*A_{16} - B_7 - 0.00992b_*^3 - \right. \\
&\quad \left. - 0.01667\frac{m}{1-m}b_*^3\right) + \tilde{a}_2\left(0.02858 - A_{14} - a\frac{n}{2}b_*A_{17} - B_8 + \right. \\
&\quad \left. + 0.0008b_*^3\right) + \tilde{a}_3\left(-A_{15} - a\frac{n}{2}b_*A_{18} - B_9 + 0.000433b_*^3\right) = 0; \\
&4.\ \varphi_1 = (6 - 2\tilde{a}_2 - 2\tilde{a}_3)\frac{1}{b_*^2}(1-m).
\end{aligned}\right\} \qquad (2.23)$$

In these equations, we have

$$\left.\begin{aligned}
A_9 &= 60J_6 - 162J_5 + 126J_4 - 27J_3; \\
A_{10} &= 10J_7 - 31J_6 + 30J_5 - 9J_4; \\
A_{11} &= 30J_7 - 96J_6 + 111J_5 - 54J_4 + 9J_3; \\
A_{12} &= 5J_8 - 18J_7 + 24J_6 - 14J_5 + 3J_4; \\
A_{13} &= 18J_6 - 45J_5 + 36J_4 - 9J_3; \\
A_{14} &= 18J_7 - 54J_6 + 57J_5 - 24J_4 + 3J_3; \\
A_{15} &= 30J_8 - 96J_7 + 111J_6 - 54J_5 + 9J_4; \\
A_{16} &= 6J_7 - 18J_6 + 18J_5 - 6J_4; \\
A_{17} &= 4J_8 - 14J_7 + 18J_6 - 10J_5 + 2J_4; \\
A_{18} &= 5J_9 - 18J_8 + 24J_7 - 14J_6 + 3J_5; \\
B_5 &= 10j_7 - 31j_6 + 30j_5 - 9j_4; \\
B_6 &= 5j_8 - 18j_7 + 24j_6 - 14j_5 + 3j_4; \\
B_7 &= 6j_7 - 18j_6 + 18j_5 - 6j_4; \\
B_8 &= 4j_8 - 14j_7 + 18j_6 - 10j_5 + 2j_4; \\
B_9 &= 5j_9 - 18j_8 + 24j_7 - 14j_6 + 3j_5.
\end{aligned}\right\} \qquad (2.24)$$

The coefficients $A_1 \div A_3$, $B_1 \div B_4$ not listed here, as well as the expressions for $J_k$ and $j_k$ have been given above when we considered the second approximation (2.21).

We eliminate $\tilde{\alpha}_2$ and $\tilde{\alpha}_3$ from the first three equations of system (2.23). As a result of this, we obtain one equation for the variable $b_*$. The solution of this equation for $b_*$ is found graphically. Having determined $b_*$, we can use system (2.23) for the calculation of $\tilde{\alpha}_2$, $\tilde{\alpha}_3$, and $\varphi_1$.

The analysis of the approximate solutions given above can be obtained by comparing them with the exact Prandtl–Tolmin solution. For this purpose, we will first calculate the velocity profile in the boundary layer of an incompressible-gas jet in the second approximation after determining the values of $\tilde{\alpha}_2$, $b_*$, and $\varphi_1$ ($\tilde{\alpha}_2 = -1.532$, $b_* = 3.037$, $\tilde{\varphi}_1 = 0.983$),

$$Z_2 = -(2\eta^3 - 3\eta^2) - 1.532(1-\eta)^2\eta^2.$$

Let us also calculate the velocity profile in the third approximation ($\tilde{\alpha}_2 = -1.479$, $\tilde{\alpha}_3 = -0.051$, $b_* = 3.03$, $\varphi_1 = 0.988$),

$$Z_2 = -(2\eta^3 - 3\eta^2) - 1.479(1-\eta)^2\eta^2 - 0.051(1-\eta)^2\eta^3.$$

Finally, we will give the results of the Prandtl–Tolmin solution [17, 18] ($b_* = 3.021$, $\varphi_1 = 0.981$).

The results of these calculations are given in Table 1 which shows that the agreement of the second and third approximations with the Prandtl–Tolmin solution is satisfactory. Moreover, it should be noted that the third approximation does not lead to any significant improvement by comparison with the second.

To check the convergence of the solutions obtained, let us also calculate the initial region of a jet of carbon dioxide ($CO_2$) at $p = 981 \cdot 10^4$ N/m², $T_0 = 248$°K, $u_H = 0$.

The velocity profile in the second approximation ($\tilde{\alpha}_2 = 1.725$, $b_* = 1.86$, $\varphi_1 = 0.737$) is

$$Z_2 = -(2\eta^3 - 3\eta^2) + 1.725(1-\eta)^2\eta^2$$

TABLE 1

| $\eta$ | 0 | 0.1 | 0.2 | 0.3 | 0.4 | 0.5 | 0.6 |
|---|---|---|---|---|---|---|---|
| $Z_2 = \frac{\bar{u}}{u_0}$ | 0 | 0.0156 | 0.0648 | 0.1484 | 0.2637 | 0.4042 | 0.56 |
| $Z_3 = \frac{\bar{u}}{u_0}$ | 0 | 0.016 | 0.0661 | 0.1501 | 0.2656 | 0.406 | 0.5612 |
| $F' = \frac{\bar{u}}{u_0}$ | 0 | 0.0162 | 0.065 | 0.147 | 0.264 | 0.405 | 0.56 |

Continuation

| $\eta$ | 0.7 | 0.8 | 0.9 | 1 | |
|---|---|---|---|---|---|
| $Z_2 = \frac{\bar{u}}{u_0}$ | 0.7165 | 0.856 | 0.961 | 1 | Second approximation |
| $Z_3 = \frac{\bar{u}}{u_0}$ | 0.7173 | 0.8566 | 0.9611 | 1 | Third approximation |
| $F' = \frac{\bar{u}}{u_0}$ | 0.716 | 0.855 | 0.961 | 1 | Prandtl–Tolmin solution |

TABLE 2

| $\eta$ | 0 | 0,1 | 0,2 | 0,3 | 0,4 | 0,5 | 0,6 |
|---|---|---|---|---|---|---|---|
| $Z_2=\frac{\bar{u}}{u_0}$ | 0 | 0.042 | 1,1481 | 0.292 | 0,4512 | 0,6078 | 0,7471 |
| $Z_3=\frac{\bar{u}}{u_0}$ | 0 | 0,0417 | 0,1473 | 0,291 | 0,45 | 0,6064 | 0,7466 |

Continuation

| $\eta$ | 0.7 | 0,8 | 0,9 | 1,0 | |
|---|---|---|---|---|---|
| $Z_2=\frac{\bar{u}}{u_0}$ | 0.8599 | 0,9409 | 0,9804 | 1 | Second approximation |
| $Z_3=\frac{\bar{u}}{u_0}$ | 0,8595 | 0,9407 | 0,9803 | 1 | Third approximation |

and the velocity profile in the third approximation ($\tilde{\alpha}_2=1.685$, $\tilde{\alpha}_3=0.0452$, $b_*=1.85$, $\varphi_1=0.742$) is

$$Z_3=-(2\eta^3-3\eta^2)+1.685(1-\eta)^2\eta^2+0.0452(1-\eta^2)\eta^3.$$

The calculations are given in Table 2.

As shown by the calculations, the convergence of the solutions is satisfactory. The second approximation is very little different from the third, so that it is recommended that the second approximation be used in the future.

Let us now proceed to the solution of the energy equation (2.16),

$$k_1\frac{\vartheta'}{\vartheta}+k_2\frac{Z''}{Z'}+\frac{\tau''}{\tau'}=0$$

with boundary conditions (2.16a).

As the result of the integration of this equation, we obtain

$$\vartheta^{k_1}\tau'=c_1(Z')^{-k_2}. \tag{2.25}$$

Replacing $\vartheta$ by $\theta$ ($\vartheta=1/\theta$), $\varphi$ by $\eta$ [$\eta=(\varphi-\varphi_2)/(\varphi_1-\varphi_2)$] in Eq. (2.25), and introducing the equation of state $i=f(V)$ after putting it into the dimensionless form $\tau=f(\theta)$, and differentiating the latter:

$$\tau'=f'(\theta)\frac{d\theta}{d\eta},$$

we obtain the energy equation (2.25) in the form

$$\frac{f'(\theta)}{\theta^{k_1}}d\theta=\overset{*}{c_1}(Z')^{-k_2}d\eta. \tag{2.26}$$

Integrating Eq. (2.26), we obtain

$$\int\frac{f'(\theta)}{\theta^{k_1}}d\theta=\overset{*}{c_1}\int(Z')^{-k_2}d\eta+\overset{*}{c_2}. \tag{2.27}$$

The left-hand side of this equation can be easily integrated if the equation of state is taken as a polynomial in V [Eq. (1.2)]. Recommendations governing the choice of the approximating function are given in Section 1.

For jets of real gases at moderate temperatures we will use Eq. (1.1) which after differentiation becomes

$$i_0\tau' = \left(AV_0 - \frac{C}{V_0\theta^2} - \frac{2D}{V_0^2\theta^3}\right)\theta'. \tag{2.28}$$

Substituting expression (2.28) into Eq. (2.27) and integrating the left-hand side of this equation, we obtain

$$\frac{AV_0\dfrac{1}{1-k_1}\theta + \dfrac{C}{V_0(1+k_1)}\dfrac{1}{\theta} + \dfrac{2D}{V_0^2(2+k_1)}\dfrac{1}{\theta^2}}{\theta^{k_1}} = c_1^*\int (Z')^{-k_2}d\eta + c_2^*. \tag{2.29}$$

There is a remaining integral on the right-hand side of (2.29) and this can be evaluated during the simultaneous solution of the equations of motion and energy as follows. Let us take a profile for an incompressible fluid or a profile obtained from the solution with $n=2$ ($k_2=0$). Using Eq. (2.29), we determine the $\theta$ profile, while the improved profile of the velocity Z can be found from the equation of motion. Substituting the new Z profile into Eq. (2.29), we repeat the calculations.

In this way, we use the method of successive approximations to determine the Z and $\theta$ profiles. The constants $c_1^*$ and $c_2^*$ are determined from the boundary conditions (2.16a).

Making use of the solutions of the energy equation (2.29), we can find the expressions for the integrands of the integrals $J_k$ and $j_k$.

The function $\theta'/\theta$, appearing in the $J_k$ and $j_k$ integrals is of the form

$$\frac{\theta'}{\theta} = \frac{c_1^*\theta^{k_1}(Z')^{-k_2}}{AV_0\theta - \dfrac{C}{V_0\theta} - \dfrac{2D}{V^2}\dfrac{1}{\theta^2}}, \tag{2.30}$$

while the function $\theta''/\theta$ appearing in the integral $j_k$ can be written as

$$\frac{\theta''}{\theta} = \frac{c_1^{*2}(k_1+1)\theta^{2k_1}(Z')^{-2k_2}}{Y^2(\theta)} - \frac{k_2c_1^*\theta^{k_1}(Z')^{-(k_2+1)}Z''}{Y(\theta)} - \frac{c_1^{*2}\theta^{(2k_1+1)}(Z')^{-2k_2}Y'(\theta)}{Y^3(\theta)}, \tag{2.31}$$

where

$$Y(\theta) = AV_0\theta - \frac{C}{V_0}\frac{1}{\theta} - \frac{2D}{V_0^2}\frac{1}{\theta^2},$$

$$Y'(\theta) = AV_0 + \frac{C}{V_0}\frac{1}{\theta^2} + \frac{4D}{V_0^2}\frac{1}{\theta^3}.$$

In order for us to calculate the integrals $J_k$ and $j_k$, we have to construct graphs of the functions $\theta'/\theta$ and $\sigma(\eta) = \frac{1}{2}\theta''/\theta - (\theta'/\theta)^2$. In general these integrals can only be evaluated graphically [32].

If we assume that $Pr_T = 0.5$ ($n=2$, $k_2=0$), then Eq. (2.29) and the functions (2.30), (2.31) can be simplified.

The solution of the energy equation (2.16) will be

$$\frac{AV_0\dfrac{1}{1-k_1}\theta + \dfrac{C}{V_0(1+k_1)}\dfrac{1}{\theta} + \dfrac{2D}{V_0^2(2+k_1)}\dfrac{1}{\theta^2}}{\theta^{k_1}} = c_1^*\eta + c_2^*. \tag{2.32}$$

TABLE 3

| | $T_H/T_0$ | | | | | | | | | | | | | |
|---|---|---|---|---|---|---|---|---|---|---|---|---|---|---|
| $\eta$ | | 1 | 1.1065 | 1.2295 | 1.4340 | 1.6390 | 2.4590 | 3.2790 | 4.0980 | 6.1470 | 8.1970 | 10.6560 | 12.2950 | 13.9340 |
| $\tau_1$ | 8.27 | 1 | 0.9109 | 0.8380 | 0.7570 | 0.7050 | 0.6040 | 0.5560 | 0.5230 | 0.4610 | 0.412 | 0.3630 | 0.3330 | 0.3040 |
| $\tau_1$ | 6.31 | 1 | 0.9000 | 0.8186 | 0.7290 | 0.6710 | 0.5580 | 0.5040 | 0.4670 | 0.3980 | 0.3440 | 0.2880 | 0.2550 | 0.2230 |
| $\tau_1$ | 3.64 | 1 | 0.8790 | 0.7790 | 0.6710 | 0.6010 | 0.4640 | 0.3990 | 0.3530 | 0.2700 | 0.2040 | 0.1360 | 0.0950 | 0.0570 |
| $\tau$ | | 1 | 1.3110 | 1.9740 | 2.6230 | 2.9670 | 3.8890 | 4.2950 | 4.7800 | 5.7050 | 6.4330 | 7.3770 | 8.0000 | 8.5900 |
| $\gamma$ | | 1 | 1.1600 | 1.3730 | 1.5330 | 1.6670 | 1.7330 | 1.8270 | 1.9070 | 2.0270 | 2.2400 | 2.6130 | 2.9330 | 3.2270 |
| $\eta''/\eta$ | 8.27 | −1.0111 | −1.280 | −1.625 | −2.261 | −2.942 | −5.341 | −6.507 | −6.772 | −6.249 | −5.575 | −4.943 | −4.616 | −4.342 |
| $\eta'/\eta$ | 6.31 | −0.905 | −1.146 | −1.455 | −2.024 | −2.634 | −4.781 | −5.826 | −6.063 | −5.594 | −4.991 | −4.425 | −4.133 | −3.887 |
| $\eta'/\eta$ | 3.64 | −0.746 | −0.944 | −1.199 | −1.668 | −2.170 | −3.940 | −4.801 | −4.996 | −4.610 | −4.113 | −3.647 | −3.406 | −3.203 |
| $\sigma(\tau_1)$ | 8.27 | 0.695 | 1.067 | 1.614 | 2.711 | 3.767 | 3.388 | −13.220 | −22.790 | −26.220 | −22.340 | −18.022 | −15.828 | −14.036 |
| $\sigma(\tau_1)$ | 6.31 | 0.557 | 0.855 | 1.294 | 2.173 | 3.019 | 2.715 | −10.590 | −18.266 | −21.017 | −17.908 | −14.445 | −12.686 | −11.250 |
| $\sigma(\tau_1)$ | 3.64 | 0.378 | 0.581 | 0.879 | 1.476 | 2.050 | 1.845 | −7.195 | −12.405 | −14.27 | −12.161 | −9.809 | −8.616 | −7.640 |

Continuation

| | $T_H/T_0$ | | | | | | | | | | | | |
|---|---|---|---|---|---|---|---|---|---|---|---|---|---|
| $\eta$ | | 16.6230 | 18.8520 | 20.4920 | 22.1310 | 24.5900 | 26.2290 | 28.6880 | 30.3280 | 32.7870 | 35.2460 | 36.885 | 38.5250 |
| $\tau_1$ | 8.27 | 0.2620 | 0.2290 | 0.2111 | 0.1850 | 0.1540 | 0.1340 | 0.1050 | 0.0860 | 0.0590 | 0.0330 | 0.0160 | 0 |
| $\tau_1$ | 6.31 | 0.1760 | 0.1390 | 0.1140 | 0.0890 | 0.0550 | 0.0323 | 0 | | | | | |
| $\tau_1$ | 3.64 | 0 | | | | | | | | | | | |
| $\tau$ | | 9.5380 | 10.3610 | 10.9840 | 11.5740 | 12.4590 | 13.1150 | 14.0330 | 14.6560 | 15.6060 | 16.5770 | 17.2130 | 17.869 |
| $\gamma$ | | 3.7330 | 4.2270 | 4.5330 | 4.8530 | 5.3870 | 5.7330 | 6.3060 | 6.6400 | 7.1470 | 7.8400 | 8.0530 | 8.4000 |
| $\eta'/\eta$ | 8.27 | −3.980 | −3.739 | −3.588 | −3.452 | −3.276 | −3.172 | −3.033 | −2.950 | −2.837 | −2.736 | −2.675 | −2.617 |
| $\eta'/\eta$ | 6.31 | −3.564 | −3.347 | −3.212 | −3.090 | −2.933 | −2.839 | −2.715 | | | | | |
| $\eta'/\eta$ | 3.64 | −2.937 | | | | | | | | | | | |
| $\sigma(\tau_1)$ | 8.27 | −11.841 | −10.466 | −9.320 | −8.928 | −8.046 | −7.534 | −6.899 | −6.527 | −6.036 | −5.616 | −5.366 | −5.137 |
| $\sigma(\tau_1)$ | 6.31 | −9.491 | −8.389 | −7.471 | −7.156 | −6.149 | −6.045 | −5.530 | | | | | |
| $\sigma(\tau_1)$ | 3.64 | −6.445 | | | | | | | | | | | |

When Eq. (2.32) is used, the $\theta$ profile is found directly from this equation.

Expressions (2.30) and (2.31) with $Pr_T = 0.5$ become

$$\frac{\theta'}{\theta} = \frac{c_1^* \theta^{k_1}}{AV_0\theta - \frac{C}{V_0}\frac{1}{\theta} - \frac{2D}{V_0^2}\frac{1}{\theta^2}}, \tag{2.33}$$

$$\frac{\theta''}{\theta} = \frac{c_1^{*2}(k_1+1)\theta^{2k_1}}{Y^2(\theta)} - \frac{c_1^{*2}\theta^{(2k_1+1)}Y'(\theta)}{Y^3(\theta)}. \tag{2.34}$$

It can be seen from Eq. (2.32) and expressions (2.33) and (2.34) that the calculations become appreciably simpler when $Pr_T = 0.5$. The equations given above allow us to obtain the variations of velocity, density, enthalpy, and temperature across the initial section of the jet.

Sample Calculations

1. Let us consider the initial region of a plane-parallel turbulent submerged jet of nitrogen at a pressure of $392\ 10^4$ N/m$^2$ and a temperature $T_0 = 75$°K.

The propagation of the jet occurs in a medium consisting of nitrogen.

The turbulent Prandtl number is equal to 0.5 ($k_1 = 0.5$, $k_2 = 0$) and the coefficient $a$ is equal to 0.07.

The coefficients appearing in the equation of state are: A = 94.74, B = 1017.28, C = 106.99, D = –1361.23.

The approximate equation of state is shown in Fig. 3.

The parameters of nitrogen on exit from the nozzle are: $T_0 = 75$°K, $V_0 = 0.124 \cdot 10^{-3}$ m$^3$/N, $i_0 = 45.8 \cdot 10^3$ J/kg.

The parameters of the surrounding medium are:

1. $\frac{T_H}{T_0} = 3.64$, $V_H = 2.065 \cdot 10^{-3}$ m$^3$/n, $i_0 = 436 \cdot 10^3$ J/kg;

2. $\frac{T_H}{T_0} = 6.31$, $V_H = 3.57 \cdot 10^{-3}$ m$^3$/n, $i_0 = 642 \cdot 10^3$ J/kg;

3. $\frac{T_H}{T_0} = 8.27$, $V_H = 4.8 \cdot 10^{-3}$ m$^3$/n, $i_0 = 816 \cdot 10^3$ J/kg.

Selecting a number of values of $\bar{V}$ in the range $V_0$ to $V_H$, we determine $\theta = \bar{V}/V_0$.

Substituting the values of $\theta$ into the energy equation (2.32), we find the corresponding values of $\eta$. The profile of the relative specific volume is shown graphically in Fig. 7.

Making use of the graphs of Figs. 2 and 4, we find the values of $\bar{i}$ and $\bar{T}$ corresponding to the selected values of $\bar{V}$.

We now determine the profiles of $\tau = \bar{i}/i_0$ (Fig. 8) and $\gamma = \bar{T}/T_0$ (Fig. 9). Using Eqs. (2.33) and (2.34), we calculate the functions $\theta'/\theta$ (Fig. 10) and $\theta''/\theta$ and determine the function $\sigma(\eta) = \frac{1}{2}\theta''/\theta - (\theta'/\theta)^2$ (Fig. 11).

The results of all calculations are given in Table 3. In the graphs of $\theta'/\theta = f(\eta)$ and $\sigma(\eta)$ (Figs. 10 and 11), we subdivide the interval of $\eta$ (0 – 1) into r equal subdivisions of width 1/r.

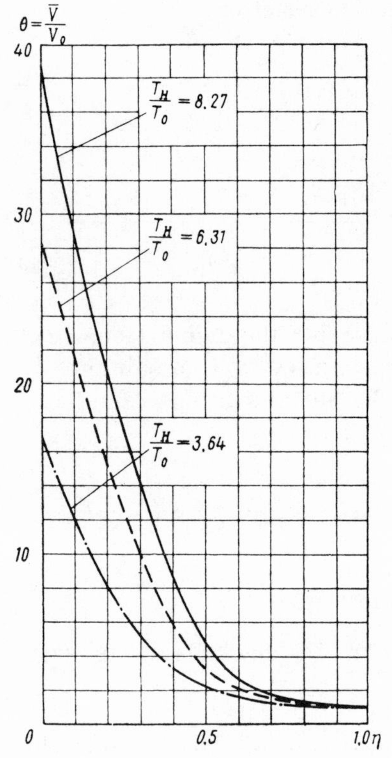


Fig. 7. The profiles of the specific volume in the boundary layer of the jet.

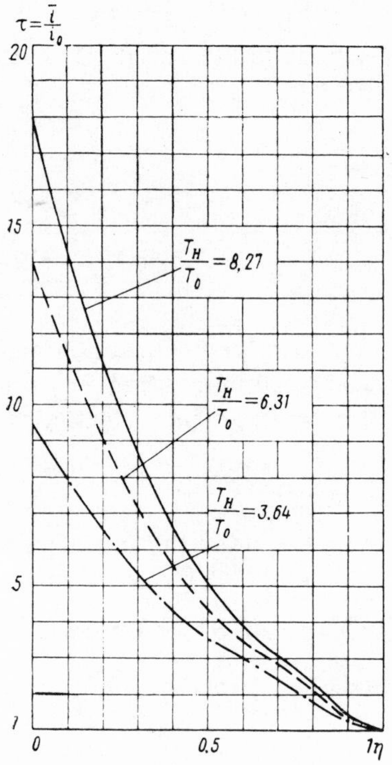


Fig. 8. Enthalpy profiles in the boundary layer of the jet.

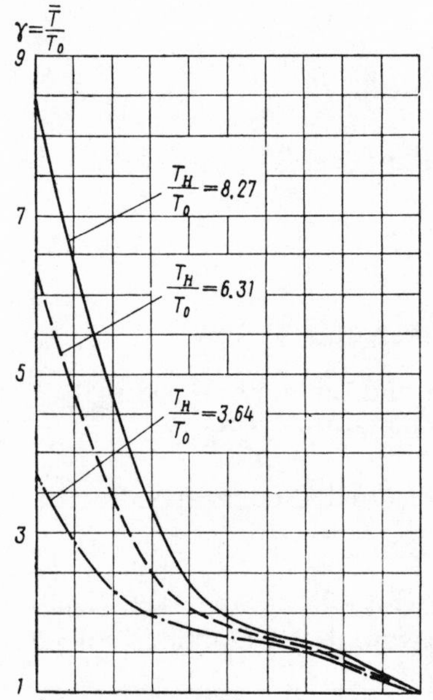


Fig. 9. Temperature profiles in the initial section of the jet.

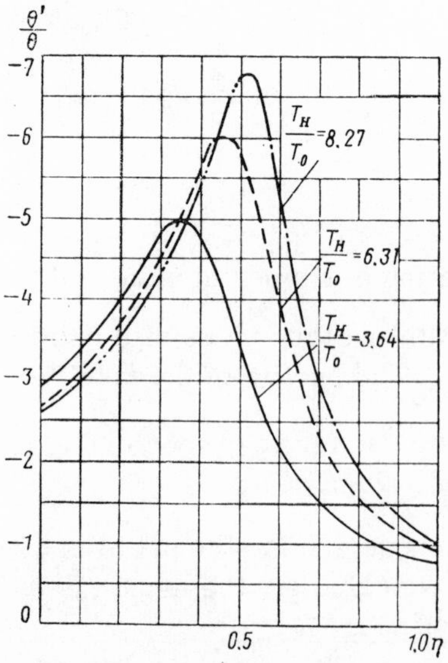


Fig. 10. Profiles of the function $\theta'/\theta$ in the boundary layer of the jet.

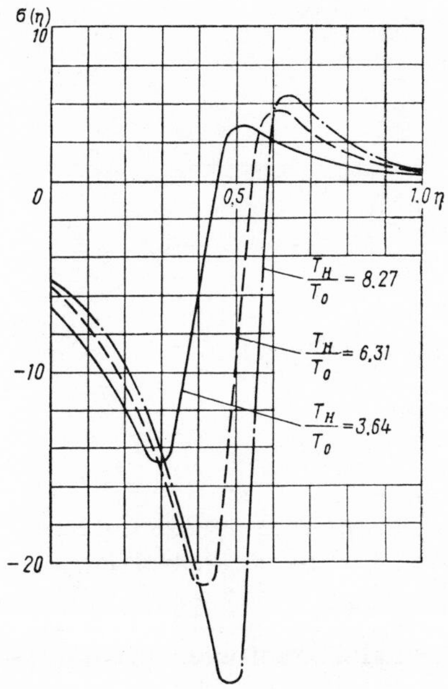


Fig. 11. Profiles of the function $\sigma(\eta)$ in the boundary layer of the jet.

The formula for the evaluation of the integral $J_k$ by the trapezoidal-rule method is of the form

$$J_k=\frac{1}{r}\left[\left(\frac{\theta'}{\theta}\right)_1\eta_1^k+\left(\frac{\theta'}{\theta}\right)_2\eta_2^k+\ldots+\left(\frac{\theta'}{\theta}\right)_{r-1}\eta_{r-1}^k+0.5\left(\frac{\theta'}{\theta}\right)_r\eta_r^k\right] \tag{2.35}$$

while the corresponding formula for the integral $j_k$ is

$$j_k=\frac{1}{r}\left[\sigma_1\eta_1^k+\sigma_2\eta_2^k+\ldots+\sigma_{r-1}\eta_{r-1}^k+0.5\sigma_r\eta_r^k\right]. \tag{2.36}$$

The integral $J_k$ has been calculated with $r=10$, the integral $j_k$ with $r=20$.

The values of the integrals are given in Table 4.

Having determined the coefficients $A_1$, $A_2$, ..., $B_1$, $B_2$, ... [from Eqs. (2.21)] for the second approximation, we solve the system of equations (2.20), find the values of $b_*$ and $\tilde{a}_2$, and determine $\varphi_1$ and $\varphi_2$ from Eq. (2.22).

The results of the calculations are given in Table 5.

The velocity profile (Fig. 12) is calculated from Eq. (2.19).

From Eqs. (2.11) and (2.19) we obtain a formula for the determination of the total head in terms of the independent variable $\eta$,

$$\frac{\overline{\rho u}\,(\overline{u}-u_{\text{н}})}{\rho_0 u_0\,(u_0-u_{\text{н}})}=\frac{1}{\theta}\,[mZ+(1-m)\,Z^2]\;-a\frac{n}{2}\,\frac{\theta'}{\theta^2}\,Z'Z\,\frac{1}{b_*^2}\,(1-m). \tag{2.37}$$

We now determine the profile of the total thrust with the condition that $u_H=0$ and $m=0$ (Fig. 13). The results of the calculations of the velocity and total-head profiles are given in Table 6.

TABLE 4

| $k$ | 2 | 3 | 4 | 5 | 6 |
|---|---|---|---|---|---|
| $J_k$ | —0.5573 | —0.3480 | —0.2443 | —0.1860 | —0.1498 |
| $j_k$ | 0.0149 | 0.1251 | 0.1287 | 0.1111 | 0.0926 |
| $J_k$ | —0.7819 | —0.4938 | —0.3436 | —0.2570 | —0.2032 |
| $j_k$ | —0.3257 | 0.0228 | 0.1227 | 0.1403 | 0.1319 |
| $J_k$ | —0.9271 | —0.5938 | —0.4147 | —0.3093 | —0.2430 |
| $j_k$ | —0.6863 | —0.1251 | 0.0767 | 0.1409 | 0.1522 |

Continuation

| $k$ | 7 | 8 | 9 | |
|---|---|---|---|---|
| $J_k$ | —0.1257 | —0.1086 | —0.0960 | $\frac{T_{\text{н}}}{T_0}=3.64$ |
| $j_k$ | 0.0774 | 0.0656 | 0.0566 | |
| $J_k$ | —0.1676 | —0.1428 | —0.1248 | $\frac{T_{\text{н}}}{T_0}=6.31$ |
| $j_k$ | 0.1168 | 0.1018 | 0.0887 | |
| $J_k$ | —0.1988 | —0.1681 | —0.1458 | $\frac{T_{\text{н}}}{T_0}=8.27$ |
| $j_k$ | 0.1441 | 0.1302 | 0.1119 | |

TABLE 5

| $\frac{T_H}{T_0}$ | $\tilde{a}_2$ | $b_*$ | $\varphi_1$ | $\varphi_2$ |
|---|---|---|---|---|
| 3.64 | 1.14 | 2.26 | 0.728 | —1.532 |
| 6.31 | 1.93 | 1.945 | 0,566 | —1.379 |
| 8,27 | 2.35 | 1.695 | 0.452 | —1.243 |

As a result of all this, we obtain the variations of the main parameters across the boundary layer of a submerged jet of nitrogen at a pressure of $p=392 \cdot 10^4$ N/m$^2$ at several temperatures of the surrounding medium.

2. Let us consider the initial region of a turbulent plane-parallel jet of incompressible fluid in a medium moving in the same direction. In this case $\theta=1$.

We select several values of the quantity $m=u_H/u_0$ in the range 0 to 1.

Solving the system of equations (2.20), we determine the values of $\tilde{a}_2$, $b_*$, and $\varphi_1$ as a function of m (Table 7).

The results of the calculation of velocity profiles in the boundary layer of a jet for values of the relative velocity of the parallel current of m = 0, m = 0.3, and m = 0.9 are given in Table 8 and are plotted graphically in the form of curves of $Z=f(\eta)$, $Z=f(\varphi)$, and $b_*/b_{*\,m=0}=f(m)$ in Figs. 14, 15, and 16.

For comparison purposes, let us plot on the graph of $b_*/b_{*\,m=0}=f(m)$ the analogous dependences obtained by G. N. Abramovich [17]:

$$\frac{b_*}{b_{*m=0}} = \frac{1-m}{1+m}$$

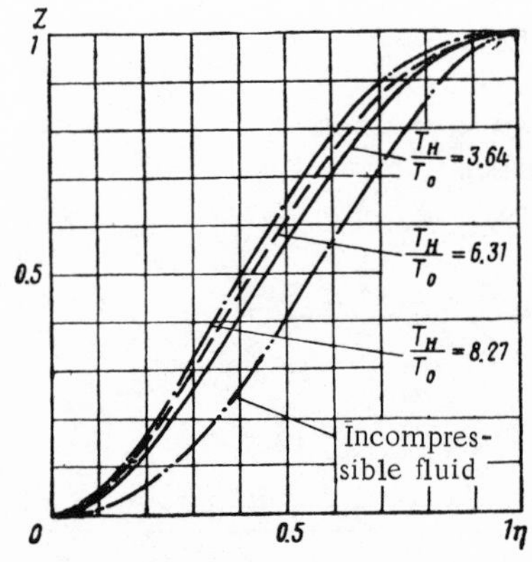


Fig. 12. Velocity profiles in the boundary layer of the jet.

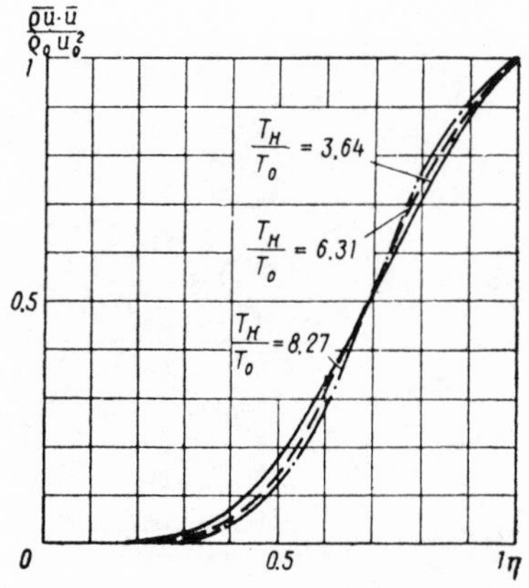


Fig. 13. Total-head profiles in the boundary layer of the jet.

TABLE 6

| $\eta$ | 0 | 0.1 | 0.2 | 0.3 | 0.4 | 0.5 | 0.6 | 0.7 | 0.8 | 0.9 | 10 | $\frac{T_H}{T_0}$ |
|---|---|---|---|---|---|---|---|---|---|---|---|---|
| $Z$ | 0 | 0.0372 | 0.1332 | 0.2663 | 0.4177 | 0.5714 | 0.7137 | 0.8343 | 0.9252 | 0.9812 | 1 | |
| $\frac{\overline{\varrho u}\cdot\bar{u}}{\varrho_0\cdot u_0^2}$ | 0 | 0.0002 | 0.0032 | 0.0216 | 0.070 | 0.1782 | 0.3277 | 0.5142 | 0.7112 | 0.8793 | 1 | 3.64 |
| $\varphi$ | −1.5317 | −1.3057 | −1.0797 | −0.8537 | −0.6277 | −0.4017 | −0.1757 | 0.0503 | 0.2763 | 0.5023 | 0.7283 | |
| $Z$ | 0 | 0.0436 | 0.1534 | 0.3012 | 0.463 | 0.6205 | 0.7590 | 0.8692 | 0.9454 | 0.9876 | 1 | |
| $\frac{\overline{\varrho u}\cdot\bar{u}}{\varrho_0\cdot u_0^2}$ | 0 | 0.0002 | 0.0019 | 0.0131 | 0.0479 | 0.1479 | 0.3215 | 0.5260 | 0.7467 | 0.8923 | 1 | 6.31 |
| $\varphi$ | −1.3793 | −1.1848 | −0.9903 | −0.7953 | −0.601 | −0.4073 | −0.2123 | −0.0193 | 0.1760 | 0.3701 | 0.5657 | |
| $Z$ | 0 | 0.0470 | 0.1642 | 0.3196 | 0.4874 | 0.6469 | 0.7837 | 0.8876 | 0.9562 | 0.9910 | 1 | |
| $\frac{\overline{\varrho u}\cdot\bar{u}}{\varrho_0\cdot u_0^2}$ | 0 | 0.0002 | 0.0014 | 0.0077 | 0.0884 | 0.1207 | 0.2865 | 0.5017 | 0.7679 | 0.8987 | 1 | 8.27 |
| $\varphi$ | −1.2425 | −1.0730 | −0.9035 | −0.7340 | −0.5645 | −0.3950 | −0.2255 | −0.0560 | 0.1135 | 0.2830 | 0.4525 | |

TABLE 7

| $m$ | 0 | 0.15 | 0.3 | 0.5 | 0.7 | 0.9 |
|---|---|---|---|---|---|---|
| $\tilde{a}_2$ | −1.532 | −1.0 | −0.705 | −0.43 | −0.22 | 0 |
| $b_*$ | 3.037 | 2.67 | 2.37 | 2.01 | 1.62 | 1.08 |
| $\varphi_1$ | 0.983 | 0.955 | 0.92 | 0.856 | 0.736 | 0.525 |

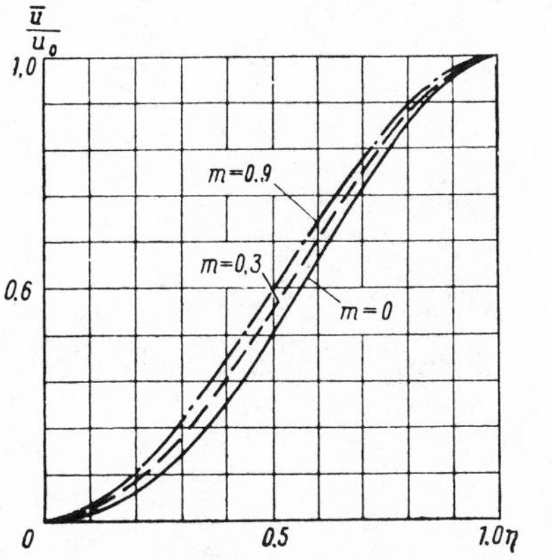


Fig. 14. Profiles of the excess velocity in the boundary layer of a jet of incompressible fluid.

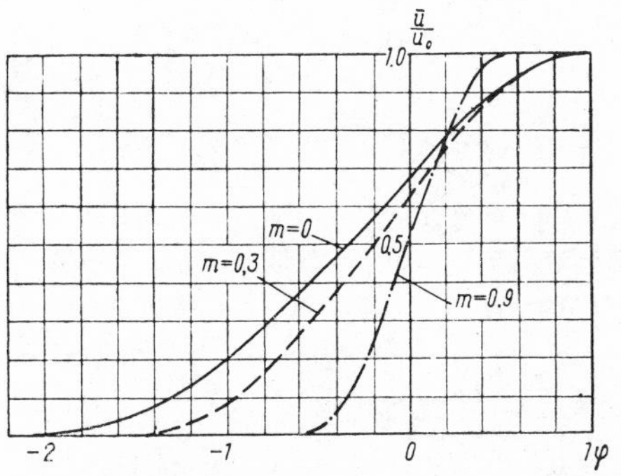


Fig. 15. Variation of the excess velocity in the boundary layer of a jet along the coordinate $\varphi$.

TABLE 8

| $\eta$ | 0 | 0,1 | 0.2 | 0,3 | 0.4 | 0.5 |
|---|---|---|---|---|---|---|
| $Z$ | 0 | 0,0156 | 0.0648 | 0.1484 | 0.2637 | 0,4042 |
| $\varphi$ | —2.054 | —1.75 | —1.446 | —1.1441 | —0,838 | —0.534 |
| $Z$ | 0 | 0.0223 | 0.086 | 0.185 | 0,3114 | 0.456 |
| $\varphi$ | —1.454 | 1.217 | —0.979 | —0.742 | —0.505 | —0.269 |
| $Z$ | 0 | 0.028 | 0.104 | 0.216 | 0,352 | 0.5 |
| $\varphi$ | —0.555 | 0.447 | —0.339 | —0.231 | —0.123 | —0.015 |

Continuation

| $\eta$ | 0,6 | 0.7 | 0.8 | 0.9 | 1.0 | |
|---|---|---|---|---|---|---|
| $Z$ | 0.56 | 0.7165 | 0.856 | 0.961 | 1.0 | $m=0$ |
| $\varphi$ | —0.23 | 0.07 | 0.376 | 0.686 | 0.983 | |
| $Z$ | 0.6074 | 0.753 | 0.878 | 0.966 | 1.0 | $m=0.3$ |
| $\varphi$ | —0.032 | 0.206 | 0.444 | 0.686 | 0.92 | |
| $Z$ | 0.648 | 0.784 | 0.896 | 0.97 | 1.0 | $m=0.9$ |
| $\varphi$ | 0.093 | 0.201 | 0.309 | 0.418 | 0.525 | |

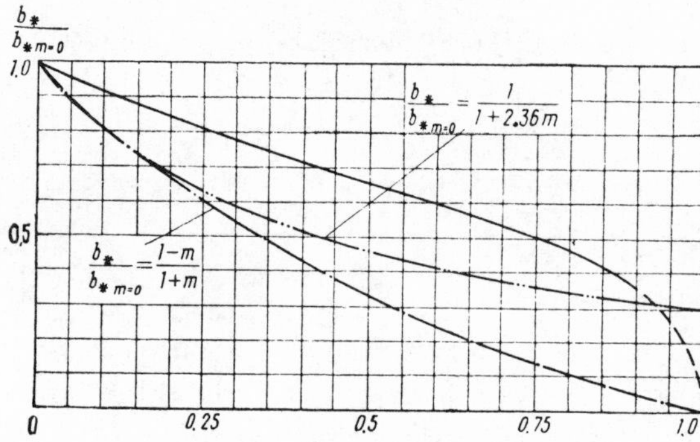


(Fig. 16) that the relative width of the boundary layer as
boundary layer of a jet of incompressible fluid with
the velocity of the surrounding medium.

and O. V. Yakovlevskii [19]:

$$\frac{b_*}{b_{*m=0}} = \frac{1}{1+2.36m}.$$

It can be seen from the graph (see Fig. 16) that the relative width of the boundary layer as obtained by us is greater than that yielded by the other theories. As the velocity of the parallel flow increases, the velocity profiles becomes fuller (Figs. 14, 15).

## 3. The Main Region of a Plane-Parallel Turbulent Jet of a Real Gas

Formulation of the Problem. Let us consider the case of the discharge of a jet of real gas from a long and infinitely narrow slit into a parallel stream (Fig. 17). We will place

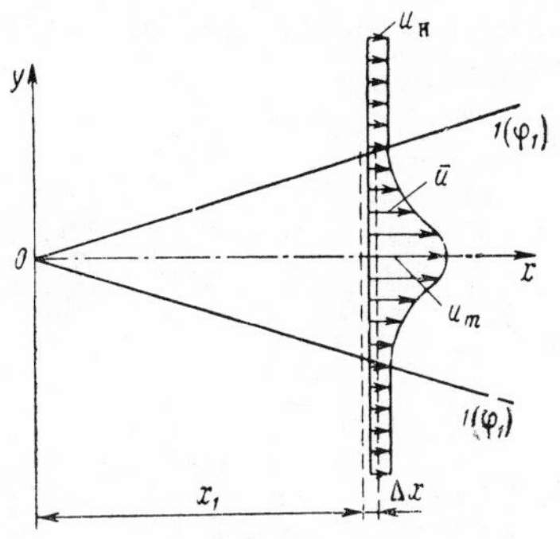


Fig. 17. Turbulent source.

the coordinate origin at the point of emergence of the jet from the slit, in other words, at the source singularity [17]. The velocity on the jet axis will be denoted by $u_m$, the density by $\rho_m$, and the temperature by $T_m$. These parameters will vary along the length of the jet. The velocity of the surrounding medium $u_H$, density $\rho_H$, and temperature $T_H$ are constant parameters along the length of the jet.

The transition section of the jet is taken to be the transverse section where the central velocity $u_m$ is equal to the velocity $u_0$ at which the jet issues from the source. We will match the solutions for the initial main regions of the jet across this transverse section.

The emerging jet in mixing with the surrounding medium forms a boundary layer whose width will gradually increase in the direction of motion of the jet. The variation of the parameters across the mixing zone will be smooth and they will vary from their values on the jet boundary 1 to their values on the jet axis. The width of the boundary layer is taken to be the distance from the jet axis to the boundary.

Let us subdivide the jet into an infinitely large number of intervals $\Delta x$. We will assume that over the interval $\Delta x$ the density and the value of the ratio $m = u_H/u_m$ are constants. We will solve the problem for an arbitrary interval $\Delta x$.

We will make use of Eqs. (2.3), (2.5), (2.9), and (1.1) for this purpose, as well as the equation of conservation of momentum

$$\int_0^{y_b} \overline{\rho u}\,(\bar{u} - u_H)\,dy = \rho_0 u_0 (u_0 - u_H)\, b_0 \tag{3.1}$$

and the equation of conservation of excess enthalpy

$$\int_0^{y_b} \overline{\rho u}\,(\bar{i} - i_H)\,dy = \rho_0 u_0 (i_0 - i_H)\, b_0, \tag{3.2}$$

where $2b_0$ is the width of the initial section of the actual jet.

Transformation of the Equations. Let us introduce new variables x, $\varphi = y/ax$, where $a = \sqrt{2c^2}$ is an experimental constant, for the solution of the system of equations (2.3), (2.5), (2.9), (1.1), (3.1), and (3.2).

We will introduce dimensionless velocities, current density, gas density, specific volume, enthalpy, and temperature defined by

$$\frac{\bar{u} - u_H}{u_m - u_H} = Z(\varphi), \quad \frac{\overline{\rho u}}{\rho_m u_m} = F'(\varphi), \quad \frac{\bar{\rho}}{\rho_m} = \vartheta(\varphi),$$
$$\frac{\bar{V}}{V_m} = \theta(\varphi), \quad \frac{\bar{i}}{i_m} = \sigma(\varphi), \quad \frac{\bar{T}}{T_m} = \gamma(\varphi). \tag{3.3}$$

In the interval $\Delta x$ (where we assume $\rho_m$ = const. and m = const.), these functions will be independent of the variable $\Delta x$.

Let us transform the equation of the conservation of excess momentum (3.1), making use of the functions (3.3) and introducing the variable $\varphi$. We obtain the equation

$$ax\rho_m u_m (u_m - u_{\text{н}}) \int_0^{\varphi_b} F'(\varphi) Z(\varphi)\, d\varphi = \rho_0 u_0 (u_0 - u_{\text{н}}) b_0. \tag{3.4}$$

From Eq. (3.4) we find that

$$u_m = \frac{M}{\sqrt{(1-m)}\sqrt{x}}; \quad \Delta u_m = \frac{M\sqrt{(1-m)}}{\sqrt{x}}, \tag{3.5}$$

where

$$M = \sqrt{\frac{\rho_0 u_0 (u_0 - u_{\text{н}}) b_0}{\int_0^{\varphi_b} F'(\varphi) Z(\varphi)\, d\varphi} \frac{1}{\sqrt{a\rho_m}}}.$$

Let us express the current in terms of the principal component of the current density

$$\psi = \int \overline{\rho u}\, dy = ax\rho_m u_m \int F'(\varphi)\, d\varphi.$$

Substituting into this equation the expression for $u_m$ from (3.5), we obtain

$$\psi = ax\rho_m \frac{M}{\sqrt{(1-m)}\sqrt{x}} F(\varphi). \tag{3.6}$$

Using the continuity equation, we find the transverse current-density component to be

$$\overline{\rho v} = -\frac{\partial\psi}{\partial x} = a\rho_m \frac{M}{\sqrt{(1-m)}\sqrt{x}} \left[\varphi F'(\varphi) - \frac{1}{2} F(\varphi)\right]. \tag{3.7}$$

This expression is correct only when $\rho_m$ and m are constants.

Let us write down the equation of motion (2.3) as follows:

$$\overline{\rho u} \frac{\partial(\overline{u} - u_{\text{н}})}{\partial x} + \overline{\rho v} \frac{\partial(\overline{u} - u_{\text{н}})}{\partial y} = -c^2 x^2 \frac{\partial}{\partial y} \left\{\overline{\rho} \left[\frac{\partial(\overline{u} - u_{\text{н}})}{\partial y}\right]^2\right\}. \tag{3.8}$$

Substituting into this equation expressions (3.3), (3.5), and (3.7) and taking into account that

$$\frac{\partial(\overline{u} - u_{\text{н}})}{\partial y} = \frac{1}{ax} \frac{d(\overline{u} - u_{\text{н}})}{d\varphi}; \quad \frac{\partial(\overline{u} - u_{\text{н}})}{\partial x} = -\frac{\varphi}{x} \frac{d(\overline{u} - u_{\text{н}})}{d\varphi},$$

we obtain the equation of motion in the form

$$FZ = (1-m)\vartheta (Z')^2. \tag{3.9}$$

We can eliminate F between Eqs. (3.9) and (2.11) to obtain the equation of motion in the following form:

$$\frac{m}{1-m} Z^2 + Z^3 + a\frac{n}{2}\frac{\vartheta'}{\vartheta} Z^2 Z' - \frac{\vartheta'}{\vartheta}(Z')^2 Z - 2ZZ'Z'' + (Z')^3 = 0.$$

Replacing in this equation the density $\vartheta$ by the specific volume ($\vartheta = 1/\theta$) and transforming to a new independent variable $\eta$ ($\eta = \varphi/b_*$), we obtain the equation of motion for the boundary layer of a plane-parallel turbulent jet valid in an infinitesimal interval $\Delta x$ ($\rho_m$ = const. and m = const.),

$$L(Z) = \frac{m}{1-m} Z^2 b_*^3 + Z^3 b_*^3 - a\frac{n}{2} b_* \frac{\theta'}{\theta} Z^2 Z' + \frac{\theta'}{\theta} Z (Z')^2 - 2ZZ'Z'' + (Z')^3 = 0, \tag{3.10}$$

where $b_*$ is the dimensionless width of the boundary layer. In solving these equations, we use the following boundary conditions:

1. On the jet axis with $\eta = 0$ ($\varphi = 0$)

a) the velocity is equal to $u_m$ and, consequently,

$$Z(0) = 1; \tag{3.11}$$

b) the transverse component of the current density must be zero on the jet axis ($\overline{\rho v} = 0$), so that

$$Z'(0) = 0. \tag{3.11a}$$

2. On the boundary of the jet where $\eta = 1$ ($\varphi = \varphi_b$) the velocity is equal to $u_H$ and, consequently,

$$Z(1) = 0. \tag{3.11b}$$

Let us investigate the behavior of Eq. (3.10) on the boundaries. In order for the solution of this equation to satisfy the boundary conditions on the axis, the following relation must hold when $\eta = 0$:

$$\frac{b_*^3}{1-m} = 2Z'(0)\, Z''(0). \tag{3.12}$$

Since $Z'(0) = 0$, whereas the left-hand side of expression (3.12) is not zero, then $Z''(0) \to \infty$.

On the jet boundary when $\eta = 1$, the solution of Eq. (3.10) will satisfy boundary condition (3.11) provided that

$$Z'(1) = 0. \tag{3.12a}$$

The function $\theta'/\theta$ appears in Eq. (3.10) and the form of this function will be determined when the equations of motion and energy are solved simultaneously.

Let us transform the equation of excess enthalpy (3.2) making use of functions (3.3), the variable $\varphi$, and the dimensionless enthalpy

$$\varepsilon(\varphi) = \frac{\overline{i} - i_H}{i_m - i_H} = \frac{\Delta \overline{i}}{\Delta i_m}.$$

The equation of conservation of excess enthalpy will then become

$$ax\rho_m u_m \Delta i_m \int_0^{\varphi_b} \varepsilon F' d\varphi = \rho_0 u_0 (i_0 - i_H)\, b_0. \tag{3.13}$$

Equation (3.13) is now used to find $\Delta i_m$:

$$\Delta i_m = \frac{\rho_0 u_0 (i_0 - i_H) b_0}{\rho_m u_m \int_0^{\varphi_b} \varepsilon F' d\varphi} \frac{1}{ax}.$$

Substituting into this equation the expression for $u_m$ (3.5), we obtain

$$\Delta i_m = \frac{k}{M} \sqrt{(1-m)} \frac{1}{\sqrt{x}}, \qquad (3.14)$$

where

$$k = \frac{\rho_0 u_0 (i_0 - i_H) b_0}{\rho_m a \int_0^{\varphi_b} \varepsilon F' d\varphi}.$$

Let us write the energy equation (2.9) in the following form:

$$\overline{\rho u} \frac{\partial (\overline{i} - i_H)}{\partial x} + \overline{\rho v} \frac{\partial (\overline{i} - i_H)}{\partial y} = -nc^2x^2 \frac{\partial}{\partial y} \left[ \rho \frac{\partial (\overline{u} - u_H)}{\partial y} \frac{\partial (\overline{i} - i_H)}{\partial u} \right], \qquad (3.15)$$

where

$$n = 1/\mathrm{Pr}_T.$$

In the case of appreciably subsonic flow, the last term in Eq. (2.9) can be neglected since it is small by comparison with the other terms of Eq. (3.15). Substituting relations (3.3), (3.5), (3.7), and (3.14) into Eq. (3.15), we obtain the energy equation in the following form:

$$F\varepsilon = n(1-m)\vartheta Z'\varepsilon'. \qquad (3.15a)$$

Dividing the energy equation (3.15) by the equation of motion (3.9), we obtain an energy equation that is valid for both variable $\varphi$ and variable $\eta$,

$$\mathrm{Pr}_T \frac{Z'}{Z} = \frac{\varepsilon'}{\varepsilon} \qquad (3.16)$$

with the boundary conditions

a) on the jet axis $\varphi = 0$ $(\eta = 0)$; $Z(0) = 1$. The enthalpy on the jet axis is equal to $i_m$ and, consequently,

$$\varepsilon(0) = 1; \qquad (3.17)$$

b) on the jet boundary $\varphi = \varphi_b$ $(\eta = 1)$; $Z(\varphi_b) = 0$. The enthalpy on the boundary is equal to $i_H$ and, consequently,

$$\varepsilon(\varphi_b) = 0. \qquad (3.17a)$$

Making use of the boundary conditions, we will obtain the solution of the energy equation (3.16) in the form

$$\varepsilon = Z^{\mathrm{Pr}_T}. \qquad (3.18)$$

Solution of the Equation of Motion. We will solve the equation of motion (3.10) with the main boundary conditions (3.11), (3.11a), and (3.11b) and supplementary conditions (3.12) and (3.12a) for the general case, by Galerkin's method [30]

$$Z_k = \sum_{j=0}^{j=k} \widetilde{a}_j \widetilde{\varphi}_j \quad (j=0, 1, 2, 3, \ldots k). \tag{3.19}$$

The system of functions $\widetilde{\varphi}_j$ must satisfy the main and supplementary conditions on the boundaries.

Let us consider the following system of functions:

$$\widetilde{\varphi}_0 = 1; \quad \widetilde{\varphi}_1 = (\eta^3 - 2\eta^{3/2}); \quad \widetilde{\varphi}_2 = (1 - \eta^{3/2})^2 \eta^{3/2};$$

$$\widetilde{\varphi}_3 = (1 - \eta^{3/2})^2 \eta^3, \ldots \widetilde{\varphi}_k = (1 - \eta^{3/2})^2 \eta^{\frac{3(k-1)}{2}}. \tag{3.19a}$$

If we take $\widetilde{a}_0 = 1$ and $\widetilde{a}_1 = 1$, then the sum of functions (3.19a) satisfies the boundary conditions for any values of the coefficients $\widetilde{a}_2, \widetilde{a}_3, \ldots, \widetilde{a}_k$.

We will seek the solution of the equation of motion (3.10) with the help of the first three functions of system (3.19a). The solution will then be of the form

$$Z_2 = 1 + (\eta^3 - 2\eta^{3/2}) + \widetilde{a}_2 (1 - \eta^{3/2})^2 \eta^{3/2}. \tag{3.20}$$

In this case, $\widetilde{a}_2$ and $b_* = \varphi_b$ will be the unknowns to be found.

Using Galerkin's method, we will write down two equations for the determination of these unknowns

$$\int_0^1 L(Z_2) \widetilde{\varphi}_1 d\eta = 0; \quad \int_0^1 L(Z_2) \widetilde{\varphi}_2 d\eta = 0. \tag{3.21}$$

Transforming Eqs. (3.21), we obtain two equations for the determination of the unknowns $\widetilde{a}_2$ and $b_*$

$$A_1^* + A_3^* - b_*^3 B_1^* - b_* B_3^* = 0; \quad A_2^* + A_4^* + b_*^3 B_2^* - b_* B_4^* = 0. \tag{3.22}$$

In the first equation of system (3.22), the functions A* and B* are given by

$$\left.\begin{aligned}
A_1^* &= 0.58478 + 0.38136\widetilde{a}_2 + 0.24747\widetilde{a}_2^2 + 0.01891\widetilde{a}_2^3;\\
A_3^* &= A_1 + \widetilde{a}_2 A_3 + \widetilde{a}_2^2 A_5 + \widetilde{a}_2^3 A_7;\\
B_1^* &= \left[\left(0.0394 + 0.065\frac{m}{1-m}\right) + \left(0.02167 + 0.0307\frac{m}{1-m}\right)\widetilde{a}_2 + \right.\\
&\quad + \left(0.00574 + 0.0051\frac{m}{1-m}\right)\widetilde{a}_2^2 + 0.00064\widetilde{a}_2^3;\\
B_3^* &= a\frac{n}{2}(B_1 + \widetilde{a}_2 B_3 + \widetilde{a}_2^2 B_5 + \widetilde{a}_2^3 B_7),
\end{aligned}\right\} \tag{3.23}$$

where

$$
\left.\begin{aligned}
A_1 &= 9J_{10} - 54J_{17/2} + 126J_7 - 144J_{11/2} + 81J_4 - 18J_{5/2};\\
A_3 &= 36J_{23/2} - 225J_{10} + 558J_{17/2} - 702J_7 + 468J_{11/2} - 153J_4 + 18J_{5/2};\\
A_5 &= \frac{189}{4}J_{13} - 306J_{23/2} + \frac{3195}{4}J_{10} - \frac{2169}{2}J_{17/2} + \frac{3267}{4}J_7 - 333J_{11/2} + \frac{261}{4}J_4 - \frac{9}{2}J_{5/2};\\
A_7 &= \frac{81}{4}J_{29/2} - 135J_{13} + \frac{1467}{4}J_{23/2} - \frac{1053}{2}J_{10} + \frac{1719}{4}J_{17/2} - 198J_7 + \frac{189}{4}J_{11/2} - \frac{9}{2}J_4;\\
B_1 &= 3J_{11} - 21J_{19/2} + 60J_8 - 90J_{13/2} + 75J_5 - 33J_{7/2} + 6J_2;\\
B_3 &= \frac{21}{2}J_{25/2} - 75J_{11} + \frac{441}{2}J_{19/2} - 345J_8 + \frac{615}{2}J_{13/2} - 153J_5 + \frac{75}{2}J_{7/2} - 3J_2;\\
B_5 &= 12J_{14} - 87J_{25/2} + 261J_{11} - 420J_{19/2} + 390J_8 - 207J_{13/2} + 57J_5 - 6J_{7/2};\\
B_7 &= \frac{9}{2}J_{31/2} - 33J_{14} + \frac{201}{2}J_{25/2} - 165J_{11} + \frac{315}{2}J_{19/2} - 87J_8 + \frac{51}{2}J_{13/2} - 3J_5.
\end{aligned}\right\} \qquad (3.23a)
$$

In the second equation of system (3.22), the functions A* and B* are given by

$$
\left.\begin{aligned}
\overset{*}{A_2} &= -(0.19612 + 0.06797\tilde{a}_2 + 0.0514\tilde{a}_2^2 - 0.00023\tilde{a}_2^3);\\
\overset{*}{A_4} &= (A_2 + \tilde{a}_2A_4 + \tilde{a}_2^2A_6 + \tilde{a}_2^3A_8);\\
\overset{*}{B_2} &= \left[\left(0.01458 + 0.0218\frac{m}{1-m}\right) + \left(0.00683 + 0.0084\frac{m}{1-m}\right)\tilde{a}_2 + \right.\\
&\quad \left. + \left(0.00155 + 0.00117\frac{m}{1-m}\right)\tilde{a}_2^2 + 0.00015\tilde{a}_2^3\right];\\
\overset{*}{B_4} &= a\frac{n}{2}\left[B_2 + \tilde{a}_2B_4 + \tilde{a}_2^2B_6 + \tilde{a}_2^3B_8\right],
\end{aligned}\right\} \qquad (3.24)
$$

where

$$
\left.\begin{aligned}
A_2 &= 9J_{23/2} - 54J_{10} + 135J_{17/2} - 180J_7 + 135J_{11/2} - 54J_4 + 9J_{5/2};\\
A_4 &= 36J_{13} - 225J_{23/2} + 594J_{10} - 855J_{17/2} + 720J_7 - 351J_{11/2} + 90J_4 - 9J_{5/2};\\
A_6 &= \frac{189}{4}J_{29/2} - 306J_{13} + 846J_{23/2} - 1296J_{10} + \frac{2385}{2}J_{17/2} - 666J_7 + 216J_{11/2} - 36J_4 + \frac{9}{4}J_{5/2};\\
A_8 &= \frac{81}{4}J_{16} - \frac{270}{2}J_{29/2} + 387J_{13} - 621J_{23/2} + 607.5J_{10} - 369J_{17/2} + 135J_7 - 27J_{11/2} + \frac{9}{4}J_4;\\
B_2 &= 3J_{25/2} - 21J_{11} + 63J_{19/2} - 105J_8 + 105J_{13/2} - 63J_5 + 21J_{7/2} - 3J_2;\\
B_4 &= \frac{21}{2}J_{14} - 75J_{25/2} + 231J_{11} - 399J_{19/2} + 420J_8 - 273J_{13/2} + 105J_5 - 21J_{7/2} + \frac{3}{2}J_2;\\
B_6 &= 12J_{31/2} - 87J_{14} + 273J_{25/2} - 483J_{11} + 525J_{19/2} - 357J_8 + 147J_{13/2} - 33J_5 + 3J_{7/2};\\
B_8 &= \frac{9}{2}J_{17} - 33J_{31/2} + 105J_{14} - 185J_{25/2} + 210J_{11} - 147J_{19/2} + 63J_8 - 15J_{13/2} + \frac{3}{2}J_5.
\end{aligned}\right\} \qquad (3.24a)
$$

The quantity $J_k$ appearing in these functions is defined by

$$
J_k = \int_0^1 \frac{\theta'}{\theta}\eta^k d\eta, \qquad (k = 1,\ {}^3/_2,\ 2,\ {}^5/_2,\ 3\ \ldots). \qquad (3.25)
$$

In order to solve the first equation of system (3.22) for $b_*$, we will write it in the form [33]

$$
b_*^3 + 3P_1b_* + 2Q_1 = 0 \qquad (3.26)
$$

where

$$P_1 = \frac{1}{3}\frac{B_3^*}{B_1^*}, \quad Q = -\frac{A_1^* + A_3^*}{2B_1^*}.$$

Since according to its physical meaning $b_*$ is a real quantity then, rejecting the irrational roots, we obtain the solution of Eq. (3.26) in the following form:

$$b_* = u_{*1} + v_{*1}, \tag{3.26a}$$

where

$$u_{*1} = \sqrt[3]{-Q_1 + \sqrt{Q_1^2 + P_1^3}}; \quad v_{*1} = \sqrt[3]{-Q_1 - \sqrt{Q_1^2 + P_1^3}}.$$

The second equation of system (3.22) is solved in an analogous manner. Let us write down the second equation of system (3.22) in a manner analogous to (3.26)

$$b_*^3 + 3P_2 b_* + 2Q_2 = 0, \tag{3.27}$$

where

$$P_2 = -\frac{1}{3}\frac{B_4^*}{B_2^*}, \quad Q_2 = \frac{A_2^* + A_4^*}{2B_2^*}.$$

The real root of this equation will be

$$b_* = u_{*2} + v_{*2}, \tag{3.27a}$$

where

$$u_{*2} = \sqrt[3]{-Q_2 + \sqrt{Q_2^2 + P_2^3}}, \quad v_{*2} = \sqrt[3]{-Q_2 - \sqrt{Q_2^2 + P_2^3}}.$$

The system of equations (3.26) and (3.27) is solved graphically. The point of intersection of two curves gives the solution of the system.

The Calculation of a Jet of Real Gas. Let us specify the value of the density $\rho_m$ (or the specific volume $V_m$) on the jet axis and let us assume that the axial density does not change over the interval $\Delta x$. In the first approximation, we assume that the relative specific volume can be described by

$$\theta = \left(\frac{V_H}{V_m}\right)^{\eta} = \theta_H^{\eta}. \tag{3.28}$$

In this case

$$\frac{\theta'}{\theta} = \ln \theta_H = \text{const}. \tag{3.28a}$$

In the first equation of system (3.22), the functions $A_3^*$ and $B_3^*$ of the first approximation will be

$$\left.\begin{aligned} A_3^* &= -\ln \theta_H (0.21273 + 0.04485\tilde{a}_2 + 0.022\tilde{a}_2^2 + 0.00397\tilde{a}_2^3), \\ B_3^* &= a\frac{n}{2} \ln \theta_H (0.08335 + 0.02779\tilde{a}_2 + 0.00556\tilde{a}_2^2 + 0.0005\tilde{a}_2^3), \end{aligned}\right\} \tag{3.29}$$

while the functions $A_4^*$ and $B_4^*$ of the second approximation will be

$$\left.\begin{aligned} A_4^* &= \ln \theta_{\text{H}} (0.0621 + 0.003\tilde{a}_2^2 + 0.00068\tilde{a}_2^3), \\ B_4^* &= -a \frac{n}{2} \ln \theta_{\text{H}} (0.02778 + 0.00557\tilde{a}_2 + 0.00051\tilde{a}_2^2). \end{aligned}\right\} \tag{3.30}$$

We will solve the system of two equations (3.26) and (3.27), making use of the expressions (3.23) and (3.24) for $A_1^*$, $B_1^*$, $A_2^*$, $B_2^*$, and expressions (3.29) and (3.30) for $A_3^*$, $B_3^*$, $A_4^*$, $B_4^*$.

We first find $\tilde{a}_2$ and $b_*$.

From Eq. (3.20) we determine the velocity profile $Z = f(\eta)$ in the boundary layer of the jet corresponding to the specific-volume profile adopted in the first approximation. Then, we determine the enthalpy profile from the solution of the energy equation (3.18). The dimensionless enthalpy profile can be used to calculate the enthalpy $\bar{i}$ at any point of the transverse section of the boundary layer

$$\bar{i} = \varepsilon\,(i_m - i_{\text{H}}) + i_{\text{H}}. \tag{3.31}$$

In this equation, the enthalpy of the parallel flow $i_{\text{H}}$ is known, while $i_m$ is found from the graph of $i = f(V)$ since $\rho_m(V)_m$ is known.

Knowing the enthalpy at any point on a transverse section of the boundary layer, we make use of the graph of $i = f(V)$ to determine the specific volume V and to find $\theta = V/V_m$, i.e., the new specific-volume profile across the transverse section of the boundary layer.

Next, we write down the equation of state (1.1) in the following form:

$$\varepsilon\,(i_m - i_{\text{H}}) + i_{\text{H}} = AV_m\theta + B + \frac{C}{V_m\theta} + \frac{D}{V_m^2\theta^2}. \tag{3.32}$$

Differentiating Eq. (3.32), we determine the function $\theta'/\theta$

$$\frac{\theta'}{\theta} = \frac{\varepsilon'\,(i_m - i_{\text{H}})}{AV_m\theta - \dfrac{C}{V_m\theta} - \dfrac{2D}{V_m^2\theta^2}}. \tag{3.33}$$

In this equation, the derivative with respect to $\varepsilon$ is

$$\varepsilon' = \text{Pr}_{\text{T}} Z^{(\text{Pr}_{\text{T}} - 1)} Z'. \tag{3.34}$$

Making use of the expressions (3.33) and (3.34), we can find the function $\theta'/\theta = f(\eta)$ and calculate the integrals (3.25) in the following manner. On the graph of $\theta'/\theta = f(\eta)$, we subdivide the range of $\eta(0-1)$ into an equal number r of intervals each of length 1/r.

The formula for the calculation of the integral $J_k$ by the trapezoidal method is

$$J_k = \frac{1}{r}\left[\left(\frac{\theta'}{\theta}\right)_1 \eta_1^k + \left(\frac{\theta'}{\theta}\right)_2 \eta_2^k + \ldots + \left(\frac{\theta'}{\theta}\right)_{r-1} \eta_{r-1}^k + 0.5\left(\frac{\theta'}{\theta}\right)_r \eta_r^k\right]. \tag{3.35}$$

We now determine the functions $A_1$, $A_2$, ... and $B_1$, $B_2$, ... [Eqs. (3.23a) and (3.24a)] and, solving the system of two equations (3.26) and (3.27), we determine the new values of the quantities $\tilde{a}_2$ and $b_*$.

In this manner we determine the variation of the parameters across the jet. It now remains for us to calculate the variation of the parameters along the jet.

Let us write down the equation of conservation of excess momentum (3.4) in the following manner

$$\frac{u_m}{u_0}=\frac{\sqrt{\dfrac{1-m_0}{1-m}}\sqrt{\dfrac{\rho_0}{\rho_m}}}{\sqrt{\dfrac{ax}{b_0}}\sqrt{b_*\int\limits_0^1 \dfrac{1}{b_*}F'Z\,d\eta}}, \tag{3.36}$$

where $m_0 = u_H/u_0$ and $b_0$ are parameters evaluated at the jet nozzle.

In this equation, F' is

$$F'=\frac{1}{\theta}\,[m+(1-m)\,Z]\,b_*-a\frac{n}{2}\,(1-m)\frac{\theta'}{\theta^2}\,Z'\frac{1}{b_*}\,. \tag{3.37}$$

The equation of conservation of excess enthalpy can be written as follows:

$$\frac{ax}{b_0}=\frac{\dfrac{\rho_0}{\rho_m}\left[\int\limits_0^1\dfrac{1}{b_*}F'Z\,d\eta\right]\left[\dfrac{1-m}{1-m_0}\right]}{b_*\left(\dfrac{i_m-i_H}{i_0-i_H}\right)^2\left[\int\limits_0^1\dfrac{1}{b_*}F'\varepsilon\,d\eta\right]^2}. \tag{3.38}$$

We determine the magnitude of the parameter $ax/b_0$ from Eq. (3.38) and, substituting its value into Eq. (3.26), we find the relative velocity $u_m/u_0$ on the jet axis.

If the jet is propagating in a parallel stream, then the calculation has to be carried out by a trial-and-error method with m the adjustable parameter.

In order to match the initial and main section of the jet, we calculate the transitional transverse section of the jet ($\rho_m = \rho_0$, $\Delta i_m = \Delta i_0$). The relative velocity $u_m/u_0$ on the axis in the transitional section ($\rho_m = \rho_0$) is found to be greater than unity, i.e., the transitional section of scalar quantities lies closer to the nozzle than that for vector quantities. The intersection of the curve $u_m/u_0 = f(ax/b_0)$ with the line $u_m/u_0 = 1$ gives the coordinate of the dynamic transitional section.

The calculations are performed for several transverse sections.

In this way, we can obtain the variation of parameters along the length of the jet.

## Sample Calculations

1. Incompressible Jet. Let us compare the approximate solution with the exact Prandtl–Tolmin solution for the main region of a plane-parallel jet [17].

Using Eqs. (3.26) and (3.27), we find the values $\tilde{a}_2 = -0.5$, $b_* = 2.477$.

The velocity profile is calculated from Eq. (3.20).

The results of the calculation are given in Table 9.

For comparison, Table 9 also contains the Prandtl–Tolmin data on the velocity profile F'. The dimensionless width of the boundary layer according to the Prandtl–Tolmin theory is $b_* = 2.4$.

TABLE 9

| | | | | | | |
|---|---|---|---|---|---|---|
| $\varphi$ | 0 | 0.2 | 0.5 | 0.8 | 1.0 | 1.2 |
| $Z$ | 1.0 | 0.941 | 0.792 | 0.607 | 0.475 | 0.36 |
| $F'$ | 1.0 | 0.94 | 0.782 | 0.604 | 0.474 | 0.357 |

Continuation

| | | | | | | |
|---|---|---|---|---|---|---|
| $\varphi$ | 1.5 | 1.7 | 2 | 2.2 | 2.4 | 2.477 |
| $Z$ | 0.21 | 0.13 | 0.05 | 0.022 | 0.0005 | 0 |
| $F'$ | 0.2 | 0.125 | 0.046 | 0.02 | 0 | 0 |

Let us calculate the integral appearing in Eq. (3.26)

$$b_* \int_0^1 \frac{1}{b_*} F'Zd\eta = 0.695.$$

Substituting the numerical value of this integral into Eq. (3.26), we obtain an expression for the axial velocity of a plane-parallel jet

$$\frac{u_m}{u_0} = \frac{1.2}{\sqrt{\frac{ax}{b_0}}}, \tag{3.39}$$

analogous to the Prandtl–Tolmin formula [17]. It can be seen from Table 9 and formula (3.39) that the agreement of our solution with the Prandtl–Tolmin solution is satisfactory.

2. Main Region of a Plane-Parallel Submerged Jet of carbon dioxide at a pressure of $p=981 \cdot 10^4$ N/m$^2$ and temperature $T_0=248$°K.

The parameters of the surrounding medium are: $T_H=908$°K, $V_H=1.82 \cdot 10^{-3}$ m$^3$/N, $i_H=137 \cdot 10^4$ J/kg.

In the calculations, the turbulent Prandtl number is taken equal to 0.5 and the coefficient $a$ is taken to be 0.1. Let us take several values of the specific volume $V_m$ on the jet axis. We will determine the function $\theta'/\theta$ by means of Eq. (3.28a).

We first of all solve the system of equations (3.26) and (3.27). To do this, we take a series of values of $\tilde{a}_2$ and determine the values of $A_1^*$, $A_2^*$, $A_3^*$, $A_4^*$ and $B_1^*$, $B_2^*$, $B_3^*$, $B_4^*$ from Eqs. (3.29) and (3.30) for each value of $\tilde{a}_2$ selected.

We then construct a graph of $b_* = f(\tilde{a}_2)$ for Eqs. (3.26) and (3.27) and from the intersection of the two curves we obtain the solution of the system of equations.

The results of the calculations are given in Table 10.

TABLE 10

| | $V_m$ | $\theta_H$ | $i_m$ | $T_H$ | $\tilde{a}_2$ | $b_*$ |
|---|---|---|---|---|---|---|
| Section I | $9.5 \cdot 10^{-4}$ | 18.8 | 90 | 248 | 0.7 | 1.44 |
| Section II | $12.5 \cdot 10^{-4}$ | 14.28 | 120 | 298 | 0.7 | 1.6 |
| Section III | $60 \cdot 10^{-4}$ | 2.98 | 180 | 388 | 0 | 1.64 |

TABLE 11

| | | | | | | | | | | | | |
|---|---|---|---|---|---|---|---|---|---|---|---|---|
| Section I | $\eta$ | 0 | 0,1 | 0.2 | 0.3 | 0.4 | 0.5 | 0,6 | 0.7 | 0.8 | 0,9 | 1.0 |
| | $Z$ | 1 | 0,958 | 0.882 | 0.779 | 0.657 | 0.521 | 0.381 | 0.242 | 0.123 | 0.037 | 0 |
| | $\varepsilon$ | 1 | 0.979 | 0.939 | 0.883 | 0.810 | 0.722 | 0.617 | 0.492 | 0.35 | 0.192 | 0 |
| | $\theta$ | 1 | 1.05 | 1.105 | 1.37 | 1.9 | 3.79 | 6.42 | 9.05 | 12.0 | 15.3 | 18.8 |
| | $\frac{\overline{\varrho u}\cdot\overline{u}}{\varrho_m\cdot u_m^2}$ | 1 | 0.888 | 0.737 | 0.525 | 0.367 | 0.147 | 0.0395 | 0.0118 | 0.0026 | 0.0003 | 0 |
| | $\frac{\overline{\varrho u}\cdot\Delta i}{\varrho_m u_m\cdot\Delta i_m}$ | 1 | 0.906 | 0.784 | 0.595 | 0.454 | 0.2035 | 0.0642 | 0.0239 | 0.0075 | 0.0012 | 0 |
| Section II | $Z$ | 1 | 0,958 | 0,882 | 0,779 | 0,657 | 0.521 | 0.381 | 0.242 | 0.123 | 0,037 | 0 |
| | $\varepsilon$ | 1 | 0.979 | 0.939 | 0.883 | 0.810 | 0.722 | 0.617 | 0.492 | 0.35 | 0.192 | 0 |
| | $\theta$ | 1 | 1.12 | 1.295 | 1.76 | 3.16 | 4.6 | 6.08 | 7.8 | 9.68 | 11.87 | 14.28 |
| | $\frac{\overline{\varrho u}\cdot\overline{u}}{\varrho_m\cdot u_m^2}$ | 1 | 0.845 | 0.663 | 0.458 | 0.185 | 0.0789 | 0.0331 | 0.0112 | 0.0027 | 0.0003 | 0 |
| | $\frac{\overline{\varrho u}\cdot\Delta i}{\varrho_m u_m\cdot\Delta i_m}$ | 1 | 0.864 | 0.705 | 0.519 | 0.228 | 0.109 | 0.054 | 0.023 | 0.0076 | 0.0013 | 0 |
| Section III | $Z$ | 1 | 0.938 | 0.83 | 0.698 | 0.558 | 0.418 | 0.288 | 0,172 | 0,082 | 0.024 | 0 |
| | $\varepsilon$ | 1 | 0.967 | 0.91 | 0.835 | 0.746 | 0.646 | 0.537 | 0.416 | 0.286 | 0.155 | 0 |
| | $\theta$ | 1 | 1.07 | 1.19 | 1.33 | 1.52 | 1.71 | 1.93 | 2.18 | 2.44 | 2.7 | 2.98 |
| | $\frac{\overline{\varrho u}\cdot\overline{u}}{\varrho_m\cdot u_m^2}$ | 1 | 0.852 | 0,618 | 0.40 | 0.228 | 0.117 | 0.051 | 0.0175 | 0.004 | 0.0003 | 0 |
| | $\frac{\overline{\varrho u}\cdot\overline{\Delta i}}{\varrho_m u_m\cdot\Delta i_m}$ | 1 | 0.879 | 0.678 | 0.478 | 0.305 | 0.181 | 0.095 | 0.042 | 0.013 | 0.0022 | 0 |

Using Eq. (3.26), we calculate the velocity profile (see Fig. 18), and from Eq. (3.18) we calculate the enthalpy profile (see Fig. 19). Making use of Eq. (3.31), we find the value of the enthalpy for the given transverse section and from the graph of Fig. 2 we determine the value of the specific volume.

We now find the improved specific-volume profile (Fig. 20)

$$\theta = \frac{V}{V_m}.$$

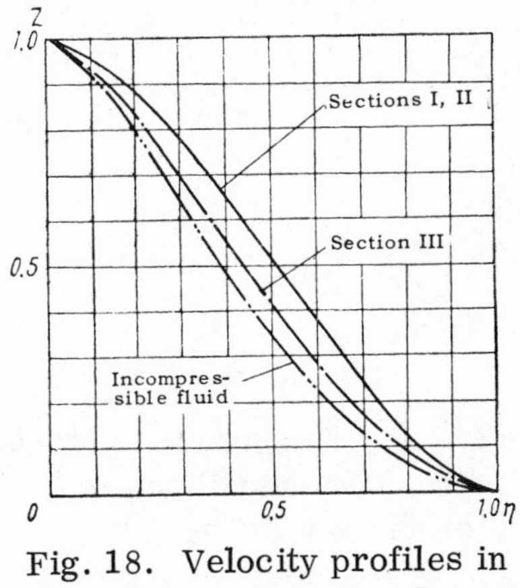


Fig. 18. Velocity profiles in the main region of a flat jet.

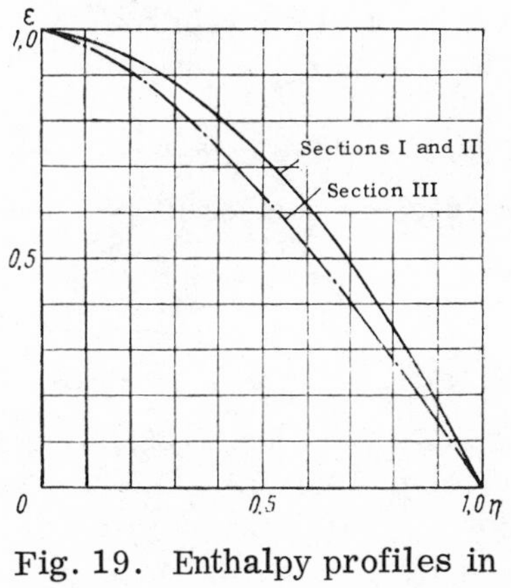


Fig. 19. Enthalpy profiles in the main region of a flat jet.

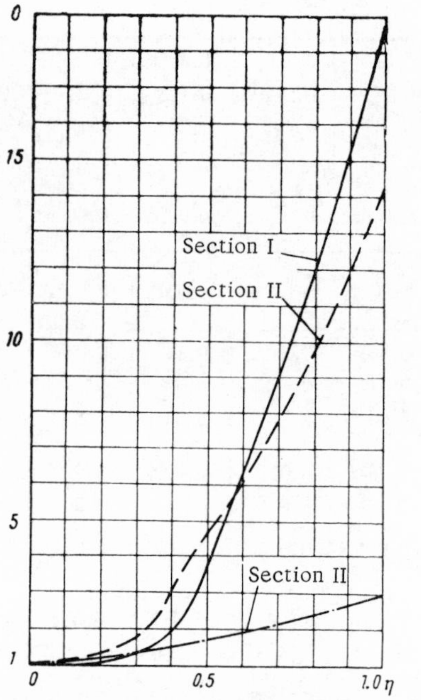


Fig. 20. The specific-volume profiles in the main region of a flat jet.

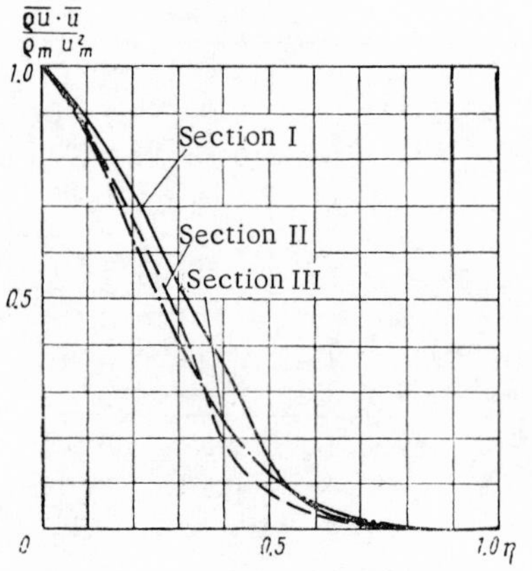


Fig. 21. Total-head profiles in the main region of a flat jet.

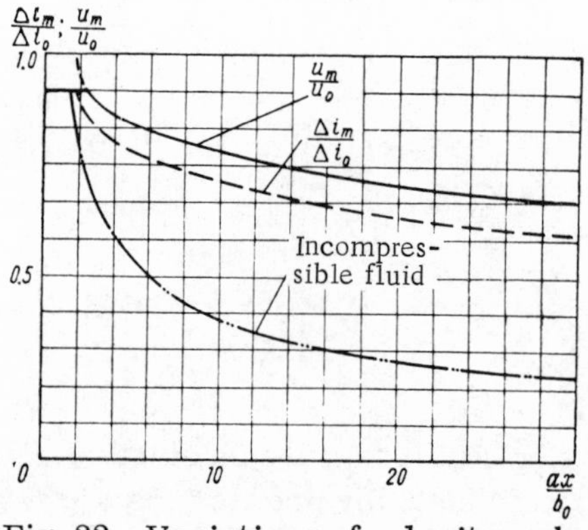


Fig. 22. Variations of velocity and enthalpy along the axis of a flat jet.

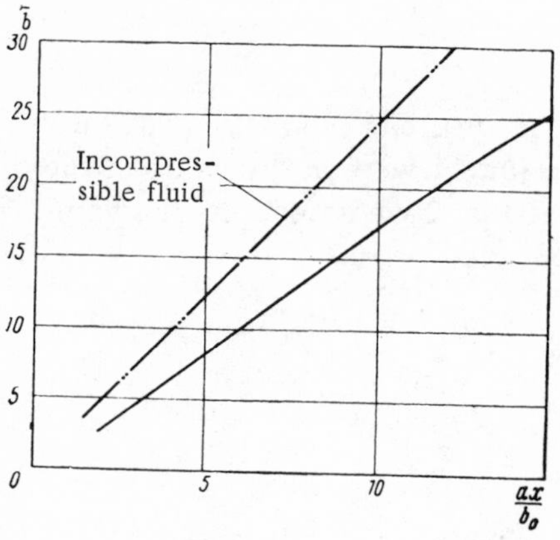


Fig. 23. Variation of the relative width of a flat jet along its length.

Making use of the equation of state (1.1), we find the function $\theta'/\theta$ from Eq. (3.33). Using Eqs. (3.20), (3.37), and (3.18), and (3.33), we determine total thrust and enthalpy profiles (see Fig. 21)

$$\frac{\overline{\rho u \cdot u}}{\rho_m \cdot u_m^2} = f(\eta), \quad \frac{\overline{\rho u \cdot \Delta i}}{\rho_m u_m \Delta i_m} = f(\eta).$$

The results of the calculation are given in Table 11.

By a graphical method [32] we evaluate the integrals

$$\int_0^1 \left(\frac{1}{b_*} F'\right) Z d\eta \quad \text{and} \quad \int_0^1 \left(\frac{1}{b_*} F'\right) \varepsilon d\eta,$$

then, using Eqs. (3.38) and (3.36), we determine $ax/b_0$ and $u_m/u_0$. The results of these calculations are given in Table 12. Figure 22 shows the fall of the relative velocity $u_m/u_0$ and the relative enthalpy $\Delta i_m/\Delta i_0$ along the jet axis as functions of the coordinate $ax/b_0$. The variation of relative velocity along the axis of an incompressible-fluid jet is shown in Fig. 22 for comparison purposes.

TABLE 12

| | Section I | Section II | Section III |
|---|---|---|---|
| $\frac{\varrho_0}{\varrho_m}$ | 1 | 1.32 | 6.3 |
| $\frac{\Delta i_m}{\Delta i_0}$ | 1 | 0.872 | 0.62 |
| $\int_0^1 \left(\frac{1}{b_*} F'\right) Z d\eta$ | 0.3218 | 0.278 | 0.279 |
| $\int_0^1 \left(\frac{1}{b_*} F'\right) \varepsilon d\eta$ | 0.354 | 0.301 | 0.317 |
| $\frac{ax}{b_0}$ | 1.78 | 3.22 | 27.9 |
| $\frac{u_m}{u_0}$ | 1.1 | 0.945 | 0.703 |

Figure 23 shows the relative width of the boundary layer of a jet of carbon dioxide and the relative width of a jet of incompressible fluid.

It can be seen from Figs. 18 and 19 that as the density ratio $\rho_m/\rho_0$ increases, the velocity and relative-enthalpy profiles become more convex. The decrease in the velocity along the axis of a jet of carbon dioxide is less rapid than that in the case of a jet of incompressible fluid (see Fig. 22), while the width of the boundary layer increases more slowly in the case of a jet of carbon monoxide than in the case of an incompressible fluid (see Fig. 23).

## 4. The Main Region of an Axially Symmetric Turbulent Jet of Real Gas

Formulation of the Problem. Let us consider the case of the outflow of a jet of a real gas from a turbulent point source (see Fig. 17). As in the case of the main region of a plane-parallel jet, we place the coordinate origin at the source singularity [17]. We will use the same notation as in the case of the plane-parallel motion. We will match the initial and main regions of the jet in the transitional transverse section.

We will subdivide the jet into intervals $\Delta x$ along its length and we will assume that the density remains constant ($\rho_m = \text{const.}$) in each of these intervals. We also assume that $m = u_H/u_m$ is constant in $\Delta x$.

We will make use of the following equations to solve the problem:

1. Equation of motion

$$\overline{\rho u} \frac{\partial \overline{u}}{\partial x} + \overline{\rho v} \frac{\partial \overline{u}}{\partial y} = -c^2 x^2 \frac{1}{y} \frac{\partial}{\partial y} \left[ y \overline{\rho} \left( \frac{\partial \overline{u}}{\partial y} \right)^2 \right]. \quad (4.1)$$

2. Continuity equation

$$\frac{\partial \overline{\rho u}}{\partial x} + \frac{\partial \overline{\rho v}}{\partial y} + \frac{\overline{\rho v}}{y} = 0. \quad (4.2)$$

3. Energy equation

$$\overline{\rho u}\frac{\partial \overline{i}}{\partial x}+\overline{\rho v}\frac{\partial \overline{i}}{\partial y}=-nc^2x^2\frac{1}{y}\frac{\partial}{\partial y}\left[y\overline{\rho}\frac{\partial \overline{u}}{\partial y}\frac{\partial \overline{i}}{\partial y}\right]. \quad (4.3)$$

The averaging of these equations was carried out according to Reynold's method in the same way as in the case of plane-parallel flow.

4. Equation of conservation of excess momentum

$$2\pi\int_0^{y_b}\overline{\rho u}(\overline{u}-u_H)\,ydy=\rho_0u_0(u_0-u_H)\pi R_0^2. \quad (4.4)$$

5. Equation of conservation of excess enthalpy

$$2\pi\int_0^{y_b}\overline{\rho u}(\overline{i}-i_H)\,ydy=\rho_0u_0(i_0-i_H)\pi R_0^2. \quad (4.5)$$

6. Equation of state (1.1).

Transformation of the Equations. Let us transform Eqs. (4.1), (4.2), (4.3), (4.4), (4.5) and (1.1) into the coordinate system x, $\varphi=y/ax$ with the help of the functions (3.3). Here, $a=\sqrt[3]{c^2}$ is an experimental constant.

Let us transform the equation of conservation of excess momentum (4.4) making use of functions (3.3) and the new variable $\varphi$. We will obtain this equation in the following form:

$$\frac{\rho_m u_m}{\rho_0 u_0}\,\frac{(u_m-u_H)}{(u_0-u_H)}\left(\frac{ax}{R_0}\right)^2\int_0^{\varphi_b}f(\varphi)Z(\varphi)\varphi d\varphi=0.5. \quad (4.6)$$

From Eq. (4.6) we can obtain the values of $u_m$ and $\Delta u_m=u_m-u_H$

$$u_m=\frac{M}{\sqrt{1-m}\,x};\qquad \Delta u_m=\frac{M\sqrt{1-m}}{x}, \quad (4.7)$$

where

$$M=\sqrt{\frac{1}{2}\frac{\rho_0u_0(u_0-u_H)R_0^2}{\int_0^{\varphi_b}f(\varphi)Z(\varphi)\varphi d\varphi}}\,\frac{1}{a\sqrt{\rho_m}},\qquad f(\varphi)=\frac{\overline{\rho u}}{\rho_m u_m}.$$

Using the continuity equation (4.2), we can express the current density components in terms of the current function $\psi$:

$$\overline{\rho u}=\frac{1}{y}\frac{\partial\psi}{\partial y};\qquad \overline{\rho v}=-\frac{1}{y}\frac{\partial\psi}{\partial x}. \quad (4.8)$$

From the first equation of system (4.8), we find the current function to be

$$\psi=\int\overline{\rho u}\cdot ydy=\rho_m u_m a^2x^2\int f(\varphi)\varphi d\varphi.$$

Replacing in this expression $u_m$ by its value (4.7) and denoting the integral by $F(\varphi)$, we obtain

$$\psi=\rho_m\frac{M}{\sqrt{1-m}}a^2xF(\varphi). \tag{4.9}$$

From Eq. (4.9) we then find the main component of the current density

$$\overline{\rho u}=\rho_m\frac{M}{\sqrt{1-m}}\frac{1}{x}\frac{F'(\varphi)}{\varphi}. \tag{4.10}$$

Using the second equation of system (4.8) and Eq. (4.9), we find that the transverse component of the current density is

$$\overline{\rho v}=\rho_m\frac{Ma}{\sqrt{1-m}}\frac{1}{x}\left[F'(\varphi)-\frac{F(\varphi)}{\varphi}\right]. \tag{4.11}$$

This expression is valid in an interval $\Delta x$ where $\rho_m$ and m are independent of x.

Let us write down the equation of motion (4.1) in the form

$$\overline{\rho u}\frac{\partial(\bar{u}-u_{\text{н}})}{\partial x}+\overline{\rho v}\frac{\partial(\bar{u}-u_{\text{н}})}{\partial y}=-a^3x^2\frac{1}{y}\frac{\partial}{\partial y}\left\{y\bar{\rho}\left[\frac{\partial(\bar{u}-u_{\text{н}})}{\partial y}\right]^2\right\}. \tag{4.12}$$

We can transform this equation with the help of expressions (3.3) (4.10), and (4.11), as well as the expressions describing the equalities of the derivatives of the velocity with respect to x and y,

$$\frac{\partial(\bar{u}-u_{\text{н}})}{\partial x}=-\frac{\varphi}{x}\frac{d(\bar{u}-u_{\text{н}})}{d\varphi},$$

$$\frac{\partial(\bar{u}-u_{\text{н}})}{\partial y}=\frac{1}{ax}\frac{d(\bar{u}-u_{\text{н}})}{d\varphi}.$$

As a result of this, the equation of motion will become

$$\frac{ZF}{\varphi}=(1-m)\vartheta(Z')^2. \tag{4.13}$$

The relation between the velocity component $\bar{u}$ and the current density $\overline{\rho u}$ can be found from

$$\overline{\rho u}=\bar{\rho}\bar{u}+\overline{\rho' u'}.$$

Substituting this expression into Eqs. (3.3) and (4.10) and making use of the Prandtl turbulence model, we obtain an equation connecting the functions Z and F

$$\frac{F'}{\varphi}=\vartheta[m+(1-m)Z]+na\vartheta'Z'(1-m). \tag{4.14}$$

Eliminating F from Eqs. (4.13) and (4.14), we obtain the equation of motion with respect to the variable $\varphi$

$$\frac{m}{1-m}Z^2+Z^3-\frac{\vartheta'}{\vartheta}(Z')^2Z-2Z''Z'Z+(Z')^3-(Z')^2Z\frac{1}{\varphi}+na\frac{\vartheta'}{\vartheta}Z'Z^2=0. \tag{4.15}$$

Replacing in the equation of motion (4.15) the current density function $\vartheta$ by the specific volume function $\theta(\vartheta=1/\theta)$ and introducing the independent variable $\eta(\eta=\varphi/b_*)$, we obtain an equation of motion which is valid over an infinitesimally small section $\Delta x$ where we can assume that $\rho_m$ = const. and m = const.

$$L(Z)=\frac{m}{1-m}Z^2b_*^3+Z^3b_*^3+\frac{\theta'}{\theta}(Z')^2Z-2Z''Z'Z+(Z')^3-Z(Z')^2\frac{1}{\eta}-na\frac{\theta'}{\theta}Z'Z^2b_*=0. \quad (4.16)$$

In solving this equation, we will make use of three boundary conditions analogous to conditions (3.11),

1. On the jet axis $\eta = 0$ ($\varphi = 0$);

$$Z(0)=1, \quad (4.17)$$
$$Z'(0)=0. \quad (4.17a)$$

2. On the jet boundary $\eta = 1$ ($\varphi = b_*$);

$$Z(1)=0. \quad (4.17b)$$

Let us investigate the equation of motion (4.16) on the boundaries. In order for the solution of the equation of motion to satisfy the boundary conditions on the axis, the following equality must hold on the jet axis:

$$\frac{b_*^3}{1-m}=2Z'(0)Z''(0). \quad (4.18)$$

Since $Z'(0) = 0$ on the jet axis, while the left-hand side of equality (4.18) is not equal to zero, then $Z''(0) \to \infty$. On the jet boundary ($\eta = 1$), the solution of the equation of motion (4.16) will satisfy the third boundary condition (4.17a) provided that

$$Z'(1)=0. \quad (4.18a)$$

Let us transform the equation of conservation of excess enthalpy (4.5) with the help of the functions (3.3) and the variable $\varphi$. We obtain

$$\frac{\rho_m u_m (i_m - i_H)}{\rho_0 u_0 (i_0 - i_H)}\left(\frac{ax}{R_0}\right)^2 \int_0^{\varphi_b} \frac{\bar{i}-i_H}{i_m - i_H} f(\varphi)\varphi d\varphi = 0.5. \quad (4.19)$$

Let us introduce the abbreviations: $\Delta i_m = i_m - i_H$, $\overline{\Delta i} = \bar{i} - i_H$, $\Delta i_0 = i_0 - i_H$, and $\varepsilon = \overline{\Delta i}/\Delta i_m$. We can find $\Delta i_m$ from Eq. (4.19),

$$\Delta i_m = \frac{K}{M}\sqrt{1-m}\,\frac{1}{x}, \quad (4.20)$$

where

$$K=\frac{0.5\rho_0 u_0 \Delta i_0}{\left(\frac{a}{R_0}\right)^2 \rho_m \int_0^{\varphi_b} \varepsilon(\varphi) f(\varphi)\varphi d\varphi}.$$

Let us write the energy equation (4.3) as follows:

$$\overline{\rho u}\frac{\partial(\bar{i}-i_H)}{\partial x}+\overline{\rho v}\frac{\partial(\bar{i}-i_H)}{\partial y}=-na^3x^2\frac{1}{y}\frac{\partial}{\partial y}\left[y\bar{\rho}\frac{\partial(\bar{u}-u_H)}{\partial y}\frac{\partial\overline{\Delta i}}{\partial y}\right]. \quad (4.21)$$

Let us transform the energy equation (4.21) with the help of expressions (3.3), (4.10), (4.11), and (4.20) and it will become

$$\frac{F\varepsilon}{\varphi}=n(1-m)\vartheta Z'\varepsilon', \tag{4.22}$$

where $n = 1/Pr_T$.

Dividing the energy equation (4.22) by the equation of motion (4.13), we obtain the energy equation

$$Pr_T\frac{Z'}{Z}=\frac{\varepsilon'}{\varepsilon}. \tag{4.23}$$

For solving Eq. (4.23) we will use boundary conditions analogous to boundary conditions (3.17):

1. On the jet axis $\varphi = 0$ ($\eta = 0$); $Z(0) = 1$; $\varepsilon(0) = 1$.
2. On the jet boundary $\varphi = \varphi_b$ ($\eta = 1$); $Z(\varphi_b) = 0$; $\varepsilon(\varphi_b) = 0$.

The solution of the energy equation (4.23) together with the boundary conditions is of the form

$$\varepsilon=Z^{Pr_T}. \tag{4.24}$$

Equation (4.24) allows us to calculate the enthalpy profile across the jet.

Solution of the Equation of Motion. We will solve the equation of motion (4.16) with the main boundary conditions (4.17), (4.17a), and (4.17b) and the supplementary conditions on the jet boundary.

In Eq. (4.16) $\theta'/\theta$ is an unknown function and $\eta$ a quantity which will be determined from a simultaneous solution of the equations of motion and energy, together with the equation of state (1.1). We will seek the general solution of the equation of motion by Galerkin's method [30]. Let us write down the solution in its general form as

$$Z_k=\sum_{j=0}^{j=k}\tilde{a}_j\tilde{\varphi}_j \quad (j=0,\ 1,\ 2,\ 3\ldots\ldots k). \tag{4.25}$$

The system of functions $\tilde{\varphi}_j$ will be chosen to satisfy the boundary conditions (4.17), (4.17a), and (4.17b), as well as the supplementary boundary conditions (4.18) and (4.18a). Let us consider the following system of functions:

$$\tilde{\varphi}_0=1,\quad \tilde{\varphi}_1=3\eta^2-4\eta^{3/2},\quad \tilde{\varphi}_2=(1-\eta)^2\eta^{3/2},$$
$$\varphi_3=(1-\eta)^2\eta^3,\ \ldots\ldots\tilde{\varphi}_k=(1-\eta)^2\eta^{\frac{3(k-1)}{2}}. \tag{4.26}$$

If we set $\tilde{a}_0 = 1$ and $\tilde{a}_1 = 1$, then the sum of functions (4.26) will satisfy all boundary conditions for any values of the coefficients $\tilde{a}_2, \tilde{a}_3, \ldots, \tilde{a}_k$. We will seek the solution of the equation of motion (4.16) with the help of the first three functions of system (4.26). The solution will be of the form

$$Z_2=1+(3\eta^2-4\eta^{3/2})+\tilde{a}_2(1-\eta)^2\eta^{3/2}. \tag{4.27}$$

In this case, the solution of Eq. (4.16) reduces to the determination of the two unknowns $\tilde{a}_2$ and $b_*$. We can write down two equations according to the Galerkin method for the determination of these unknowns,

$$1.\ \int_0^1 L(Z_2)\tilde{\varphi}_1 d\eta = 0, \qquad 2.\ \int_0^1 L(Z_2)\tilde{\varphi}_2 d\eta = 0. \tag{4.28}$$

Transforming Eqs. (4.28), we obtain two equations for the determination of the unknowns $\tilde{a}_2$ and $b_*$,

$$\left.\begin{aligned} &1.\ A_1^* + A_3^* - b_*^3 B_1^* - b_* B_3^* = 0, \\ &2.\ A_2^* + A_4^* + b_*^3 B_2^* - b_* B_4^* = 0. \end{aligned}\right\} \tag{4.29}$$

In the first equation of system (4.29), the functions A* and B* are given by

$$\left.\begin{aligned} &A_1^* = 1.18697 + 0.10579\tilde{a}_2 + 0.10306\tilde{a}_2^2 + 0.0044\tilde{a}_2^3, \\ &A_3^* = A_1 + \tilde{a}_2 A_3 + \tilde{a}_2^3 A_5 + \tilde{a}_2^3 A_7, \\ &B_1^* = \left(0.03591 + 0.0613\frac{m}{1-m}\right) + \left(0.01275 + 0.01884\frac{m}{1-m}\right)\tilde{a}_2 + \\ &\qquad + \left(0.00219 + 0.00204\frac{m}{1-m}\right)\tilde{a}_2^2 + 0.00018\tilde{a}_2^3, \\ &B_3^* = an\,(B_1 + \tilde{a}_2 B_3 + \tilde{a}_2^2 B_5 + \tilde{a}_2^3 B_7), \end{aligned}\right\} \tag{4.30}$$

where

$$\left.\begin{aligned} &A_1 = 324J_6 - 1512J_{11/2} + 2628J_5 - 2016J_{9/2} + 684J_4 - 360J_{7/2} + 396J_3 - 144J_{5/2}, \\ &A_3 = 486J_{15/2} - 1746J_7 + 1320J_{13/2} + 1884J_6 - 2796J_{11/2} + 1104J_{9/2} - 12J_4 - 186J_{7/2} - 126J_3 + 72J_{5/2}, \\ &A_5 = \frac{945}{4}J_9 - 588J_{17/2} - 383J_8 + 1848J_{15/2} - \frac{959}{4}J_7 - 2161J_{13/2} + \\ &\qquad + 760J_6 + 1172J_{11/2} - \frac{1773}{4}J_5 - 322J_{9/2} + 63J_4 + 60J_{7/2} + \frac{27}{4}J_3 - 9J_{5/2}, \\ &A_7 = \frac{147}{4}J_{21/2} - 49J_{10} - \frac{357}{2}J_{19/2} + 238J_9 + \frac{1413}{4}J_{17/2} - 471J_8 - \\ &\qquad - 363J_{15/2} + 484J_7 + \frac{813}{4}J_{13/2} - 271J_6 - \frac{117}{2}J_{11/2} + 78J_5 + \frac{27}{4}J_{9/2} - 9J_4, \\ &B_1 = 162J_7 - 810J_{13/2} + 1512J_6 - 1248J_{11/2} + 492J_5 - 396J + 480J_4 - 192J_{7/2} + 18J_3 - 42J_{5/2} + 24J_2, \\ &B_3 = \frac{405}{2}J_{17/2} - 774J_8 + 633J_{15/2} + 916J_7 - \frac{2865}{2}J_{13/2} - 106J_6 + \\ &\qquad + 694J_{11/2} + 120J_5 - \frac{365}{2}J_{9/2} - 170J_4 + 81J_{7/2} + 20J_3 + \frac{9}{2}J_{5/2} - 6J_2, \\ &B_5 = 81J_{10} - 210J_{19/2} - 152J_9 + 744J_{17/2} - 81J_8 - 1000J_{15/2} + \\ &\qquad + 336J_7 + 648J_{13/2} - 217J_6 - 234J_{11/2} + 24J_5 + 64J_{9/2} + 9J_4 - 12J_{7/2}, \\ &B_7 = \frac{21}{2}J_{23/2} - 14J_{11} - 57J_{21/2} + 76J_{10} + \frac{255}{2}J_{19/2} - 170J_9 - \\ &\qquad - 150J_{17/2} + 200J_8 + \frac{195}{2}J_{15/2} - 130J_7 - 33J_{13/2} + 44J_6 + \frac{9}{2}J_{11/2} - 6J_5. \end{aligned}\right\} \tag{4.31}$$

In the second equation of system (4.29), the functions A* and B* are given by

$$\left.\begin{aligned}
&A_2^* = -0.25095 + 0.00836\tilde{a}_2 - 0.01454\tilde{a}_2^2 - 0.00005\tilde{a}_2^3;\\
&A_4^* = A_2 + \tilde{a}_2 A_4 + \tilde{a}_2^2 A_6 + \tilde{a}_2^3 A_8;\\
&B_2^* = \left(0.00772 + 0.01198\frac{m}{1-m}\right) + \left(0.00237 + 0.00303\frac{m}{1-m}\right)\times\\
&\quad\times\tilde{a}_2 + \left(0.00035 + 0.00027\frac{m}{1-m}\right)\tilde{a}_2^2 + 0.00003\tilde{a}_2^3;\\
&B_4^* = an\,(B_2 + \tilde{a}_2 B_4 + \tilde{a}_2^2 B_6 + \tilde{a}_2^3 B_8),
\end{aligned}\right\} \tag{4.32}$$

where

$$\left.\begin{aligned}
&A_2 = 108J_{15/2} - 360J_7 + 180J_{13/2} + 576J_6 - 648J_{11/2} - 144J_5 + 360J_{9/2} - 36J_{7/2} - 72J_3 + 36J_{5/2};\\
&A_4 = 162J_9 - 366J_{17/2} - 372J_8 + 1296J_{15/2} + 78J_7 - 1734J_{13/2} +\\
&\quad + 360J_6 + 1104J_{11/2} - 258J_5 - 378J_{9/2} + 12J_4 + 96J_{7/2} + 18J_3 - 18J_{5/2};\\
&A_6 = \frac{315}{4}J_{21/2} - 91J_{10} - \frac{813}{2}J_{19/2} + 466J_9 + \frac{3502}{4}J_{17/2} - 981J_8 - \frac{2045}{2}J_{15/2} + 1084J_7\\
&\quad + 711J_{13/2} - 661J_6 - \frac{623}{2}J_{11/2} + 210J_5 + \frac{370}{4}J_{9/2} - 27J_4 - \frac{39}{2}J_{7/2} + \frac{9}{4}J_{5/2};\\
&A_8 = \frac{49}{4}J_{12} - 84J_{11} + \frac{996}{4}J_{10} - 416J_9 + \frac{1710}{4}J_8 - 276J_7 + 109J_6 - 24J_5 + \frac{9}{4}J_4;\\
&B_2 = 54J_{17/2} - 198J_8 + 132J_{15/2} + 300J_7 - 390J_{13/2} - 90J_6 +\\
&\quad + 216J_{11/2} + 72J_5 - 54J_{9/2} - 90J_4 + 36J_{7/2} + 12J_3 + 6J_{5/2} - 6J_2;\\
&B_4 = \frac{135}{2}J_{10} - 168J_{19/2} - 148J_9 + 624J_{17/2} - 904J_{15/2} + 192J_7 +\\
&\quad + 672J_{13/2} - 105J_6 - 312J_{11/2} - 36J_5 + 112J_{9/2} + 36J_4 - 24J_{7/2} - 8J_3 + \frac{3}{2}J_2;\\
&B_6 = 27J_{23/2} - 34J_{11} - 150J_{21/2} + 188J_{10} + 352J_{19/2} + 430J_9 - 458J_{17/2} + 520J_8 + 370J_{15/2} - 350J_7 - 202J_{13/2} +\\
&\quad + 124J_6 + 80J_{11/2} - 18J_5 - 22J_{9/2} + 3J_{7/2};\\
&B_8 = \frac{7}{2}J_{13} - 26J_{12} + 84J_{11} - 154J_{10} + 175J_9 - 126J_8 + 56J_7 - 14J_6 + \frac{3}{2}J_5.
\end{aligned}\right\} \tag{4.33}$$

The integral $J_k$ appearing in these functions is given by

$$J_k = \int_0^1 \frac{\theta'}{\theta}\eta^k d\eta \quad (k = 1,\ {}^3/_2,\ 2,\ {}^5/_2,\ 3\ldots). \tag{4.34}$$

The first equation of system (4.29) can be written as [33]

$$b_*^3 + 3P_1 b_* + 2Q_1 = 0, \tag{4.35}$$

where

$$P_1 = \frac{1}{3}\frac{B_3^*}{B_1^*}, \quad Q_1 = -\frac{A_2^* + A_3^*}{2B_1^*}.$$

The solution of this equation yields the value of $b_*$. Since according to its physical meaning $b_*$ should be a real positive number, we can immediately reject irrational roots to obtain

$$b_* = u_{*1} + v_{*1}, \tag{4.35a}$$

where

$$u_{*1}=\sqrt[3]{-Q_1+\sqrt{Q_1^2+P_1^3}},\quad v_{*1}=\sqrt[3]{-Q_1-\sqrt{Q_1^2+P_1^3}}.$$

The second equation of system (4.29) is solved in the same manner. This equation is

$$b_*^3+3P_2b_*+2Q_2=0, \tag{4.36}$$

where

$$P_2=-\frac{1}{3}\frac{B_4^*}{B_2^*},\quad Q_2=\frac{A_2^*+A_4^*}{2B_2^*}.$$

The real root of this equation is

$$b_*=u_{*2}+v_{*2}, \tag{4.36a}$$

where

$$u_{*2}=\sqrt[3]{-Q_2+\sqrt{Q_2^2+P_2^3}},\quad v_{*2}=\sqrt[3]{-Q_2-\sqrt{Q_2^2+P_2^3}}.$$

The system of equations (4.35) and (4.36) is solved graphically, i.e., we determine the point of intersection of the two curves.

The Calculation of an Axially Symmetric Jet of Real Gas. We take several values of the density $\rho_m$ (or the specific volume $V_m$) on the jet axis, assuming that the density is constant over an infinitesimally small region of the axis.

We will perform the calculations for each value of the density $\rho_m$ = const.

In the first approximation, we assume that the variation of the specific volume across a section of the jet is as follows:

$$\theta=\left(\frac{V_{\text{н}}}{V_m}\right)^{\eta}=\theta_{\text{н}}^{\eta}. \tag{4.37}$$

In this case, the known function $\theta'/\theta$ is of the form

$$\frac{\theta'}{\theta}=\ln\theta_{\text{н}}=\text{const}. \tag{4.37a}$$

Then, the functions $A_3^*$, $B_3^*$, $A_4^*$, and $B_4^*$ of system (4.29) will become

$$\left.\begin{aligned}
A_3^*&=\ln\theta_{\text{н}}(-0.21797-0.01916\tilde{a}_2-0.00756\tilde{a}_2^2-0.0009\tilde{a}_2^3);\\
B_3^*&=an\ln\theta_{\text{н}}(0.0833+0.01664\tilde{a}_2+0.00204\tilde{a}_2^2+0.00012\tilde{a}_2^3);\\
A_4^*&=\ln\theta_{\text{н}}(0.03954-0.00114\tilde{a}_2+0.00065\tilde{a}_2^2+0.0001\tilde{a}_2^3);\\
B_4^*&=an\ln\theta_{\text{н}}(-0.01663-0.00206\tilde{a}_2-0.0001\tilde{a}_2^2).
\end{aligned}\right\} \tag{4.38}$$

Taking several values of $\tilde{a}_2$, we now solve the system of two equations (4.35) and (4.36) and making use of expressions (4.30) and (4.32) for the functions $A_1^*$, $B_1^*$, $A_2^*$, $B_2^*$ and expressions (4.38) for $A_3^*$, $B_3^*$, $A_4^*$, $B_4^*$, we determine $b_*$. From Eqs. (4.27) and (4.24) we find the velocity and enthalpy profiles in the boundary layer of the jet. Knowing the function $\varepsilon(\eta)$, we can easily find the enthalpy $\bar{i}$ at any point of the cross section of the jet boundary layer

$$\bar{i}=\varepsilon(i_m-i_H)+i_H. \quad (4.39)$$

In Eq. (4.39), the enthalpy of the parallel flow is known, while the value of $i_m$ can be easily found from the known value of $\rho_m(V_m)$ on the jet axis by means of the graph of $i=f(V)$. Knowing the enthalpy across the jet, we can determine the values of the specific volume from the graph of $i=f(V)$ and thus we can find $\theta=\bar{V}/V_m$.

In other words, we find the new improved specific-volume profile over the cross section of the jet.

Equation (1.1) can be written as

$$\varepsilon(i_m-i_H)+i_H=AV_m\theta+B+\frac{C}{V_m\theta}+\frac{D}{V_m^2\theta^2}.$$

Differentiating this equation, we find an expression for $\theta'/\theta$

$$\frac{\theta'}{\theta}=\frac{\varepsilon'(i_m-i_H)}{AV_m\theta-\dfrac{C}{V_m\theta}-\dfrac{2D}{V_m^2\theta^2}}. \quad (4.40)$$

Using Eqs. (4.40) and (3.34), we can calculate the function $\theta'/\theta$ and hence evaluate the integral (4.34) by the trapezoidal method [32]. To do this, we subdivide the range of $\eta(0-1)$ in the graph of $\theta'/\theta=f(\eta)$ into r subintervals each of length 1/r. The trapezoidal rule for the evaluation of the integral $J_k$ is

$$J_k=\frac{1}{r}\left[\left(\frac{\theta'}{\theta}\right)_1\eta_1^k+\left(\frac{\theta'}{\theta}\right)_2\eta_2^k+\cdots+\left(\frac{\theta'}{\theta}\right)_{r-1}\eta_{r-1}^k+0.5\left(\frac{\theta'}{\theta}\right)_r\eta_r^k\right]. \quad (4.41)$$

Having obtained the values of the integrals $J_k$, we calculate the functions $A_1$, $A_2$, ..., $B_1$, $B_2$, ... from (4.31) and (4.33) and then find the values of $A_1^*$, $A_2^*$, . . . , $B_1^*$, $B_2^*$ from Eqs. (4.30) and (4.32).

Solving the system of equations (4.29), we find new values of $\tilde{a}_2$ and $b_*$.

Having calculated several cross sections in this manner, we can proceed to the determination of the variations of the jet parameters along the axis.

With the help of expression (4.7), we can write down the equation of conservation of excess momentum (4.4) as follows:

$$\frac{u_m}{u_0}=\frac{0.707\sqrt{\dfrac{1-m_0}{1-m}}\sqrt{\dfrac{\rho_0}{\rho_m}}}{\dfrac{ax}{R_0}b_*\sqrt{\displaystyle\int_0^1 F'Z\,d\eta}}, \quad (4.42)$$

where $m_0=u_H/u_0$, and $\rho_0$ are parameters at exit from the nozzle.

In this equation, F' is given by

$$F'=\frac{1}{\theta}[m+(1-m)Z]\eta-an\frac{\theta'}{\theta^2}Z'(1-m)\frac{1}{b_*^2}\eta. \quad (4.43)$$

We can find the value of $ax/R_0$ from the equation of conservation of excess enthalpy (4.5)

$$\frac{ax}{R_0}=\frac{0.707\sqrt{\frac{1-m}{1-m_0}}\sqrt{\int\limits_0^1 F'Z\,d\eta}\sqrt{\frac{\rho_0}{\rho_m}}}{\frac{\Delta i_m}{\Delta i_0}\,b_*\int\limits_0^1 F'\varepsilon\,d\eta}. \tag{4.44}$$

We can now use Eqs. (4.43) and (4.44) to determine the variation of velocity along the jet axis and the coordinate of the given cross section. If the jet is emitted into a parallel stream, then the calculation is performed by means of a trial-and-error method involving a variation of m.

In order to match the initial and main regions of the jet, we calculate the transitional section of the jet where $\rho_m=\rho_0$, and $\Delta i_m=\Delta i_0$. The value of $u_m/u_0$ in this transitional section is larger than unity or, in other words, the thermal transitional section is situated closer to the jet nozzle than the dynamic transitional section. From the intersection of the curve $u_m/u_0=f(ax/R_0)$ with the line $u_m/u_0=1$, we find the coordinate of the dynamic transitional section.

In this way we can obtain all of the parameters of the jet and their variations along the axis and cross section of the jet and, finally, we can match the initial and main regions of the jet.

## Sample Calculations

1. Incompressible Case. We determine the velocity profile in the main region of an axially symmetric jet of an incompressible fluid.

Let us solve the system of equations (4.29) taking into account the fact that $\bar{\rho}(\bar{V})=\text{const.}$ and $u_H=0$. We find the values of the coefficient $\tilde{a}_2$ and the dimensionless width of the boundary layer $b_*$ to be

$$\tilde{a}_2=-0.34;\; b_*=3.32.$$

Substituting the value of the coefficient $\tilde{a}_2$ into Eq. (4.27), we determine the velocity profile across the cross section of the jet.

The results of the calculation are given in Table 13.

Let us compare this approximate solution for the velocity profile of an axially symmetric jet of incompressible fluid with the more accurate Prandtl–Tolmin solution. The relative width of the boundary layer in the latter solution is $b_*=3.4$ [17]. The velocity profile $\bar{u}/u_m=F'/\eta$ obtained from the Prandtl–Tolmin solution is given in Table 13.

Let us determine the variation of velocity along the axis of a jet with a circular cross section. To do this, we first of all evaluate the integral

$$b_*^2\int\limits_0^1 Z^2\eta\,d\eta=0.506.$$

Substituting the value of the integral into Eq. (4.42), we obtain the formula for the axial velocity in the main region of a circular jet of incompressible fluid

$$\frac{u_m}{u_0}=\frac{0.99}{\frac{ax}{R_0}}.$$

TABLE 13

| | | | | | | | | | | |
|---|---|---|---|---|---|---|---|---|---|---|
| $\eta$ | 0 | 0.1 | 0.2 | 0.3 | 0.4 | 0.5 | 0.6 | 0.7 | 0.8 | 0.9 | 1.0 |
| $Z$ | 1 | 0.8953 | 0.7436 | 0.5846 | 0.437 | 0.305 | 0.1978 | 0.1101 | 0.0473 | 0.0171 | 0 |
| $\frac{\bar{u}}{u_m}=\frac{F'}{\eta}$ | 1 | 0.904 | 0.755 | 0.59 | 0.44 | 0.302 | 0.187 | 0.1 | 0.044 | 0.017 | 0 |

TABLE 14

| | $V_m$ | $\theta_H$ | $i_m$ | $T_m$ | $\tilde{a}_2$ | $b_*$ |
|---|---|---|---|---|---|---|
| Section I | $9.5\cdot10^{-4}$ | 18.8 | 90 | 248 | 1.55 | 2.21 |
| Section II | $12.5\cdot10^{-4}$ | 14.28 | 120 | 298 | 1.1 | 2.3 |
| Section III | $20.5\cdot10^{-4}$ | 8.71 | 140 | 318 | 1.0 | 2.45 |
| Section IV | $40\cdot10^{-4}$ | 4.46 | 160 | 334 | 0.6 | 2.7 |
| Section V | $60\cdot10^{-4}$ | 2.98 | 180 | 388 | 0.3 | 2.87 |

The formula for the axial velocity obtained by Tolmin [17] is of the form

$$\frac{u_m}{u_0}=\frac{0.96}{\frac{ax}{R_0}}.$$

A comparison of the approximate solution for the case of an incompressible fluid with the more accurate Prandtl–Tolmin solution shows that the agreement between the two solutions is satisfactory.

2. The Main Region of An Axially-Symmetric Jet of a Real Gas. Let us calculate a jet of carbon dioxide at $p=981\cdot10^4$ N/m$^2$ and an initial temperature $T_0=248$°K. The parameters of the surrounding medium are: $T_H=908$°K, $V_H=1.82\cdot10^{-3}$ m$^3$/N, $i_H=137\cdot10^4$ J/kg. We assume that $Pr_T=0.5$ and $a=0.1$.

We take several values of the specific volume on the jet axis, $V_m$. Using these values of $V_m$, we find from Figs. 2 and 3 the values of $i_m$ and $T_m$. As a first approximation, we take the

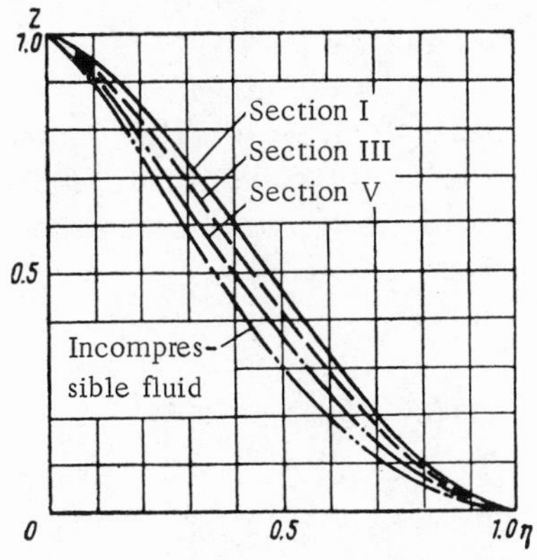


Fig. 24. Velocity profiles in the main region of an axially symmetric jet.

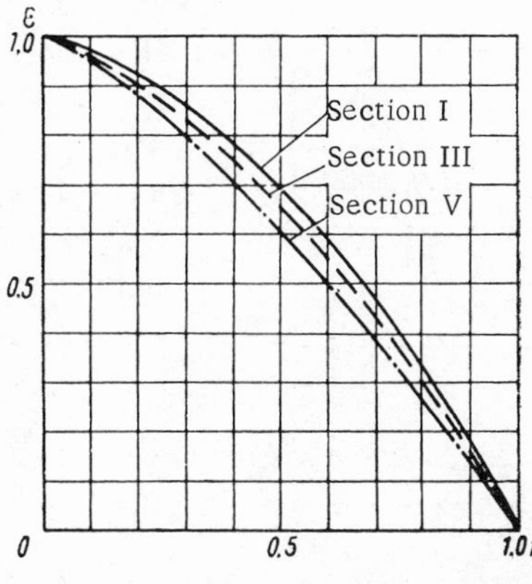


Fig. 25. Enthalpy profiles in the main region of an axially symmetric jet.

TABLE 15

| Section | | | | | | | | | | | | |
|---|---|---|---|---|---|---|---|---|---|---|---|---|
| Section I | $\eta$ | 0 | 0.1 | 0.2 | 0.3 | 0.4 | 0.5 | 0.6 | 0.7 | 0.8 | 0.9 | 1.0 |
| | $Z$ | 1.0 | 0.944 | 0.852 | 0.737 | 0.609 | 0.472 | 0.338 | 0.21 | 0.101 | 0.0333 | 0 |
| | $\varepsilon$ | 1.0 | 0.972 | 0.923 | 0.859 | 0.78 | 0.687 | 0.581 | 0.458 | 0.318 | 0.183 | 0 |
| | $\theta$ | 1.0 | 1.05 | 1.16 | 1.47 | 2.26 | 4.74 | 7.16 | 9.64 | 12.5 | 15.25 | 18.8 |
| | $\frac{\overline{\varrho u}\cdot\overline{u}}{\varrho_m\cdot u_m^2}$ | 1 | 0.868 | 0.665 | 0.444 | 0.313 | 0.0775 | 0.0248 | 0.0075 | 0.0015 | 0.0001 | 0 |
| | $\frac{\overline{\varrho u}\cdot\overline{\Delta i}}{\varrho_m u_m\cdot\Delta i_m}$ | 1 | 0.894 | 0.721 | 0.518 | 0.401 | 0.113 | 0.0428 | 0.0164 | 0.0049 | 0.0005 | 0 |
| Section III | $Z$ | 1 | 0.93 | 0.82 | 0.693 | 0.559 | 0.423 | 0.297 | 0.181 | 0.086 | 0.029 | 0 |
| | $\varepsilon$ | 1 | 0.965 | 0.906 | 0.834 | 0.748 | 0.651 | 0.546 | 0.426 | 0.292 | 0.169 | 0 |
| | $\theta$ | 1 | 1.22 | 1.83 | 2.54 | 3.22 | 3.95 | 4.71 | 5.61 | 6.64 | 7.56 | 8.71 |
| | $\frac{\overline{\varrho u}\cdot\overline{u}}{\varrho_m\cdot u_m^2}$ | 1 | 0.814 | 0.434 | 0.222 | 0.1183 | 0.0547 | 0.0232 | 0.0077 | 0.0016 | 0.0002 | 0 |
| | $\frac{\overline{\varrho u}\cdot\overline{\Delta i}}{\varrho_m u_m\cdot\Delta i_m}$ | 1 | 0.845 | 0.479 | 0.268 | 0.1586 | 0.0842 | 0.0427 | 0.0181 | 0.0054 | 0.0011 | 0 |
| Section V | $Z$ | 1 | 0.9117 | 0.78 | 0.636 | 0.495 | 0.362 | 0.245 | 0.144 | 0.066 | 0.023 | 0 |
| | $\varepsilon$ | 1 | 0.955 | 0.884 | 0.797 | 0.704 | 0.602 | 0.496 | 0.379 | 0.256 | 0.151 | 0 |
| | $\theta$ | 1 | 1.088 | 1.24 | 1.415 | 1.6 | 1.8 | 2.03 | 2.26 | 2.5 | 2.7 | 2.98 |
| | $\frac{\overline{\varrho u}\cdot\overline{u}}{\varrho_m\cdot u_m^2}$ | 1 | 0.796 | 0.52 | 0.307 | 0.166 | 0.0796 | 0.033 | 0.0105 | 0.0021 | 0.0002 | 0 |
| | $\frac{\overline{\varrho u}\cdot\overline{\Delta i}}{\varrho_m u_m\cdot\Delta i_m}$ | 1 | 0.834 | 0.588 | 0.384 | 0.236 | 0.133 | 0.067 | 0.0278 | 0.0082 | 0.0016 | 0 |

function $\theta'/\theta$ to be given by Eq. (4.37). Taking several values of $\tilde{a}_2$, we determine the values of the coefficients A* and B* corresponding to these $\tilde{a}_2$ from Eqs. (4.30), (4.32), and (4.38). From the point of intersection of the two curves $b_* = f(\tilde{a}_2)$, we find the solution of the system of equations (4.35) and (4.36) (see Table 14). From Eqs. (4.27) and (4.24), we find the velocity and enthalpy profiles in Figs. 24 and 25. The results of these calculations are given in Table 15.

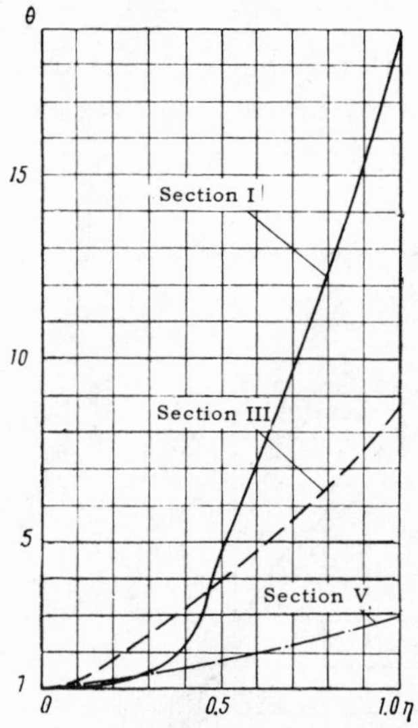


Fig. 26. Specific-volume profiles in the main region of an axially symmetric jet.

Using Eq. (4.39), we find the variation of enthalpy across the jet and from the graph of Fig. 2 we determine the value of the specific volume $\overline{V}$ and the quantity $\theta = \overline{V}/V_m$ (see Fig. 26).

Using the equation of state (1.1), we find the improved value of the function $\theta'/\theta$ from Eq. (4.40). From Eqs. (4.27), (4.43), and (4.24) we determine the total-head profiles and the excess-enthalpy profiles (see Fig. 27),

$$\left.\begin{aligned} \frac{\overline{\rho u}\cdot\overline{u}}{\rho_m u_m^2} &= f(\eta), \\ \frac{\overline{\rho u}\cdot\overline{\Delta i}}{\rho_m u_m\cdot\Delta i_m} &= f(\eta). \end{aligned}\right\}$$

The results of these calculations are given in Table 15. The

TABLE 16

| | Section I | Section II | Section III | Section IV | Section V |
|---|---|---|---|---|---|
| $\frac{\varrho_0}{\varrho_m}$ | 1 | 1.32 | 2.16 | 4.21 | 6.31 |
| $\frac{\Delta i_0}{\Delta i_m}$ | 1 | 0.874 | 0.788 | 0.704 | 0.62 |
| $\int_0^1 F' Z d\eta$ | 0.0538 | 0.03423 | 0.03302 | 0.03705 | 0.0411 |
| $\int_0^1 Z' \varepsilon d\eta$ | 0.0647 | 0.04161 | 0.041 | 0.04783 | 0.0545 |
| $\frac{ax}{R_0}$ | 1.145 | 1.8 | 2.38 | 3.07 | 3.73 |
| $\frac{u_m}{u_0}$ | 1.205 | 1.055 | 0.945 | 0.900 | 0.818 |

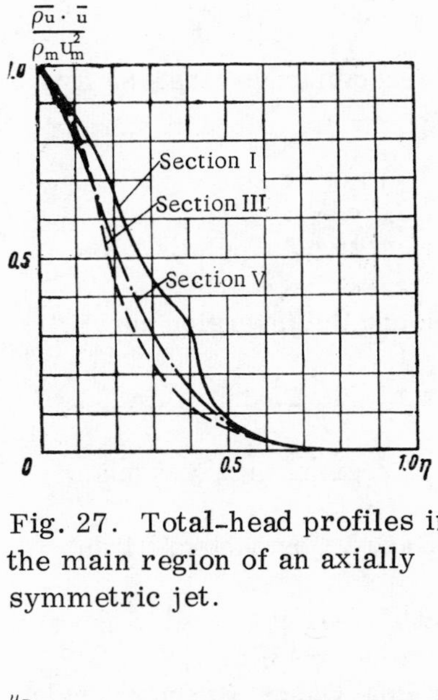


Fig. 27. Total-head profiles in the main region of an axially symmetric jet.

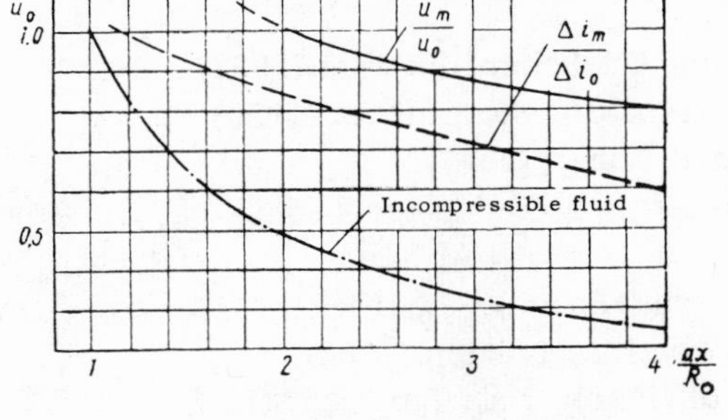


Fig. 28. Variation of velocity and enthalpy along the axis of an axially symmetric jet.

calculation of the integrals

$$\int_0^1 F'Zd\eta \text{ and } \int_0^1 F'\varepsilon d\eta$$

is carried out graphically.

The dimensionless quantities $ax/R_0$ and $u_m/u_0$, calculated from Eqs. (4.44) and (4.42), are shown in Table 16. The results of the calculations were used to construct graphs showing the variation of the relative velocity $u_m/u_0$ and the relative enthalpy $\Delta i_m/\Delta i_0$ along the jet axis (see Fig. 28).

The same figure also shows for comparison the variation of the relative velocity $u_m/u_0$ for a jet of incompressible fluid. For each section we determine the relative width of the jet boundary layer

$$\bar{b} = b_* \frac{ax}{R_0} .$$

The variation of the relative width $\bar{b}$ along the jet is shown in Fig. 29. The relative width of a jet of incompressible fluid is also shown in the same figure.

The results of the calculations show that as the ratio $\rho_m/\rho_H$ increases, the velocity (Fig. 24) and enthalpy (Fig. 25) profiles become more convex. In the case of the carbon dioxide jet, the velocity falls more slowly along the axis (Fig. 28) and the boundary is less steep (Fig. 29) than in the case of a jet of incompressible fluid.

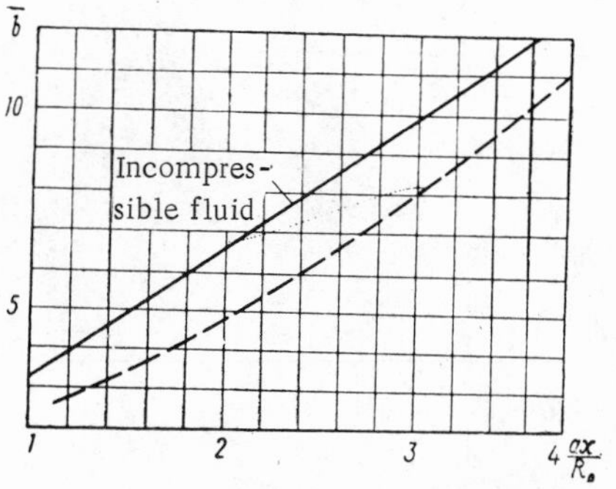


Fig. 29. The variation of the width of an axially symmetric jet.

In the calculation of a jet of carbon dioxide, we have replaced the true variation of the function $\theta'/\theta$ appearing in the equation of motion by the constant

$$\frac{\theta'}{\theta} = \ln \theta_{н}.$$

Let us carry out a more accurate calculation (second approximation) for the third cross section ($\Delta i_m/\Delta i_0 = 0.788$) of the jet by introducing the function $\theta'/\theta$ obtained in the first approximation. To do this, we use Eq. (4.34) to evaluate the integrals $J_k$ and Eqs. (4.31) and (4.33) to find the values of the coefficients A and B.

Solving the system of equations (4.29), we find new values of the quantities $\tilde{a}_2$ and $b_*$, namely,

$$\tilde{a}_2 = 1.3; \; b_* = 2.56.$$

Using the same equations as in the first approximation, we determine $u_m/u_0$ and $ax/R_0$ ($U_m/u_0 = 0.957$, $ax/R_0 = 2.24$). A comparison of these values with the results obtained in the first approximation shows that the first approximation is satisfactory, while it is much simpler than the second approximation.

Therefore, for future calculations of jets of real gases, it is recommended that the first approximation be used.

## Literature Cited


1. A. E. Sheindlin, "The behavior of matter in the super-critical region," Teplofiz., No. 3 (1954).
2. D. D. Kalafati, "Phase transitions in the supercritical region and the inversion curve," Teploenerg., Vol. 33, No. 1 (1961).
3. V. Yu. Urbakh, "On the critical state in liquid–gas transitions," Zh. Tekhn. Khim., Vol. 31, No. 2 (1959), p. 332.
4. M. I. Kulakova, "The gas–liquid transition in the supercritical region," Izv. Vysshikh. Uchebn. Zavendenii Ener. No. 2 (1963).
5. M. P. Vukalovich et al., The Thermodynamic Properties of Gases, Gostekhteoretizdat (1955).
6. A. M. Litvin, Technical Thermodynamics, Gostekhteoretizdat (1956).
7. P. S. Epshtein, A Course in Thermodynamics, Gostekhteoretizdat (1948).
8. M. P. Vukalovich and I. I. Novikov, The Equation of State for Real Gases, Gosenergoizdat (1948).
9. I. S. Badyl'kes, Working Substances for Refrigerators, Pishchepromizdat (1952).
10. N. B. Vargaftik, Physico-Thermal Properties of Matter, Gosenergoizdat (1956).
11. S. Ya. Gersh, Deep Cooling, Vols. I and II, Sovetskaya Nauka (1947).
12. M. P. Malkov and K. F. Pavlov, Handbook of Deep Cooling Methods for Technology, Gostekhteoretizdat (1947).
13. R. B. Scott, Low Temperature Techniques [Russian translation], IL, (1962).
14. F. Din, Thermodynamic Functions of Gases, Butterworth's, London (1956).
15. J. Hilsenrath et al., Tables of Thermal Properties of Gases, Nat. Bur. Std. (U. S.) Circ. 564 (1955).
16. E. S. Wentzel, Theory of Probability [Russian translation], Fizmatgiz (1962).
17. G. N. Abramovich, Theory of Turbulent Jets, Fizmatgiz (1960).

18. G. N. Abramovich, Turbulent Free Jets of Liquids and Gases, Gosenergoizdat (1948).
19. O. V. Yakovlevskii, "The hypothesis of the universal nature of the ejection properties of gas jets and its applications," Izv. Akad. Nauk SSSR, Otdel. Tekhn. Nauk, No. 3 (1961).
20. Pai Shih-yi, Theory of Jets, Fizmatgiz (1960).
21. V. A. Golubev, "The calculation of turbulent jets with very high temperatures," Inzh. Zh., Vol. 1, No. 4 (1961).
22. V. I. Bakulev, "Calculations of turbulent submerged jets of a real gas," Inzh. Zh., Vol. 1, No. 3 (1961).
23. N. E. Kochin, I. A. Kibel', and N. V. Roze, Theoretical Hydromechanics, Vols. I and II, Ogiz (1948).
24. L. G. Loitsyanskii, Fluid and Gas Mechanics, Fizmatgiz (1959).
25. A. N. Patrashev, Hydromechanics, Voenmorizdat (1953).
26. H. Schlichting, Boundary Layer Theory, McGraw-Hill, New York (1960).
27. E. van Dreist, "Turbulent boundary layer in compressible fluids," in: Mechanics, No. 1/11 [Russian translation], IL (1952).
28. V. A. Golubev, "Theoretical investigations into turbulent plane-parallel high-temperature jets with dissociation and ionization included," Inzh.-Fiz. Zh., Vol. 4, No. 6 (1961).
29. I. I. Mezhirov and E. E. Solodkin, "The dynamic and thermal boundary layers in a compressible gas," Trudy Tsent. Aerogidrodinam. Inst., No. 1 (1951).
30. L. V. Kantorovich and V. I. Krylov, Approximate Methods of Higher Analysis, Gostekhteoretizdat (1952).
31. N. A. Pratusevich, Variational Methods in Structural Mechanics, Gostekhteoretizdat, (1948).
32. A. N. Krylov, Lectures on Approximate Calculations, Gostekhteoretizdat (1954).
33. I. N. Bronshtein and K. A. Semendyaev, Handbook of Mathematics, Gostekhteoretizdat (1957).

# THE CALCULATION OF THE SHAPE OF AN ISOBARIC MIXING CHAMBER

O. V. Yakovlevskii

One of the main problems facing designers of ejectors, as well as various mixing chambers, is the determination of the optimal length and shape of the channel in which turbulent intermixing takes place. Some authors have used for this purpose the laws of propagation of free turbulent jets in a parallel stream.

Two papers by A. Ya. Cherkez [1] and M. V. Polikovskii [2] have been devoted to the calculation of flow in a mixing chamber. However, as was pointed out in [3], the method of Cherkez based on the experimentally observed analogy between the velocity fields in a cross section of the gas stream in an ejector and in a free turbulent jet is only of limited validity. The limitation arises because the nominal velocity of the parallel stream introduced into the calculation is found to be imaginary under some conditions.

The method proposed in [2] for the calculation of the inlet (initial) region of the ejector involves the determination of successive approximations to the stream parameters for a number of transverse sections. This method leads to laborious calculations and does not allow us to make an analysis of the influence of hydrodynamic and geometric parameters on the properties of flow in the mixing chamber.

The attempt made by I. S. Bogolyubov [4] to determine the shape of the isobaric inlet region of an ejector has been based on the theory of intermixing of parallel streams developed by A. Kuethe. However, A. Kuethe's theory contradicts experimental data on free jets (for example, see [1]), so that the use of its results for the calculation of flow in a mixing chamber has no practical meaning.

Moreover, the papers [1, 2, 4] listed above do not allow us to calculate the turbulent jet flow of fluid in a channel when the active stream, i.e., the stream possessing the higher momentum is the peripheral (annular) stream and not the central jet.

An analysis of the ejection properties of turbulent gas jets led the author in 1960 to formulate the hypothesis of the universality of these properties [5]. Calculations carried out on the basis of this hypothesis were found to be in satisfactory agreement with the corresponding experimental data for turbulent jets propagating under various conditions (jet of hot gas, including plasma, in a parallel stream; supersonic jet under various conditions of outflow; gas-liquid double-phase jet).

It was shown in [5] that the method based on the universality of the ejection properties of gas jets can be extended to the solution of other jet problems.

In the present paper, this method is applied to the solution of the problem of determining the shape of a mixing chamber which results in the intermixing of fluid streams under isobaric conditions. As is known, other conditions being equal, an isobaric mixing chamber is always more effective than a cylindrical chamber, i.e., it secures lower total-pressure loss for the mixture.

It should be noted, that for the calculation of flow in an isobaric mixing chamber and the determinination of its shape we could use the well-known theory of turbulent jets. However, as has already been noted in [5], the theory of jets propagating in a parallel stream [1] does not agree with experimental data over a certain range of the principal parameters. It was for this reason that a new approach to the calculation of gas jets propagating in parallel streams became necessary. On the other hand, the application of the laws of turbulent-jet theory [1] to isobaric mixing chambers does not allow us to obtain the required relations in explicit form, which considerably complicates the analysis of the dependence of the chamber shape on the principal flow parameters.

Therefore, the method of calculating turbulent jets based on the hypothesis of the universality of ejection properties of jets [5] has been used for the solution of the above problem.

## 1. Description of Flow, Principal Assumptions, and the System of Equations

Let us consider flow in an axially symmetric channel (see Fig. 1) in the initial region of which there are two streams with unequal velocities $U_{10}$ (central jet) and $U_{20}$ (annular jet) separated by the wall of the central nozzle. Because of vortices that are present on the unstable boundary separating the two streams, an intense turbulent intermixing of the central and annular jets takes place. The region in which mixing takes place widens with distance from the initial section and penetrates more and more deeply into each of the two streams. As a result of this, in some transverse section (which we will call the transition section), one of the streams becomes completely involved in intense turbulent mixing and the unperturbed core of this stream disappears. If the central nozzle is of small dimensions (by comparison with the transverse section of the whole channel), the unperturbed core of the central jet ceases to exist first and the inner boundary of the mixing zone intersects the axis of the channel. On the other hand, if the transverse dimensions of the central and annular jets are comparable in the initial region (see Fig. 2), the unperturbed core of the annular jet is the first to disappear and the outer boundary of the mixing zone touches the channel wall. The flow depicted in Fig. 1 will be called for brevity Scheme A, that depicted in Fig. 2 will be called Scheme B.

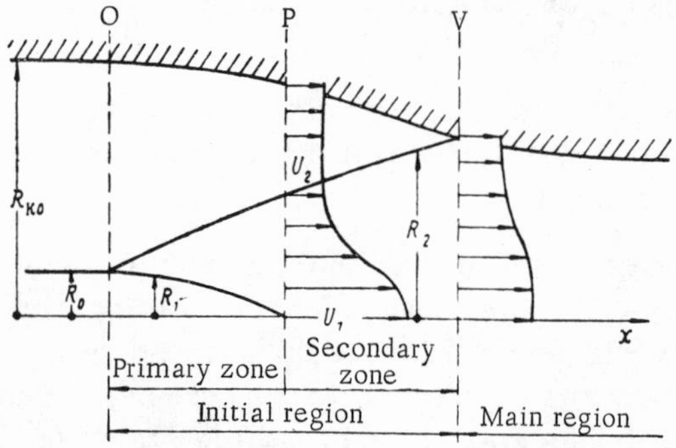


Fig. 1. Flow associated with the propagation of a jet in a restricted parallel stream according to Scheme A.

Downstream from the transition section, further broadening of the mixing zone leads to the disappearance of the core of the second stream also (the annular jet in the case of Fig. 1 or the central jet in the case of Fig. 2) and this occurs at a certain distance from the nozzle at the position of the section labelled V. In section V the entire flow is found to be completely subject to strong turbulent intermixing. Downstream from section V – in the main region of flow – a further decrease in the nonuniformity of the velocity profile takes place due to the action of the process of turbulent diffusion. Flow in the main region has been studied in detail in the author's papers [3, 6] in which formulas for the calculation of the stream

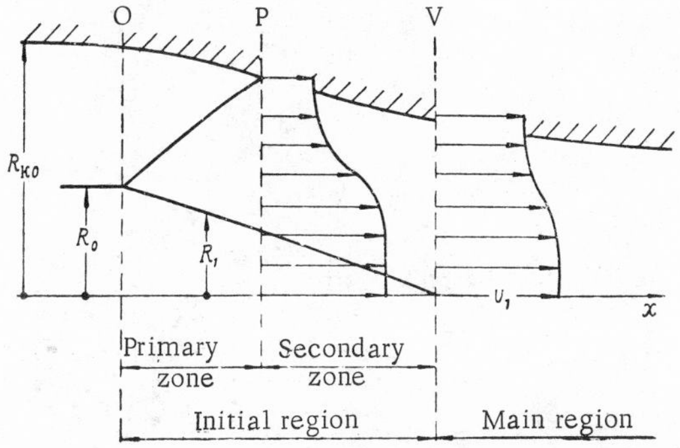


Fig. 2. Flow associated with the propagation of a jet in a restricted parallel stream according to Scheme B.

parameters for an arbitrarily shaped channel were derived.

In the present paper we will consider the calculation of flow in the initial region of the mixing chamber between the cross sections labelled O and V. In the case of an ejector, this region is called the inlet region; it is in this region that the ejected medium becomes entrained by the active stream in a process which is completed by section b.

The problem can thus be formulated as follows: To find the shape of the initial region of the channel which with the given geometric and hydrodynamic parameters of the flow in the initial section would result in a constant static pressure along the stream (p = const.).

We will assume that the velocity distribution of the two streams are uniform in the initial region and that the magnitudes of the velocities in the central and annular regions are $U_{10}$ and $U_{20}$, respectively. The densities of both streams will be assumed to be constant ($\rho$ = const.). With pressure constant, the velocity in the unperturbed core of each stream will not vary. By analogy with a free turbulent stream, we will assume that the profile of the dimensionless excess velocity in the mixing zone is self-similar. In the system of coordinates illustrated in Figs. 1 and 2, this assumption can be expressed as

$$\Delta U^0 \equiv \frac{U - U_2}{U_1 - U_2} = \varphi(\xi), \quad \xi = \frac{R - R_1}{R_2 - R_1}. \tag{1.1}$$

Here U is the velocity of the stream at an arbitrary point on the X axis; the indices 0, 1, and 2 correspond to the initial section, the central jet, and the annular stream; R is a transverse coordinate measured from the axis of the channel; $R_1$ and $R_2$ are the inner and outer boundaries of the mixing zone; $R_c$ is the channel radius.

It should be noted that in the primary zone (between section O and V), the velocities $U_1$ and $U_2$ are constant and equal to $U_{10}$ and $U_{20}$, respectively; in the secondary zone, either the velocity $U_2 = U_{20}$ (in the case of flow according to scheme A) or the velocity $U_1 = U_{10}$ (in the case of flow according to scheme B) remain constant.

Thus, to solve the problem formulated above, we have to determine the X-dependence of the channel radius $R_c$, as well as of two other quantities: either $R_1$ and $R_2$ of the primary zone, or $U_1$ and $R_2$, or $U_2$ and $R_1$ for the secondary zone, or $U_1$ and $U_2$ for the initial region. In order to determine these three unknowns, we have three equations at our disposal, namely, the equations of continuity and conservation of momentum, as well as the ejection equation based on the hypothesis of the universality of the ejection properties of turbulent jets [5].

The flow rate and the momentum of the liquid in the initial region at constant specific gravity are given by

$$G_0 = \pi R_0^2 \gamma U_{10} + \pi (R_{c0}^2 - R_0^2) \gamma U_{20}$$

and

$$K_0 = \pi R_0^2 \gamma U_{10}^2 + \pi (R_{c0}^2 - R_0^2) \gamma U_{20}^2.$$

For convenience in subsequent transformations, we will introduce the area-averaged velocity $g_0$ in the initial region of the channel

$$g_0 = \frac{G_0}{\pi R_{c0}^2 \gamma},$$

as well as the flow-rate averaged velocity $k_0$ in the initial section of the channel

$$k_0 = \frac{K_0}{\pi R_{c0}^2 \gamma}.$$

In the following we will also use the quantity $i_0 = k_0/g_0^2$, the so-called field coefficient [3], which characterizes the kinematic nonuniformity of the flow in the initial region of the channel.

As a geometric parameter of the problem characterizing the flow conditions in the initial region, we choose the dimensionless quantity $\alpha$ defined as the ratio

$$\alpha = \left(\frac{R_0}{R_{c0}}\right)^2.$$

It is not difficult to see that all of the dimensionless flow parameters in section o will be completely determined by two dimensionless quantities which we take to be the parameter $\alpha$ and the relative velocity of the annular stream in the initial section, $u_{20} = U_{20}/g_0$. It is easy to show that the other characteristics of the flow can be expressed in terms of $U_{20}$ and $\alpha$ as follows:

$$\left.\begin{aligned} u_{10} = u_{20} + \frac{1-u_{20}}{\alpha}, \quad i_0 = 1 + \frac{1-\alpha}{\alpha}(1-u_{20})^2, \\ m_0 \equiv \frac{u_{20}}{u_{10}} = \frac{\alpha u_{20}}{1-u_{20}(1-\alpha)}, \\ N \equiv \frac{G_{20}}{G_{10}} = \frac{u_{20}(1-\alpha)}{1-u_{20}(1-\alpha)}. \end{aligned}\right\} \tag{1.2}$$

The equation for the conservation of flow rate in the initial region of an axially symmetric channel can be written as

$$g_0 R_{c0}^2 = R_1^2 U_1 + 2\int_{R_1}^{R_2} URdR + (R_c^2 - R_2^2) U_2, \tag{1.3}$$

while the equation of conservation of momentum will be

$$k_0 R_{c0}^2 = R_1^2 U_1^2 + 2\int_{R_1}^{R_2} U^2 RdR + (R_c^2 - R_2^2) U_2^2. \tag{1.4}$$

If in the integrands of Eqs. (1.3) and (1.4) we replace U and R by $\Delta U^0$ and $\xi$ with the help of formula (1.1), then after a series of transformations these equations become

$$a_1 r_1^2 + 2b_1 r_1 r_2 + c_1 r_2^2 = M_1 \tag{1.5}$$

and

$$a_2 r_1^2 + 2b_2 r_1 r_2 + c_2 r_2^2 = M_2. \tag{1.6}$$

Here, we have introduced the following abbreviations

$$M_1=\frac{1-r_c^2u_2}{u_1-u_2},\quad M_2=\frac{i_0-2u_2+r_c^2u_2^2}{(u_1-u_2)^2},$$

$$r_1=\frac{R_1}{R_{c0}},\quad r_2=\frac{R_2}{R_{c0}},\quad r_c=\frac{R_c}{R_{c0}},$$

$$a_1=1+A_*-2A_{**},\quad b_1=A_{**}-A_*,\quad c_1=A_*,$$

$$a_2=1+B_*-2B_{**},\quad b_2=B_{**}-B_*,\quad c_2=B_*,$$

$$A_{**}=\int_0^1\varphi(\xi)\,d\xi,\quad B_{**}=\int_0^1\varphi^2(\xi)\,d\xi,$$

$$A_*=2\int_0^1\varphi(\xi)\,\xi d\xi,\quad B_*=2\int_0^1\varphi^2(\xi)\,\xi d\xi.$$

If, for the description of the velocity profile in the mixing zone we make use of Schlichting's formula [1]

$$\varphi(\xi)=(1-\xi^{3/2})^2, \tag{1.7}$$

which is used extensively in the theory of turbulent jets, then the coefficients listed above will have the following numerical values:

$$\left.\begin{array}{lll} & A_{**}=0.450, \quad B_{**}=0.316, & \\ a_1=0.357, & b_1=0.193, & c_1=A_*=0.257,\\ a_2=0.502, & b_2=0.182, & c_2=B_*=0.134.\end{array}\right\} \tag{1.8}$$

As the third equation required for the determination of the three unknowns, we use the ejection equation. According to the hypothesis of the universality of the ejection properties of jets [5] mentioned above, the rate of increase of the relative mass of the jet is independent of the relative velocity of the surrounding medium,† but is completely determined by the ratio of the densities of the surrounding medium and the jet. Since we are considering the mixing of incompressible-fluid jets at constant density, then, consequently, the ejection equation will be of the same form as that for a submerged jet. An analysis of the experimental and theoretical data obtained by various authors [1, 5, 8] shows that the variation in the relative flow rate with increasing distance from the initial section of the jet can be described by the following function:

$$G_c^0(x)=\begin{cases}1+\mu x & \text{for } x\leqslant x_*,\\ \omega(x+\delta) & \text{for } x\geqslant x_*.\end{cases} \tag{1.9}$$

Here, $G_c^0=G_c/G_{10}$, $x=X/R_0$, while $\mu$, $\omega$, and $\delta$ are constant coefficients. The coefficient $\omega$ according to [1, 5, 8, 9] is a constant and equal to 0.155. The magnitude of the coefficient $\mu$, as well as the values of $\delta$ and $x_*$ will, in general, depend on the initial turbulence of the jet. However, for the case of turbulent channel flow most frequently encountered in practice (turbulence intensity of 1-5%), experiments [1, 5] show that the coefficient $\mu$ can be taken as 0.072. The remaining constants in Eq. (1.9) then are $x_*=12.4$ and $\delta\approx 0$.

In order to make use of the ejection equation when $u_{20}<1$, we will write the equation of conservation of flow rate in the channel as

$$G_0=G_c+\pi(R_c^2-R_2^2)\gamma U_{20}.$$

† This assertion is valid as long as the jet is active, i.e., as long as its momentum per unit cross sectional area is high than that of the parallel stream. If the parallel stream becomes active, then all arguments refer to it.

Putting this equation into dimensionless form, we obtain

$$G_c^0 = \frac{1 - u_{20}(r_c^2 - r_2^2)}{\alpha u_{10}},$$

which taken together with the ejection equation (1.9) allows us to determine the variation of all variables of interest to us along the channel

$$r_c^2 - r_2^2 = \frac{1 - \alpha u_{10} G_c^0(x)}{u_{20}} \equiv \psi_1(x). \tag{1.10}$$

In the case where the annular and not the central jet is active in the mixing process ($u_{20} > 1$), the ejection equation with the help of the hypothesis of the universality of ejection properties [5] can be written as

$$G_{10} - G_1 = \mu' U_2 \gamma 2\pi R_0 X,$$

where $G_1$ is the flow rate of the fluid in the unperturbed core of the central jet and $\mu'$ is a coefficient which, according to the data of [10], is equal to 0.035. Since $G_1 = \pi R_1^2 \gamma U_1$, this equation transformed to dimensionless form becomes

$$r_1^2 = \alpha \frac{u_{10} - 2\mu' u_2 x}{u_1}. \tag{1.11}$$

For the analysis of the primary zone of the initial region where the unperturbed cores of both jets still exist, we obviously have $U_1 = U_{10}$ and $U_2 = U_{20}$, so that formula (1.11) can be simplified to

$$r_1^2 = \alpha \left(1 - 2\mu' \frac{u_{20}}{u_{10}} x\right) \equiv \psi_2(x). \tag{1.12}$$

## 2. Determination of the Boundaries of the Flow Regimes In the ($u_{20}$, $\alpha$) Diagram and the Solution of the System of Equations

Before we proceed to the solution of the problem, i.e., the calculation of the function $r_c(x)$ for various values of the parameters $u_{20}$ and $\alpha$, let us attempt to establish the conditions for the existence of the flow regimes A and B as functions of the parameters $u_{20}$ and $\alpha$. In this connection, as a criterion characterizing the transition from one flow scheme to the other we will use the simultaneity of the disappearance (in the one transverse section) of the unperturbed cores in the central and annular streams, namely,

$$r_1 = 0, \quad r_2 = r_c. \tag{2.1}$$

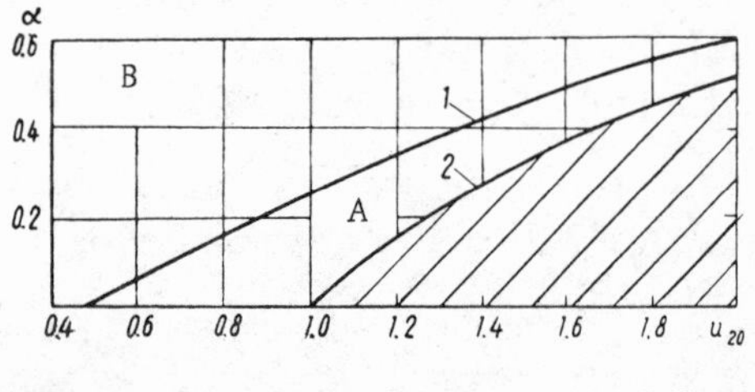


Fig. 3. Regions of existence of flow according to schemes A and B as a function of the parameters $u_{20}$ and $\alpha$.

Turning to Eqs. (1.5)-(1.6), we see that their simultaneous solution together with conditions (2.1) yields the connection between $u_{20}$ and $\alpha$ which must be satisfied by the geometric and kinematic characteristics when conditions (2.1) hold:

$$\alpha = \frac{\sqrt{0.508 - 0.994 u_{20} + 0.552 u_{20}^2} - 1 + 1.257 u_{20}}{2 u_{20}}. \tag{2.2}$$

The curve representing dependence (2.2) is shown in Fig. 3 (curve 1); it subdivides the whole domain of the parameters $u_{20}$ and $\alpha$ into two regions: A and B, the first of which corresponds to channel flow according to scheme A, the second to flow according to scheme B. In the shaded portion of the $u_{20}$, $\alpha$ plane, the values of the parameter $u_{10}$ are negative, so that this region of parameters $u_{20}$ and $\alpha$ must be excluded from consideration (curve 2 corresponds to $u_{10} = 0$).

Having determined the boundary between the two flow regimes, we will proceed to the solution of the system of equations describing the flow of intermixing jets in the channel.

The flow of fluid in the main region of an isobaric mixing chamber (see Figs. 1, 2), as well as the shape of the channel can be determined by the method described by the author in [6]. As shown by calculations, the variation in the form of the isobaric mixing chamber in this region is small by comparison with that in the initial region. In the present paper we give the solution for the initial region of an isobaric chamber, while for convenience and for greater definiteness of the resulting formulas, we will consider separately the primary and secondary zones of the initial region.

The Primary Zone of the Initial Region. This region is characterized by the existence of cores of unperturbed flow in both the central and peripheral jets. In view of the condition p = const., the velocity in each core is constant and equal to the corresponding initial value ($u_1 = u_{10}$, $u_2 = u_{20}$). The unknowns to be determined are $r_1$, $r_2$, and $r_c$.

The simultaneous solution of Eqs. (1.5) and (1.6) allows us to express the ordinates of the inner and outer boundaries of the mixing zone $r_1$ and $r_2$ in terms of the current chamber radius $r_c$ and the initial values of the kinematic and geometric parameters $u_{20}$ and $\alpha$

$$r_i^2 = \frac{T_i - \sqrt{T_i - h_i Q_i}}{h_i} \quad (i = 1,\ 2), \tag{2.3}$$

where

$$\left.\begin{aligned} &T_i = A_i - B_i r_c^2, \quad Q_i = (A_{i+2} - B_{i+2} r_c^2)^2, \\ &A_j = \frac{\alpha}{(1-u_{20})^2}\left[s_j(1-u_{20}) - t_j(1-u_{20})^2 + \alpha t_j u_{20}^2\right], \\ &B_j = \frac{\alpha u_{20}}{(1-u_{20})^2}\left[s_j(1-u_{20}) + \alpha t_j u_{20}\right] \quad (j = 1,\ 2,\ 3,\ 4). \end{aligned}\right\} \tag{2.4}$$

Here, we have

$$s_1 = 0.195; \quad s_2 = 0.228; \quad s_3 = 0.521; \quad s_4 = 1.406;$$
$$t_1 = 0.048; \quad t_2 = 0.130; \quad t_3 = t_4 = 1.0;$$
$$h_1 = 0.058; \quad h_2 = 0.031.$$

Since, as has been shown in Section 1, the ejection equations are different for $u_{20} < 1$ and $u_{20} > 1$, we will consider these two cases separately. When $u_{20} < 1$, we express $r_2$ in terms of $r_c$ and $\psi_1(x)$ and then substitute this expression into formula (2.3) with i = 2 to obtain an equation whose solution for $r_c^2$ yields

$$r_c^2(x) = \frac{F}{D}\left(1 - \sqrt{1 - \frac{DE}{F^2}}\right), \tag{2.5}$$

where

$$\left.\begin{aligned} &D = h_2 + 2B_2 + B_4^2, \\ &E = A_4^2 + 2A_2\psi_1(x) + h_2\psi_1^2(x), \\ &F = A_2 + A_4 B_4 + (h_2 + B_2)\psi_1(x). \end{aligned}\right\} \tag{2.6}$$

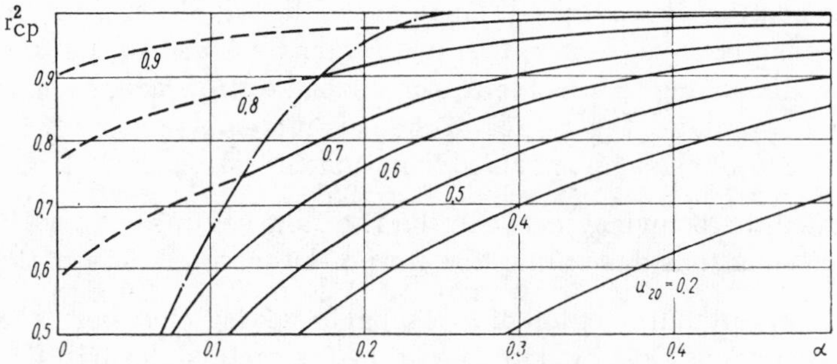


Fig. 4. The variation of the radius of the isobaric mixing chamber at the end of the primary zone as a function of the parameters $u_{20}$ and $\alpha$, where $U_{20} < 1$.

In order to obtain the function $r_c(x)$ for the case when the velocity of the peripheral stream is higher than that of the central jet ($u_{20} > 1$), we make use of Eqs. (1.12) and (2.3) with $i = 1$, the simultaneous solution of which is

$$r_c^2(x) = \frac{K}{B_3^2}\left(1 + \sqrt{1 - \frac{LB_3^2}{K^2}}\right), \tag{2.7}$$

where

$$\left.\begin{aligned} K &= A_3B_3 - B_1\psi_2(x), \\ L &= A_3^2 - 2A_1\psi_2(x) + h_1\psi_2^2(x). \end{aligned}\right\} \tag{2.8}$$

Expressions (2.5)-(2.8) obtained above allow us to determine the shape of the isobaric mixing chamber from the initial values of the kinematic and geometric parameters $u_{20}$ and $\alpha$ and then, with the help of formulas (1.1) and (2.3), to determine the fluid flow during the process of intermixing of jets in the channel at constant pressure. It should be noted that the calculation of flow and channel shape by means of formulas (2.3)-(2.8) is only valid for the primary zone of the initial region, i.e., provided that unperturbed-flow cores exist in both the central and peripheral jets. As soon as one of the unperturbed cores ceases to exist, the primary zone of the initial region terminates. It is therefore clear that formulas (2.5) and (2.7) can only be used provided that $r_c > r_{cp}$, where $r_{cp}$ is the radius of the mixing chamber at the point corresponding to the end of the primary zone.

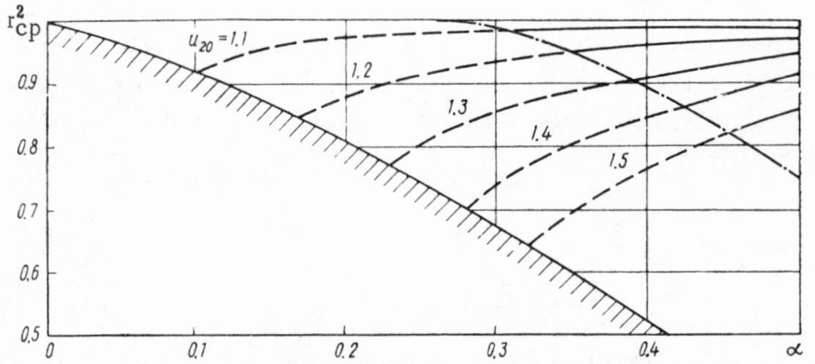


Fig. 5. The variation of the radius of the isobaric mixing chamber at the end of the primary zone as a function of the parameters $u_{20}$ and $\alpha$, where $u_{20} < 1$.

The magnitude of $r_{cp}$ is completely determined by the initial values of the kinematic and geometric parameters $u_{20}$ and $\alpha$. It can be found from the system of equations (1.5)-(1.6) subject to the following conditions:

$r_1 = 0$ for flow according to scheme A (see Fig. 1);

$r_2 = r_c$ for flow according to scheme B (see Fig. 2).

The corresponding formulas for the determination of the function $r_{cp}(u_{20}, \alpha)$ are

for scheme A

$$r^2_{cp}(u_{20}, \alpha) = \frac{A_3}{B_3}, \tag{2.9}$$

for scheme B

$$r^2_{cp}(u_{20}, \alpha) = \frac{P}{C}\left(1 - \sqrt{1 - \frac{CA_4^2}{P^2}}\right), \tag{2.10}$$

where

$$C = h_2 + 2B_2 + B_4^2,$$
$$P = A_2 + A_4 B_4.$$

The function $r_{cp}(u_{20}, \alpha)$ given by relations (2.9) and (2.10) is shown in Fig. 4 (for $u_{20} < 1$) and in Fig. 5 (for $u_{20} > 1$). The dot-dash curve in both figures gives the boundary between the flow regimes A and B (see Fig. 3), the curves lying to the left of this line corresponding to scheme A and those to the right to scheme B.

The Secondary Zone of the Initial Region. The shape of the mixing chamber and the flow parameters for the secondary zone of the initial region are found by a method analogous to that used above. The only difference is that instead of one of the boundaries of the mixing zone (the inner one in the case of scheme A and the outer one in the case of scheme B), another unknown makes its appearance – the velocity either on the axis (scheme A) or on the chamber wall (scheme B).

Let us consider the case that is most frequently encountered in practice, namely, flow according to scheme A with $u_{20} < 1$. To find three unknowns $r_c$, $r_2$, and $u_1$, we have a system of three equations (1.5), (1.6), and (1.10), which under the conditions indicated above ($r_1 = 0$, $u_2 = u_{20}$) can be written as

$$c_1 r_2^2 = \frac{1 - r_c^2 u_{20}}{u_1 - u_{20}}, \quad c_2 r_2^2 = \frac{i_0 - 2u_{20} + r_c^2 u_{20}^2}{(u_1 - u_2)^2}, \tag{2.11}$$
$$r_c^2 - r_2^2 = \varphi_1(x).$$

With the help of the first two equations of this system, we can express $u_1$ and $r_2^2$ in terms of the chamber radius and the initial parameters

$$\left.\begin{aligned} u_1 &= u_{20} + \frac{c_1}{c_2} \frac{i_0 - 2u_{20} + r_c^2 u_{20}^2}{1 - r_c^2 u_{20}}, \\ r_2^2 &= \frac{c_2}{c_1^2} \frac{(1 - r_c^2 u_{20})^2}{i_0 - 2u_{20} + r_c^2 u_{20}^2}. \end{aligned}\right\} \tag{2.12}$$

The simultaneous solution of the last equations of system (2.11) and (2.12) allows us to determine the variation of the radius of the mixing chamber along its length in the secondary zone of the initial region

$$r_c^2(x) = \frac{J}{nu_{20}}\left(1 - \sqrt{1 - \frac{nH}{J^2}}\right), \qquad (2.13)$$

where

$$J = \frac{i_0}{2u_{20}} + n - \frac{u_{20}}{2}\psi_1(x),$$

$$H = 1 + n + (i_0 - 2u_{20})\psi_1(x),$$

$$n = \frac{c_2}{c_1^2} - 1 = 1.03.$$

The radius of the isobaric mixing chamber in the final section of the initial region is found from Eq. (2.13) with $\psi_1 = 0$,

$$r_{cs}^2 = \frac{1 + 0.486\dfrac{i_0}{u_{20}}}{u_{20}}\left[1 - \sqrt{1 - \frac{1.97}{\left(1 + 0.486\dfrac{i_0}{u_{20}}\right)^2}}\right]. \qquad (2.14)$$

The position of the final section of the initial region is also found from the condition $\psi_1 = 0$

$$x_s = \frac{1}{\alpha\omega u_{10}} = \frac{1}{\omega[1 - (1 - \alpha)u_2]}$$

or, alternatively, if we make use of the concept of ejection coefficient N,

$$x_s = \frac{N + 1}{\omega}.$$

## 3. Discussion of the Results

The relations obtained in Section 2 allow us to determine the shape of the initial region of an isobaric mixing chamber from the given values of the kinematic and geometric parameters. An examination of Figs. 4 and 5 shows that the radius of the isobaric mixing chamber should decrease downstream, and this decrease will occur more rapidly as the deviation of $u_{20}$ from unity increases and as the value of $\alpha$ decreases. The reason for this is that these conditions correspond to an increase in the nonuniformity of the velocity profile in the initial section of

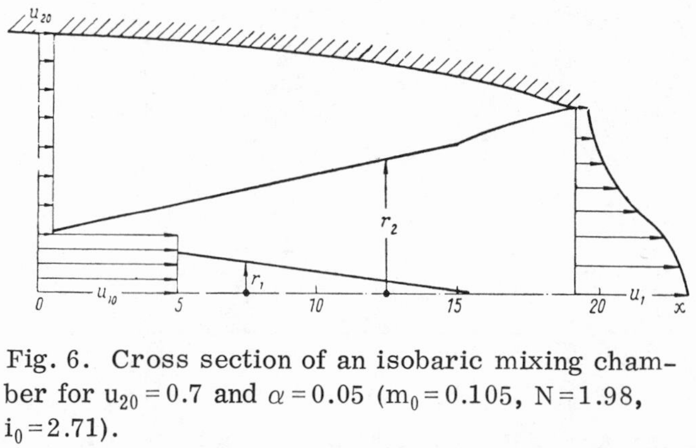


Fig. 6. Cross section of an isobaric mixing chamber for $u_{20} = 0.7$ and $\alpha = 0.05$ ($m_0 = 0.105$, $N = 1.98$, $i_0 = 2.71$).

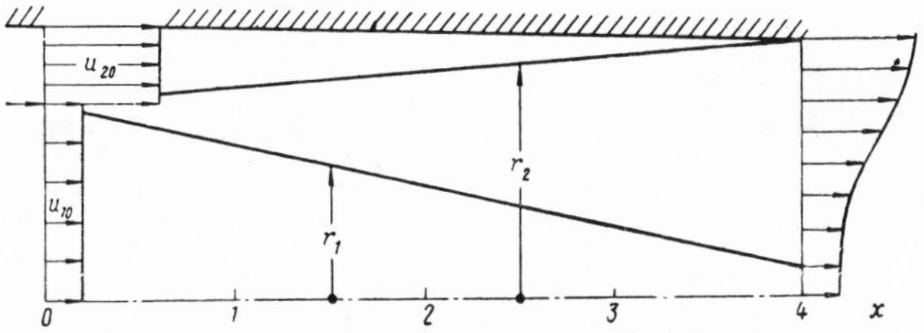


Fig. 7. Cross section of an isobaric mixing chamber for $u_{20} = 1.5$ and $\alpha = 0.5$ ($m_0 = 3.0$, $N = 3.0$, $i_0 = 1.25$).

the chamber. However, it is well known (for example, see the author's paper [3]) that as the kinematic nonuniformity of the stream in a channel of constant transverse section increases, there is a greater static-pressure increase associated with the smoothing out of the nonuniformity. Consequently, if we impose the condition that pressure in the channel is to be constant, we find that its cross sectional area (or radius) should decrease downstream and that this decrease will be greater, the larger the initial nonuniformity of the velocity profile, i.e., the smaller the value of $\alpha$ and the greater the deviation of $u_{20}$ from unity.

In conclusion, let us consider two concrete examples of a numerical calculation of the shape of an isobaric mixing chamber, taking $u_{20} = 0.7$, $\alpha = 0.05$ (Example 1) and $u_{20} = 1.5$, $\alpha = 0.5$ (Example 2). In the first example, flow is according to scheme A, in the second according to scheme B (see Fig. 3). The values of $m_0$, i, and N corresponding to the specified values of $u_{20}$ and $\alpha$ are given in Figs. 6 and 7 which show the longitudinal cross section through the initial regions of the mixing chambers, as well as outlines of the mixing zones. It can be seen that the maintenance of isobaric flow requires an appreciable decrease in the radius of the mixing chamber (especially in the first example).

The method for determining the shape of an isobaric mixing chamber and the flow parameters presented above can be used for the selection of optimal ejector parameters (for example, the velocity of the ejected stream $u_{20}$ and geometric parameter $\alpha$ for a given value of the ejection coefficient). However, the solution of this problem was not an aim of the present paper.

The author would like to express his gratitude to G. B. Krayushkina for her help with the calculations.

## Literature Cited

1. G. N. Abramovich, Theory of Turbulent Jets, Fizmatgiz (1960).
2. M. V. Polikovskii, "The calculation of the entrance section of an ejector," Izv. Akad. Nauk SSSR, Otdel. Tekhn. Nauk, No. 1 (1957).
3. O. V. Yakovlevskii, "The laws of turbulent mixing of coaxial flows in a channel with constant transverse cross section," Inzh. Zh. Vol. 1, No. 4 (1961).
4. I. S. Bogolyubov, "The initial phase of flow intermixing in an ejector," Transactions of the MAI, No. 97, Oborongiz (1958).
5. O. V. Yakovlevskii, "The hypothesis of the universality of the ejection properties of turbulent jets and its applications," Izv. Akad. Nauk SSSR, Otdel. Tekhn. Nauk, No. 3, (1961).
6. O. V. Yakovlevskii, "The mixing of jets in a channel with variable transverse cross section," Izv. Akad. Nauk SSSR, Otdel. Tekhno. Nauk, No. 1 (1962).
7. K. Viktorin, Untersuchung turbulenter Mischvorgänge, Forsch. Gebiete Ingerieurw., Vol. 12 (1941), pp. 16–30.
8. M. L. Albertson et al., Diffusion of submerged jets, Proc. Am. Soc. Civil Engrs., Vol. 11 (1948), pp. 1571–1596.

9. F. P. Ricou and D. B. Spalding, Measurement of entrainment by axisymmetrical turbulent jets, J. Fluid Mech., Vol. 11 (Aug. 1961), p. 1.

10. G. N. Abramovich, Turbulent Free Jets of Liquids and Gases, Gosenergoizdat, (1948).

# THE PROPAGATION OF A TURBULENT JET IN AN OPPOSING STREAM

A. N. Sekundov

The investigation of the propagation of jets in opposing streams is acquiring great importance at the present time in view of many technological applications. For example, the possibility of the use of aerodynamic stabilizers in afterburners of turbojet engines is pointed out in [1]. The properties of this type of stabilization of combustion in the zone of development of a jet in an opposing stream exhibit significant advantages by comparison with the properties of conventional mechanical stabilizers. The design and construction of this type of device necessitates a complete understanding of the laws of propagation of turbulent jets in opposing streams.

One of the first to investigate this problem was L. A. Vulis [2] who made an experimental determination of the "range" $l$ (the length of the circulation zone) of a jet propagating in the initial region of an opposing jet with a large diameter. In these experiments, the principal parameter m (the ratio of the jet velocity to the velocity of the opposing stream) was varied within the range 2.13 to 2.63. L. A. Vulis proposed a superposition method for theoretical calculations, but the method only leads to qualitative agreement between theoretical and experimental data.

Yu. V. Ivanov, Kh. N. Sui, and É. P. Timma [3, 4, 5] have made a detailed investigation of the velocity field in a jet propagating in an opposing current over a wide range of variation of the parameter m (1 to 20). The dependence of the range of the jet on this parameter, $l(m)$, was established. In varying the diameter of the jet source, the above authors noticed that the opposing stream can be considered to be infinitely wide when the condition $D/l \geq 2.5$, where D is the diameter of the opposing stream, is satisfied.

A paper by A. S. Ginevskii [6] has appeared recently containing a theoretical calculation of the whole flow zone. A. S. Ginevskii notes that there is good agreement between the results of this calculation and the experimental data given in [7]. However, these results differ from those of [3] and [4], for example, by approximately 20-30% with regard to the quantity $l$. Moreover, in the theoretical analysis of [6], several assumptions have been adopted without sufficient substantiation: Thus, the author assumes that the thickness of the boundary layer at the nozzle section is equal to zero and that the pressure throughout the flow zone is constant (see Fig. 1).

Thus, the problem of the propagation of a jet in an opposing stream has not yet been solved unambiguously, since there are considerable variations between the results of different authors.

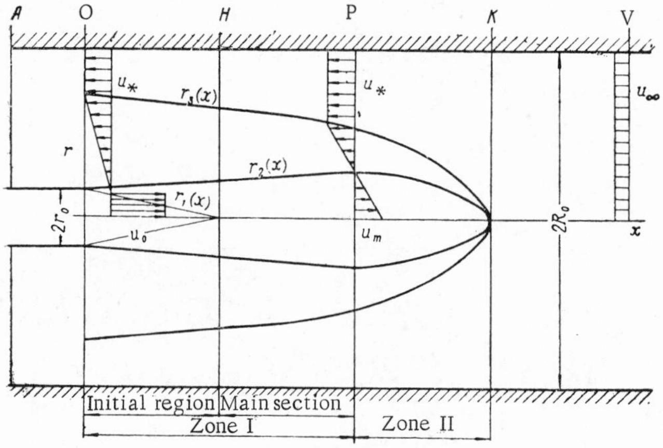


Fig. 1. The propagation of a jet in a cylindrical chamber.

In the following, an approximate solution of the above problem is obtained as a special case of a more general problem of the propagation of a jet in an opposing stream flowing in a cylindrical chamber.

## 1. The Propagation of a Jet in an Opposing Stream

Let us consider the propagation of a jet in a cylindrical chamber (see Fig. 1). A jet issues with velocity $u_0$ from a nozzle of radius $r_0$ and propagates along the axis of a cylindrical chamber of radius $R_0$; the jet expands as it is retarded by the opposing stream whose velocity $u_\infty$ is assumed to be less than the velocity $u_0$ of the jet. There exists a closed region bounded by the surface $r_2(x)$ in which the jet flow retains its initial direction. The boundedness of this region is the most typical feature which distinguishes the flow scheme under consideration from the usual cases of jet propagation. The surface $r_3(x)$ separates regions of unperturbed and perturbed flow in the opposing stream (the unperturbed flow has a uniform velocity field) and $r_1(x)$ is an analogous surface within the main jet. Experiments show that the whole region of flow in a cylindrical chamber can be subdivided in a longitudinal direction into two zones. In zone I, which adjoins the nozzle, the propagation of the jet is qualitatively similar to that of the usual submerged jet, namely, the flow rate and the thickness of the jet $r_2(x)$ increase with distance away from the nozzle, the boundaries of the jet are practically linear and subtend an angle $\alpha = \mathrm{arctg}\ 0.22$ with the chamber axis, and the static pressure is approximately constant. In zone II, the magnitudes of $r_2(x)$ and static pressure change sharply – the final retardation of the jet by the opposing stream takes place. Let us adopt as the transverse section separating these two zones the section in which the jet velocity $u_m$ becomes equal to the velocity $u_*$ of the opposing stream.

On the basis of the data given in [4], we can show that in this section the thickness of the jet $r_2$ also reaches its maximum value.

We will use a method described in [8] to obtain a closed system of equations. Let us write the equation describing the variation of the thickness of the jet in the main region as follows:

$$\frac{dr_2}{dx} = \frac{|v'|}{u_{av}} k(x), \tag{1.1}$$

where v' is the transverse fluctuation velocity, $u_{av}$ the average velocity of the jet, and k(x) a correction factor which takes into account the various features of jet propagation in an opposing stream. Let us discuss the meaning of this coefficient in greater detail. As was already pointed out above, in section P (see Fig. 1) we have $dr_2/dx = 0$, whereas in the case of jet propagation, for example, in a parallel stream we have $dr_2/dx > 0$. This behavior of the derivative $dr_2/dx$ can be explained as follows. In the general case, the increase in the thickness of a turbulent jet occurs because particles of the jet being carried by turbulent fluctuations into the surrounding medium entrain the matter of this medium and impart motion to it, as a result of which matter from the surrounding current becomes added to the jet. If the external current moves in a direction opposite to that of the jet, this process can only occur if there are particles in the jet whose velocities are higher than those of the particles in the external medium. It follows from this, that the broadening of a jet propagating in an opposing stream is governed by that component of the jet whose velocity is greater in magnitude than the velocity of the opposing stream $u_*$. Let us denote the ratio of the "active" mass of the jet to the total mass by

$$\frac{G_a}{G} = \frac{2\pi\rho \int_0^{r_a} urdr}{2\pi\rho \int_0^{r_2} urdr}, \tag{1.2}$$

where $r_a$ is the radius at which the jet velocity is $u = u_*$. Let us further assume that

$$k(x) = \left(\frac{G_a}{G}\right)^n, \tag{1.3}$$

where n is an empirical constant whose value according to preliminary determinations is 0.25. Following the method described in [8] and assuming that $|v'| \sim u_m + u_*$ and $u_{av} \sim u_m$, we finally find that

$$\frac{dr_2}{dx} = c\,\frac{u_m + u_*}{u_m}\left(\frac{G_a}{G}\right)^n. \tag{1.4}$$

The constant c can be found if we proceed to the limit $u_* \to 0$ in expression (1.4)

$$\frac{dr_2}{dx} = c,$$

so that, as in this case the jet reduces to the usual submerged jet for which

$$\frac{dr_2}{dx} = 0.22, \tag{1.5}$$

it is reasonable to assume that $c = 0.22$.

The law governing the broadening of of the turbulent boundary layer in the initial region of zone I can be obtained in the same manner as in the case of the main region, but the variations of the parameters $u_m$, G, and $G_a$ in the initial region are such that the right-hand side of expression (1.4) is close to the constant c and since we have $c = 0.27$ for the initial region of a submerged jet, we can assume that

$$\frac{d(r_2 - r_1)}{dx} = 0.27. \tag{1.6}$$

In order to be able to calculate the jet in an opposing stream, we must know the velocity profile in the zone of intermixing of the jet and the opposing stream. Several empirical expressions of varying accuracy are given in [3-6] for the description of the true velocity profiles. Calculations have shown that in view of the fact that the equations of motion are in integral form, the final results depend only weakly on the expression used for the velocity profile. Therefore, to simplify calculations, we will use a simple velocity profile in what follows; this consists of two linear sections as follows: The velocity profile from the jet axis to $r_2(x)$ is

$$\frac{u}{u_m} = \frac{r_2 - r}{r_2}, \tag{1.7}$$

while the velocity profile in the opposing stream from $r_2(x)$ to $r_3(x)$ is

$$\frac{u}{u_*} = \frac{r - r_2}{r_3 - r_2}. \tag{1.8}$$

We will assume that in the initial region the velocity profile is also linear

$$\frac{u}{u_0} = \frac{r_2 - r}{r_2 - r_1}. \tag{1.9}$$

## 2. The Propagation of a Turbulent Jet in a Cylindrical Chamber and an Infinite Opposing Stream

Let us now proceed to the solution of the problem of the propagation of an axially symmetric jet in an opposing stream inside a cylindrical chamber (see Fig. 1). The opposing stream in flowing around the broadening jet is accelerated to a velocity $u_*$. According to Bernoulli's equation, the pressure in it decreases according to

$$p_\infty - p_* = \frac{\rho}{2g}(u_*^2 - u_\infty^2). \tag{2.1}$$

Measurements of the velocity $u_*$ and pressure $p_*$ have shown that within zone I these parameters vary only slightly, so that we will assume that velocity and pressure are constant within zone I.

The equations of conservation of flow rate and momentum for the contour bounded by sections O and V can be written as follows:

$$\frac{1}{2}u_0 r_0^2 + \frac{1}{2}u_\infty R_0^2 - \int_{r_2}^{r_{03}} urdr - \frac{1}{2}u_*(R_0^2 - r_{03}^2) = 0, \tag{2.2}$$

$$\frac{1}{2}u_0^2 r_0^2 - \frac{1}{2}u_\infty^2 R_0^2 = -\int_{r_2}^{r_{03}} u^2 rdr - \frac{1}{2}u_*^2(R_0^2 - r_{03}^2) + \frac{\Delta p}{2\rho}R_0^2, \tag{2.3}$$

where $\Delta p = p_\infty - p_*$ and $r_{03}$ is to be evaluated in section 0, i.e., at $x=0$. Transforming these equations together with Eqs. (1.8) and (2.1), we obtain

$$\overline{u}_* = \frac{3(m + \overline{R}_0^2)}{3\overline{R}_0^2 - (\overline{r}_3^2 + \overline{r}_3 + 1)}, \tag{2.4}$$

$$\overline{r}_{03} = -0.333 + \sqrt{-0.222 + \frac{2m^2 + \overline{R}_0^2(\overline{u}_*^2 - 1)}{\overline{u}_*^2}}, \tag{2.5}$$

where

$$m = \frac{u_0}{u_\infty} \text{ and } \overline{R}_0 = \frac{R_0}{r_0}.$$

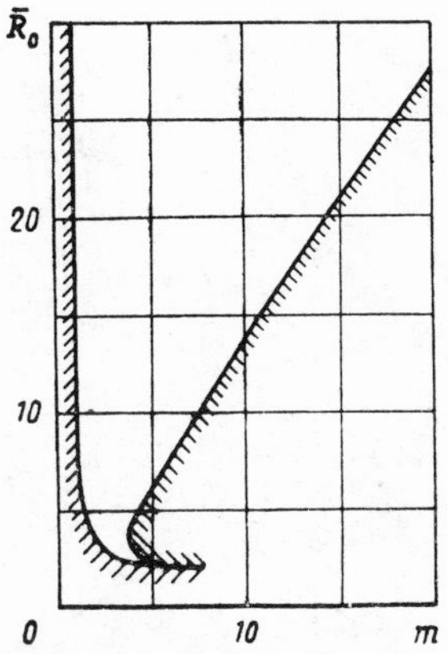


Fig. 2. The region of admissible values of the parameters m and $R_0$.

For given values of m and $\bar{R}_0$, this system of equations can be solved for $\bar{u} = u_* / u_\infty$ and $\bar{r}_{03} = r_{03}/r_0$ by the method of successive approximations. Calculations have shown that $\bar{u}_*$ increases with increasing m and decreasing $\bar{R}_0$, whereas $r_{03}$ increases with increasing m and $\bar{R}_0$.

In addition to the obvious condition

$$1 \leqslant \bar{r}_3(m, \bar{R}_0) \leqslant \bar{R}_0, \tag{2.6}$$

the admissible values of the parameters m and $R_0$ are also subject to one other condition which follows from the fact that the flow scheme under consideration cannot exist if the total pressure in the jet

$$p_c^0 = p_* + \frac{\rho u_0^2}{2}$$

is less than the total pressure in the opposing stream

$$p_\infty^0 = p_\infty + \frac{\rho u_\infty^2}{2} = p_* + \frac{\rho u_*^2}{2}.$$

This yields the following restriction on the possible values of the parameters m and $\bar{R}_0$:

$$\bar{u}_*(m, \bar{R}_0) \leqslant m. \tag{2.7}$$

Relations (2.6) and (2.7) allow us to determine completely the region of admissible values of the parameters m and $\bar{R}_0$ (see Fig. 2). The solution of the system of equations (2.4) and (2.5) simplifies considerably if $\bar{R}_0 \to \infty$, which corresponds to the case of propagation of a jet in an unbounded opposing stream

$$\bar{u}_* = 1, \tag{2.8}$$

$$\bar{r}_{03} = \sqrt{6m(m+1)+1}. \tag{2.9}$$

In particular, it follows from expressions (2.8) and (2.1) that in the propagation of a jet in an infinite opposing stream, the pressure in zone I is $p_* = p_\infty$. An "infinite" opposing stream is produced in practice by a jet with a sufficiently large diameter $D_0$. The magnitude of this diameter on the basis of the flow scheme under consideration should satisfy the inequality $D_0 > 2r_{03}$. This condition, together with relation (2.9) and expression (2.32) obtained below can be written as

$$\frac{D_0}{l} \geqslant 2. \tag{2.10}$$

It should be noted that condition (2.10) is in good agreement with the experimental result obtained in [4].

Let us now consider the main region of zone I. The equations of conservation of flow rate and momentum for a contour bounded by a section through the main region and section V can be written as

$$\int_0^{r_2} urdr + \frac{1}{2} u_\infty R_0^2 - \int_{r_2}^{r_3} urdr - \frac{1}{2} u_* (R_0^2 - r_3^2) = 0, \tag{2.11}$$

$$\int_0^{r_2} u^2rdr - \frac{1}{2} u_\infty^2 R_0^2 = - \int_{r_2}^{r_3} u^2rdr - \frac{1}{2} u_*^2 (R_0^2 - r_3^2) + \frac{\Delta p}{2\rho} R_0^2. \tag{2.12}$$

Let us transform Eqs. (2.11) and (2.12) with the help of relations (1.7), (1.8), and (2.1). into

$$N^2 + N + \beta = \frac{3a\overline{R}_0^2}{\overline{r}_2^2}, \tag{2.13}$$

$$(3 - b) N^2 + (2 - b) N + \beta (\alpha - b) = 0, \tag{2.14}$$

where

$$N = \frac{\overline{r}_3}{\overline{r}_2}, \quad \alpha = 1 - \frac{\overline{u}_m}{\overline{u}_*}, \quad \beta = 1 + \frac{\overline{u}_m}{\overline{u}_*}, \quad a = \frac{\overline{u}_* - 1}{\overline{u}_*}, \quad b = \frac{\overline{u}_* + 1}{\overline{u}_*}, \tag{2.15}$$

in which $\overline{u}_m = u_m/u_\infty$ is the dimensionless velocity on the jet axis.

This system of equations allows us to determine $\overline{r}_2(\overline{u}_m, \overline{R}_0, \overline{u}_*)$ and $\overline{r}_3(\overline{u}_m, \overline{R}_0, \overline{u}_*)$, where, as was pointed out above, $\overline{u}_*$ is found from relations (2.4) and (2.5). If in these functions we set $\overline{u}_m = m$, we will obtain the values of $\overline{r}_2$ and $\overline{r}_3$ in the transition section H between the initial and main regions: $\overline{r}_{2H} = \overline{r}_2(m, \overline{R}_0, \overline{u}_*)$ and $\overline{r}_{3H} = \overline{r}_3(m, \overline{R}_0, \overline{u}_*)$.

If we now make use of Eq. (1.6), we can easily find the length of the initial region of zone I, namely,

$$\overline{x}_H = \frac{1}{0.27} \overline{r}_{2H}. \tag{2.16}$$

Since the parameters in the initial region vary approximately linearly, then, knowing their values at the beginning and end of the initial region, as well as the length of the latter, we can find them for any intermediate section.

In order to calculate the main section, we must solve the system of equations (2.13) and (2.14) for $\overline{u}_m(\overline{r}_2, \overline{R}_0, \overline{u}_*)$, substitute into the resulting expression the value of $\overline{u}_*(m, \overline{R}_0)$, and then integrate Eq. (1.4) which, together with expressions (1.2) and (1.7), can be rewritten as

$$\frac{d\overline{r}_2}{d\overline{x}} = c \frac{\overline{u}_m + \overline{u}_*}{\overline{u}_m} \left\{ 1 - 3 \left( \frac{\overline{u}_*}{\overline{u}_m} \right) + 2 \left( \frac{\overline{u}_*}{\overline{u}_m} \right)^3 \right\}^n. \tag{2.17}$$

Since it is impossible to obtain an explict expression for $\overline{u}_m$ as a function of $\overline{r}_2$, the integration of this equation is difficult even numerically since the right-hand side of (2.17) tends to zero as $\overline{u}_m \to \overline{u}_*$. As a rough approximation we can take

$$\frac{d\overline{r}_2}{d\overline{x}} = c, \tag{2.18}$$

since the right-hand side of expression (2.17) is close to c over most of the range of variation of $\overline{u}_m$ from m to $\overline{u}_*$. In addition, an indirect confirmation of the validity of this assumption can be obtained as follows. It follows from Eq. (2.18) that the maximum thickness of the jet in the transverse section P is

$$\overline{r}_{2P} = c\overline{x}_P + c_0, \qquad (2.19)$$

where the quantity $c_0 = 0.05x_H$ can be neglected when m is large. Making use of relations (2.27) and (2.31) which will be derived below, we can determine the relative width of the jet, which is found to be independent of the parameter m,

$$\frac{2\overline{r}_{2P}}{\overline{l}} = \text{const} = 0.33. \qquad (2.20)$$

This result is confirmed by many experiments, although the numerical value of the constant differs from experiment to experiment; thus, this constant is found to be 0.36 in [5] and 0.43 in [8].

Equation (2.18) allows us to find the dependence of $\overline{r}_2$ on the distance from the end of the nozzle

$$\overline{r}_2 - \overline{r}_{2H} = 0.22(\overline{x} - \overline{x}_H). \qquad (2.21)$$

The system of equations (2.13), (2.14), and (2.21) which is a system of three algebraic equations with three unknowns $\overline{r}_2$, $\overline{r}_3$, $\overline{u}_m$ and two parameters m and $R_0$ can be easily solved.

From the condition that $\overline{u}_m = \overline{u}_*$ at the end of zone I, we can determine the length of the main region

$$\overline{x}_P - \overline{x}_H = \frac{1}{0.22}[\overline{r}_{2P} - \overline{r}_{2H}]. \qquad (2.22)$$

Calculations have shown that this quantity increases with increasing values of the parameters m and $\overline{R}_0$.

The solution of system (2.13), (2.14), and (2.21) can be obtained in explicit form if we consider the case $R_0 \to \infty$ which corresponds to the propagation of the jet in an infinite medium.

Making use of relation (2.4) and eliminating the indeterminacy in Eq. (2.13) which arises as $\overline{R}_0 \to \infty$, we obtain

$$\overline{r}_2^2 = \frac{6m^2 + 9m + 2 + \sqrt{6m(m+1)+1}}{\overline{u}_m^2 + 4\overline{u}_m + 3} = \frac{\varphi(m)}{\psi(\overline{u}_m)}, \qquad (2.23)$$

$$\overline{r}_3 = (\overline{u}_m + 1)\overline{r}_2. \qquad (2.24)$$

These relations allow us to find the lengths of the initial and main regions very simply if we take account of Eqs. (2.16) and (2.21).

$$\overline{x}_H = \frac{1}{0.27}\sqrt{\frac{\varphi(m)}{\psi(m)}}, \qquad (2.25)$$

$$\overline{x}_P - \overline{x}_H = \frac{1}{0.22}\left[\sqrt{\frac{\varphi(m)}{\psi(1)}} - \sqrt{\frac{\varphi(m)}{\psi(m)}}\right], \qquad (2.26)$$

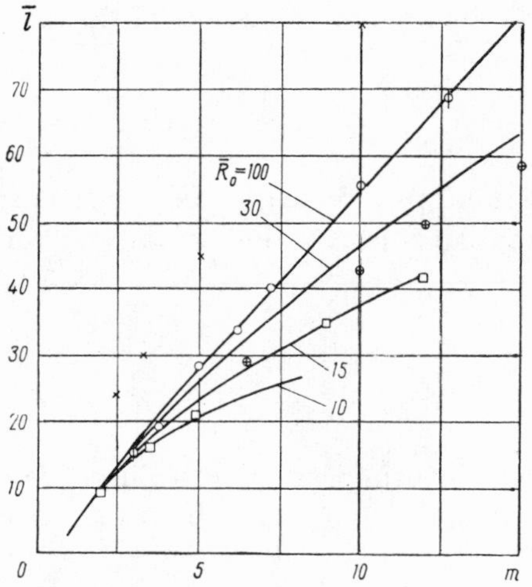


Fig. 3. Comparison of calculated and experimental values of the range $\bar{l}$ for various values of the parameters m and $\bar{R}_0$;

× $\bar{R}_0 \to \infty$, according to the data of [7];
ɸ $\bar{R}_0 \to \infty$, according to the data of [4];
○ $\bar{R}_0 \to \infty$, ⊕ $\bar{R}_0 = 30$, □ $\bar{R}_0 = 15$ } according to the author's experiments.

where

$$\varphi(m) = 6m^2 + 9m + 2 + \sqrt{6m(m+1)+1},$$
$$\psi(m) = m^2 + 4m + 3.$$

It is not possible to neglect pressure variations in zone II as was done in the case of zone I, since the pressure here is comparable with the velocity head. The velocity profiles likewise change very rapidly. Therefore, it is not possible to perform an exact calculation of the flow in zone II. Let us show how the dimensions of this zone can be estimated approximately. In view of the fact that the velocities of the direct and opposing streams in section P are equal ($\bar{u}_m = \bar{u}_*$), we can assume that the development of the jet in zone II occurs as if without energy losses. This assumption allows us to consider flow in zone II to be potential flow and to make use of the method described in [5] for the calculation of the circulatory zone behind a badly streamlined body. As a result of such a calculation we obtain

$$\bar{x}_K - \bar{x}_P = 1.56 \cdot \bar{r}_{2P} = 1.56 \sqrt{\frac{\varphi(m)}{\varphi(1)}}. \tag{2.27}$$

We will assume that this dependence remains valid when $\bar{R}_0 \neq \infty$, as well as when $\bar{R}_0 \to \infty$.

Before we proceed to the calculation of the "range" of a jet in an opposing stream, let us point out an important circumstance. As can be seen, for example, from formula (2.26), when $m \to 1$ the width of the main region in zone I is equal to zero, while the length of the initial region, as determined from expressions (2.16) or (2.23), will be a small but nevertheless nonzero quantity. However, it is obvious that with m = 1, the condition $u_m = u_*$ holds directly at the end of the nozzle and zone I will be completely absent, so that the "range" of the jet will be governed only by the dimensions of zone II. This contradiction is apparently due to the arbitrary nature of the flow model used and can be eliminated through the introduction of a correction coefficent

$$\bar{x}'_H = k(m)\, x_H, \tag{2.28}$$

where

$$k(m) = \begin{cases} 0, \text{ when } m = 1, \\ 1, \text{ when } m \to \infty. \end{cases} \tag{2.29}$$

Since we do not have any auxiliary conditions for the determination of the function k(m), we will assume that

$$k(m) = \frac{m-1}{m}. \tag{2.30}$$

Thus, the "range" of the jet is given by

$$\bar{l}=k(m)\,\bar{x}_H+(\bar{x}_P-\bar{x}_H)+(\bar{x}_K-\bar{x}_P). \tag{2.31}$$

Expressions for the individual terms in this equation have been derived above. The quantity $\bar{l}$ depends on the parameters m and $\bar{R}_0$; this dependence is shown in Fig. 3. It has been found that for $\bar{R}_0 > 100$, the value of $\bar{l}$ is insensitive to changes in $\bar{R}_0$ so that only one curve has been shown in the figure for values of $\bar{R}_0 > 100$. Thus, when $\bar{R}_0 \to \infty$, the "range" of the jet is governed only by a single parameter m,

$$\bar{l}(m)=2.16\sqrt{\varphi(m)}-\left(4.55-3.71\,\frac{m-1}{m}\right)\sqrt{\frac{\varphi(m)}{\psi(m)}}. \tag{2.32}$$

In addition to this dependence, Fig. 3 also shows the results of "range" calculations for $\bar{R}_0 = 30$, 15, and 10. It can be seen from the figure that these curves terminate abruptly at large values of m, since here we fall into the region of inadmissible values of m and $\bar{R}_0$ (see Fig. 2). It should be noted that there is satisfactory agreement between the experimental data of Kh. N. Sui and the author, and the results of the calculations.

## 3. The Additional Resistance Created by the Opposing Stream

Cases of practical application of the flow scheme under consideration, for example, aerodynamic stabilization of combustion in afterburners of turbojet engines, have been mentioned above. The flow of a jet in an afterburner is of course nonisothermal. The calculation carried out above neglected density differences between the material of the jet and the opposing stream. Let us make an approximate estimate of the influence of nonisothermal conditions on the range of the jet. It has been shown in [9] that the following expression holds for the velocity variation along the axis of a submerged nonisothermal jet:

$$u_m \sim \frac{u_0 r_0}{x\sqrt{\theta}}, \tag{3.1}$$

where $\theta = \rho_\infty/\rho_0$, $\rho_\infty$ is the density of the opposing stream, $\rho_0$ that of the jet. In view of the fact that in our scheme the law of flow in zone I which forms the major part of the total length of the jet is similar to the law of propagation of a submerged jet, we can assume on the basis of expression (3.1) that

$$\bar{L}=\frac{1}{\sqrt{\theta}}\bar{l}, \tag{3.2}$$

where $\bar{L}$ is the length of a nonisothermal jet.

This result is in satisfactory agreement with the experimental data of Yu. V. Ivanov.

In conclusion, let us determine the coefficient of hydraulic resistance $\xi$ in a cylindrical chamber containing an opposing axial stream (neglecting friction with the chamber walls),

$$\xi=\frac{p_\infty^0-p_A^0}{\frac{\rho_\infty u_\infty^2}{2}}=\frac{\left(p_\infty+\frac{\rho_\infty u_\infty^2}{2}\right)-\left(p_A+\frac{\rho_A u_A^2}{2}\right)}{\frac{\rho_\infty u_\infty^2}{2}}, \tag{3.3}$$

where $p_\infty^0$ and $p_A^0$ are the total pressures in sections at infinite distances to the left and right of the nozzle. It is assumed that the velocity and density fields are uniform in section A. In

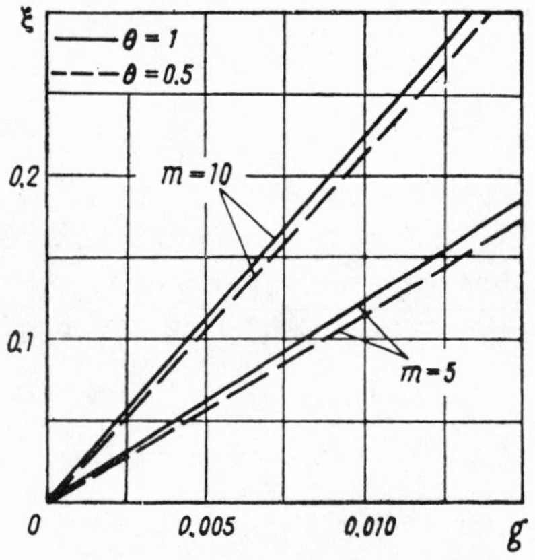


Fig. 4. Drag in a cylindrical chamber as a function of the parameters g, m, and $\theta$.

order to find the unknowns appearing in expression (3.3), we can write down the equations of conservation of momentum, flow rate, and excess enthalpy for the contour bounded by sections A and B, namely,

$$\rho_0 u_0^2 r_0^2 - \rho_\infty u_\infty^2 R_0^2 = \rho_A u_A^2 (R_0^2 - r_0^2) + + (p_\infty - p_0) r_0^2 + (p_\infty - p_A)(R_0^2 - r_0^2), \quad (3.4)$$

$$\rho_0 u_0 r_0^2 + \rho_\infty u_\infty R_0^2 = \rho_A u_A (R_0^2 - r_0^2), \quad (3.5)$$

$$\rho_\infty u_\infty R_0^2 (T_\infty - T_0) = \rho_A u_A (R_0^2 - r_0^2)(T_A - T_0). \quad (3.6)$$

Simple calculations show that with typical values of the various parameters: $\bar{R}_0 = 20$, $m = 5$, $p_\infty = 1$ atm, $u_\infty = 100$ m/sec, the ratios $\rho_0 T_0/\rho_A T_A$ and $\rho_A T_A/\rho_\infty T_\infty$ differ from unity by less than 2%. Therefore, Eq. (3.6) can be rewritten as

$$\bar{u}_\infty R_0^2 (1 - \theta) = u_A (\bar{R}_0^2 - 1)(1 - \bar{\rho}_A), \quad (3.7)$$

where $\theta = \rho_\infty/\rho_0$, $\bar{\rho}_A = \rho_A/\rho_0$. We can determine $p_A$, $\rho_A$, and $u_A$ by a simultaneous solution of Eqs. (3.4), (3.5), and (3.7). Substituting the values of these quantities into (3.3), we obtain

$$\xi = \frac{\bar{R}_0^2 [2m^2 + (1+\theta) m] - 2(p_\infty - p_0)(\bar{R}_0^2 - 1) - (m^2 - \theta)}{\theta (\bar{R}_0^2 - 1)^2}. \quad (3.8)$$

The last two terms in the numerator can be neglected when $\bar{R}_0 \geq 20$. If we introduce a parameter g characterizing the relative flow rate and defined by $G_0/G_\infty = m/\theta R_0^2$, the final expression for $\xi$ will be

$$\xi = \frac{2m^3 + (1+\theta) m^2}{(m - \theta g)^2} g. \quad (3.9)$$

This dependence is shown in Fig. 4. Since the flow velocities in combustion chambers quoted above are small, compressiblity effects have been neglected. Therefore, the total-pressure-loss in a cylindrical chamber can be calculated from the expression

$$\xi = \frac{1 - \frac{p_A^0}{p_\infty^0}}{\frac{\rho_\infty u_\infty^2}{2p_\infty^0}} = \frac{1 - \sigma}{1 - \pi(\lambda_\infty)}, \quad (3.10)$$

from which we have

$$\sigma = 1 - \xi [1 - \pi(\lambda_\infty)]. \quad (3.11)$$

## Literature Cited

1. E. Fillippi, "La stabilizzazion della fiamma degli esoreattori," L'aerotecnica, No. 1 (1958).
2. L. A. Vulis, and T. P. Leont'eva, "On parallel and opposing turbulent jets," Izv. Akad. Nauk Kaz. SSR, Ser. energ. No. 9 (1955).

3. Kh. N. Sui and Yu. V. Ivanov, "The investigation of the development of a circular jet in the initial region of an opposing jet of large dimensions," Izv. Akad. Nauk Est. SSR, Ser. Tekhn. i Fiz.-Mat. Nauk, Vol. 8, No. 2 (1959).
4. Kh. N. Sui, "The investigation of the development of circular and planar jets in parallel and opposing streams," Izv. Est. SSR, Ser. Tekhn. i Fiz.-Mat. Nauk, Vol. 10, No. 3 (1961).
5. E. Timma, "Turbulent circular and planar jets developing in an opposing stream," Izv. Est. SSR, Ser. Tekhn. i Fiz.-Mat. Nauk, Vol. 11, No. 4 (1962).
6. A. S. Ginevskii, "Turbulent jet streams with reverse liquid flows," in: Industrial Aerodynamics, No. 23, Oborongiz, (1962).
7. L. I. Ilizarova and A. S. Ginevskii, "The experimental investigation of jets in an opposing stream," in: Industrial Aerodynamics, No. 23, Oborongiz, (1962).
8. G. N. Abramovich, The Theory of Turbulent Jets, Fizmatgiz, (1960).
9. O. V. Yakovlevskii, "The hypothesis of the universality of the ejection properties of turbulent jets of gas and its applications," Izv. Akad. Nauk SSSR, Otd. Tekun. Nauk, No. 3 (1961).

# AXIALLY SYMMETRIC SUPERSONIC TURBULENT JETS DISCHARGED FROM A NOZZLE WITH UNDEREXPANSION

Chiang Chê-haing

Free turbulent jets emitted from axially symmetric supersonic nozzles under nonsimilarity conditions (pressure at the nozzle orifice not equal to the pressure of the surrounding medium) have not been extensively studied although they are of great practical interest.

If the jet flows out of an axially symmetric or planar supersonic nozzle into a uniform supersonic stream and has the same pressure as that of the surrounding medium, then only weak oscillations occur, but density discontinuities are absent. Such jets do not possess a periodic or almost periodic structure [9, 11].

A jet flowing out of a supersonic axially symmetric nozzle with underexpansion into a stationary medium or a uniform subsonic stream has a fairly complicated structure. Because of the distortion of the boundaries of the jet and expansion waves, the compression waves become superposed on one another on account of reflection from the jet boundary. As a result of this, a system of density discontinuities appears in such waves (see Fig. 1). When the coefficient of nonsimilarity $n = p_{exit}/p_H$ is only slightly higher than unity, the jet has a periodic or almost periodic structure. Here, $p_{exit}$ is the pressure at the nozzle orifice and $p_H$ the pressure of the surrounding medium.

Most of the papers devoted to the problem under consideration contain few experimental data on the first "barrel" of the jet (the zone situated between the nozzle and the first system of shock waves) obtained in the case of outflow from an axially symmetric nozzle.

One of the first such papers is by Winckler [14] published in 1948. This is a purely experimental paper devoted to a quantitative investigation of the first barrel of a jet. The velocity fields in the first barrel of an axially symmetric supersonic jet were calculated from the density fields measured by means of an interferometer; in these calculations, it was assumed that in front of the central forward discontinuity, the temperature, pressure, and Mach number are adiabatic functions of the density. Measurements of the total-pressure rise and relative measurements of the velocity profiles near the nozzle orifice by means of an interferometer confirm the validity of the last assumption. The measurements show good agreement with one another and this means that the intensity of the oblique discontinuity extending from the nozzle orifice is low, so that the entropy of the jet remains approximately constant in front of the forward discontinuity.

† This paper is based on the results of work performed by the author at the Moscow Aviation Institute under the supervision of G. N. Abramovich.

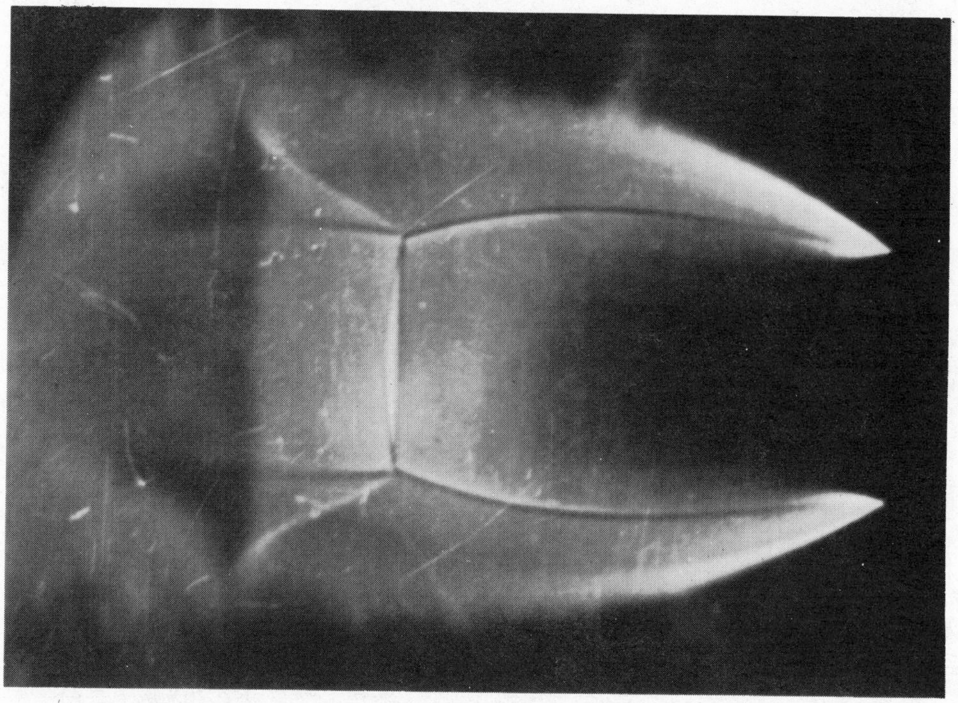

Fig. 1. Shadow photograph of a supersonic jet.

This assumption has also been made in other similar experiments.

Wang and Peterson [12] in 1958 used the method of characteristics to calculate the field of Mach numbers in front of a system of compression waves. Because of the interaction between the last rarefaction characteristic leaving the nozzle orifice and the first compression characteristic reflected from the jet boundary, a density discontinuity is produced, so that the exact calculation of the flow field behind the discontinuity becomes very difficult. However, an approximate method for the calculation of the points of intersection of the density discontinuity and the mesh formed by the characteristics by means of a digital computer has been proposed by Love [9]. If the operating regime of the nozzle differs only slightly from a similarity regime, then the boundary of the jet remains almost linear and with a small error it can be considered to be a similarity regime for $0.8 < n < 1.2$. If the operating regime of the nozzle differs markedly from a similarity regime, a system of density discontinuities appears in the jet and this causes the jet boundary to become curvilinear. At the present time, there is still no analytic method for the determination of the jet boundary in the case of outflow from an underexpanded nozzle. The theoretical boundary obtained numerically from the method of characteristics can be taken as the average line of the turbulent boundary layer. However, the method of characteristics requires a large amount of computation.

A particularly simple method for the determination of the curve giving an approximate boundary of the jet has been proposed by Love [9] on the basis of the method of characteristics. In this method, it is assumed that the boundary of the initial region of the jet can be approximated by a circle that passes through the nozzle orifice and the point where the diameter of the boundary is a maximum. The center of this circular arc lies on the normal to the jet boundary at the nozzle orifice and is situated at a distance $\delta_b = \delta_{exit}$ from it. Love's paper contains families of curves for the determination of the radius of the arc as a function of n, $M_{exit}$, and k.

## 1. Qualitative Investigations of Jets Flowing out of an Axially Symmetric Nozzle with Underexpansion

1. Distribution of Pressure Along the Jet Axis. The experimental data on the distribution of static pressures along the axis of a jet flowing out of an axially symmetric nozzle under nonsimilarity conditions are shown in Figs. 2-5 for $M_{exit}$ equal to 1.5 and 2.0, respectively. It can be seen from these graphs that in a jet flowing out of an underexpanded nozzle with $n > 1$, the static pressure on the jet axis falls away from the nozzle orifice to the discontinuity and then, after the discontinuity, it does not differ appreciably from the pressure of the surrounding medium. Subsequently, the static pressure on the jet axis varies according to a damped sinoidal curve and at some distance from the nozzle it becomes equal to the atmospheric pressure; in other words, a jet flowing out of an underexpanded nozzle periodically expands and contracts; because of energy losses in the density discontinuities, the excess pressure in the jet tends to zero.

It should be noticed that with $n > 1$ these oscillations on the jet axis rapidly die out (with the exception of the case $n \approx 2$) as a result of the strong forward discontinuity in the first barrel. With the exception of the first phase, deviations of static pressure on the jet axis from the pressure of the surrounding medium are less than 10%. The larger the value of n, the more rapid the attenuation of the pressure oscillations along the jet axis. When $n \approx 2$, the deviation of the pressure on the axis from atmospheric pressure is less than 20% during the first phase. If the value of n is only negligeably different from unity (either greater than or less than unity), the deviation of pressure on the jet axis from the atmospheric pressure is also small and less than 10%, although the pressure oscillations extend to greater distances from the nozzle orifice. This phenomenon can be explained as follows: With n large, an intense central forward discontinuity arises behind the first barrel and this leads to a large total-pressure drop. If n is negligibly different from unity and the mean pressure in the jet is only slightly above the pressure in the surrounding medium, then strong discontinuities do not arise and total-pressure drops are small. As a result of this, the static-pressure oscillations are damped out only slowly. The case $n \approx 2$ should be considered as a transition regime in which the jet already contains a central discontinuity, but its diameter is small and rarefaction in the jet before the discontinuity is not very great. This circumstance leads to a considerable increase in the pressure in the discontinuity which nevertheless decays along the jet axis at a slow rate (see Fig. 2).

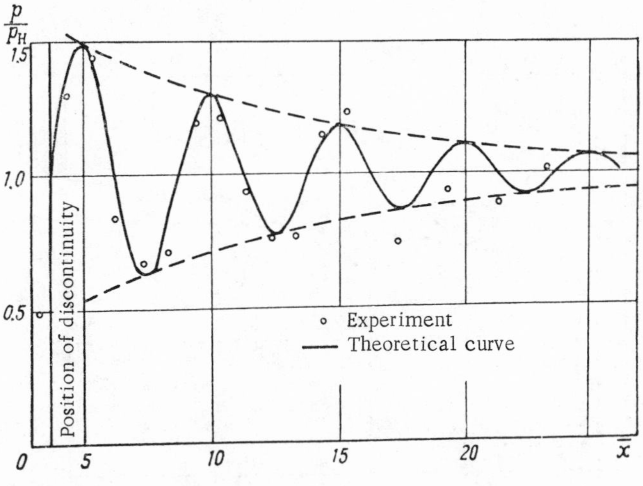


Fig. 2. Distribution of static pressure along the jet axis, $M_{exit} = 1.5$, $n = 2$.

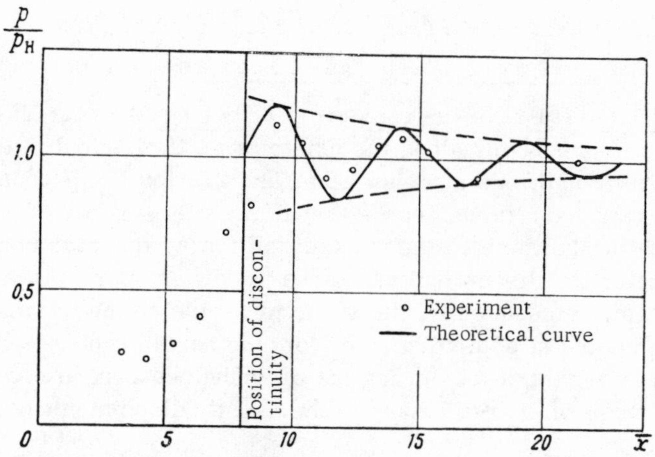


Fig. 3. Distribution of static pressure along the jet axis, $M_{exit}=1.5$, $n=2$.

The experimental curves of the distribution of static pressure along the jet axis can be described by expressions for damped oscillations whose period and amplitude depend on the Mach number at the nozzle exit, $M_{exit}$, and the degree of nonsimilarity n. Some of these calculated curves are shown in Figs. 2 and 3 and these were obtained from the formula

$$\frac{p}{p_H}-1=Ae^{-a\bar{x}}\sin\omega\bar{x}. \tag{1.1}$$

The following values of A, $a$ , and $\omega$ were chosen for the calculations:

| $M_{exit}$ | 1.5 | | | | | 2.0 | |
|---|---|---|---|---|---|---|---|
| $n$ | 2 | 3 | 4.09 | 5 | 5.45 | 4 | 2.56 |
| $A$ | 0.55 | 0.22 | 0.22 | 0.22 | 0.22 | 0.3 | 0.24 |
| $a$ | 0.1 | 0.1 | 0.1 | 0.1 | 0.1 | 0.1 | 0.1 |
| $\omega$ | $\frac{\pi}{2.5}$ | $\frac{\pi}{2.5}$ | $\frac{\pi}{2.5}$ | $\frac{\pi}{2.5}$ | $\frac{\pi}{2.5}$ | $\frac{\pi}{4}$ | $\frac{\pi}{2.5}$ |

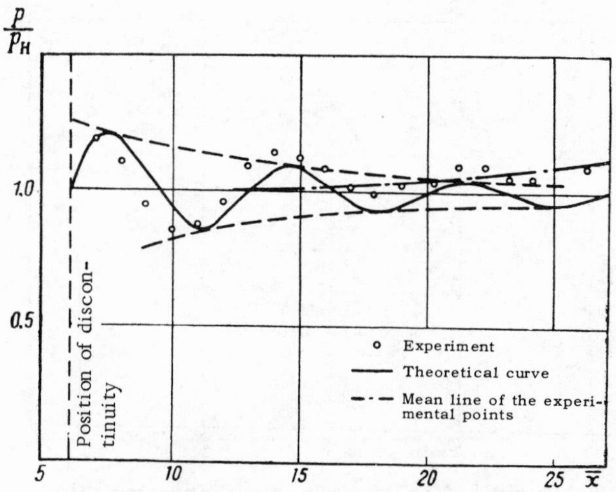


Fig. 4. Distribution of static pressure along the jet axis, $M_{exit}=2$, $p_0/p_H=20$, $p_{exit}/p_H=2.56$.

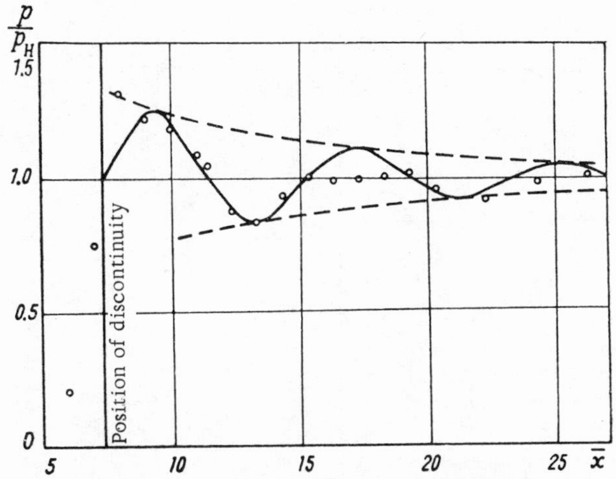


Fig. 5. Distribution of static pressures along the jet axis, $M_{exit}=2.0$, n=4.

We were unable to find the theoretical expressions for the coefficients A, a, and $\omega$ as functions of the degree of nonsimilarity n and the Mach number at the nozzle exit, $M_{exit}$.

The experimental points shown in Figs. 2 and 3 are in satisfactory agreement with the curves obtained from formula (1.1).

2. Determination of the Length of the First Barrel of the Jet. The lengths of the first barrel of a jet were measured on shadow photographs obtained with the IAB-451 instrument for various regimes of a jet from a nozzle. Figures 6-8 show the variations of the relative lengths $\bar{w}$ as functions of the degree of nonsimilarity n for three values of the Mach number at the nozzle orifice. Here, $\bar{w}$ is defined by

$$\bar{w} = \frac{w}{R_{exit}}, \tag{1.1a}$$

where w is the length of the first barrel of the jet.

These figures give the experimental points obtained by the author and the results of [9]. It can be seen from these figures that at a given value of $M_{exit}$, the length of the first barrel of the jet increases with increasing air pressure in the receiver. The rate at which the length of the first barrel increases with increasing value of n grows with increasing value of the Mach number $M_{exit}$ at the nozzle orifice. At the present time, there is no method for the deter-

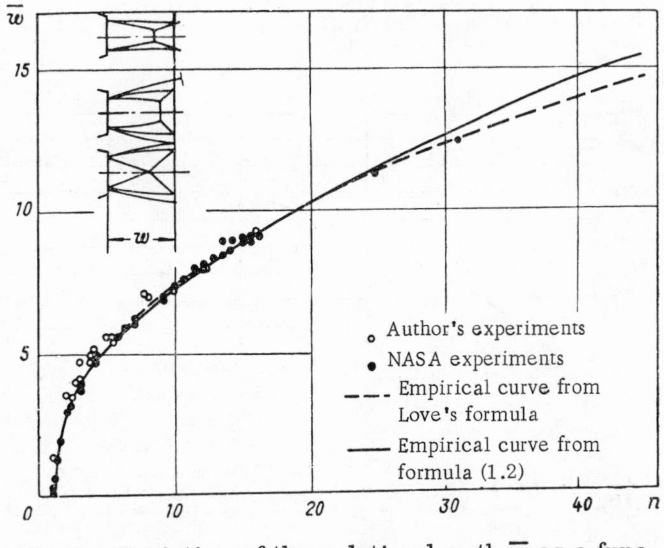


Fig. 6. Variation of the relative length $\bar{w}$ as a function of the degree of nonsimilarity n at the nozzle orifice for $M_{exit}=1$.

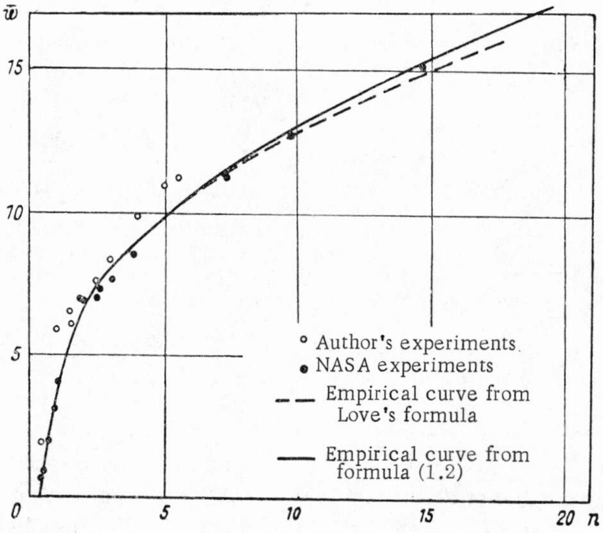


Fig. 7. Variation of the relative length $\bar{w}$ as a function of the degree of nonsimilarity n at the nozzle orifice for $M_{exit}=2$.

mination of the theoretical relation between the quantities $\bar{w}$, n, and $M_{exit}$. However, the experimental data reveal that for $n>2$, the variation of w with n is linear on a logarithmic scale. The gradient of this line depends on $M_{exit}$. This fact allows us to find the following empirical formula for the determination of the length of the first barrel for any values of n and $M_{exit}$:

when $n \leq 2$

$$\bar{w}=3.1M_{exit}^{\frac{1}{5}}\left[(nM_{exit}^2-1)^{\frac{1}{2}}-(M_{exit}^2-1)^{\frac{1}{2}}\right]+2(M_{exit}^2-1)^{\frac{1}{2}}, \tag{1.2a}$$

when $n \geq 2$

$$\bar{w}=\left\{3.1M_{exit}^{\frac{1}{5}}\left[(nM_{exit}^2-1)^{\frac{1}{2}}-(M_{exit}^2-1)^{\frac{1}{2}}\right]+2(M_{exit}^2-1)^{\frac{1}{2}}\right\}\left(\frac{n}{2}\right)^t. \tag{1.2b}$$

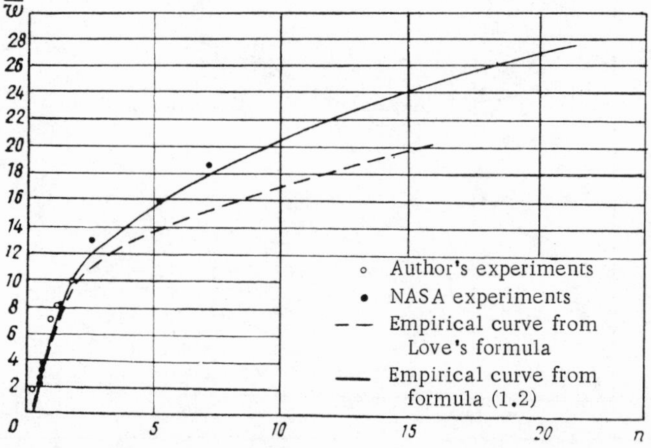


Fig. 8. Variation of the relative length $\bar{w}$ as a function of the degree of nonsimilarity n at the nozzle orifice for $M_{exit}=3$.

Formula (1.2b) differs from (1.2a) only by multiplier $(n/2)^t$. The magnitude of the exponent t depends on $M_{exit}$ as follows:

$$\text{when } M_{exit} \leqslant 1.5, \qquad t = \frac{0.523}{\sqrt{M_{exit}}}, \tag{1.3a}$$

$$\text{when } M_{exit} \geqslant 1.5, \qquad t = 0.451 - 0.016 M_{exit}. \tag{1.3b}$$

In addition to the experimental points, Figs. 6-8 give the calculated curves for the variation of $\bar{w}$ with n obtained from formula (1.2) for values of $M_{exit}$ of 1.0, 2.0, and 3.0. These curves are in good agreement with the experimental points.

An empirical formula for the determination of $\bar{w}$ as a function of n and $M_{exit}$ has also been obtained in [9]. A comparison of the author's empirical curve with Love's empirical curve (see Figs. 6-8) shows that the empirical formula (1.2) is in better agreement with experimental data than Love's formula with the exception of outflow from a sonic nozzle. In the latter case, the two curves coincide when $n \leq 20$, while for $n > 20$ and $M_{exit} = 1$, empirical curve (1.2b) shows worse agreement with experiment than Love's curve, although formula (1.2) can be used for practical calculations even in this region.

3. Determination of the Distance between the Orifice and the Central Forward Discontinuity in the First Barrel of the Jet. Figures 9-11 show the experimental data on the variation of the distance between the nozzle orifice and the central forward discontinuity, $\bar{l}_c = l_c/R_{exit}$, as a function of the degree of nonsimilarity n for the following values of the Mach number at the nozzle orifice: $M_{exit} = 1.0$, 2.0, and 3.0. If the operating regime of the nozzle is appreciably different from a similarity regime and there is no direct forward discontinuity in the jet, then the distance $l_c$ is measured from the nozzle orifice to the point of intersection of the oblique discontinuities (see Fig. 9). The variation of the relative quantity $\bar{l}_c = l_c/R_{exit}$ with n and $M_{exit}$ is similar to that of $\bar{w}$.

It was possible to obtain a simple relation holding between $\bar{l}_c$ and $\bar{w}$ for fixed values of n and $M_{exit}$,

$$\bar{l}_c = 0.8\,\bar{w}. \tag{1.4}$$

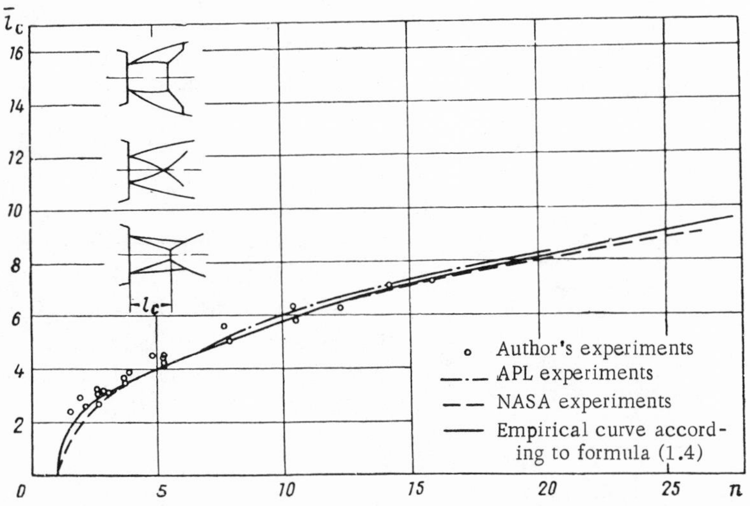


Fig. 9. The relative length of the first barrel $\bar{l}_c$ as a function of the degree of nonsimilarity n for $M_{exit} = 1$.

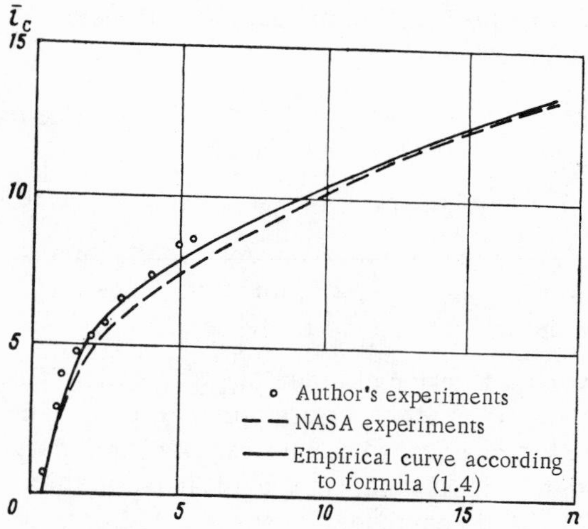


Fig. 10. The relative length of the first "barrel" $\bar{l}_c$ as a function of the degree of nonsimilarity n for $M_{exit} = 3$.

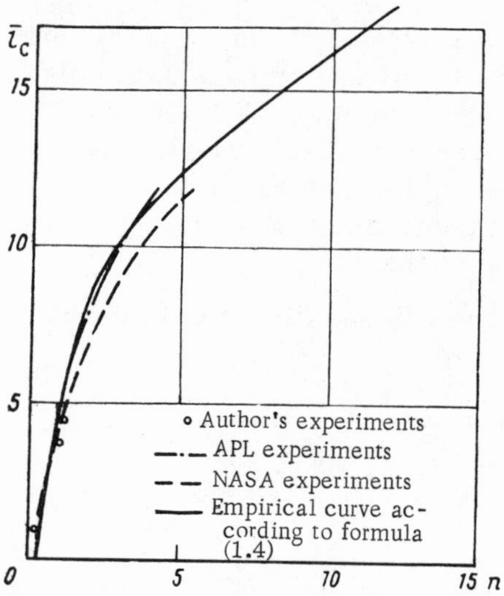


Fig. 11. The relative length of the first "barrel" $\bar{l}_c$ as a function of the degree of nonsimilarity n for $M_{exit} = 3$.

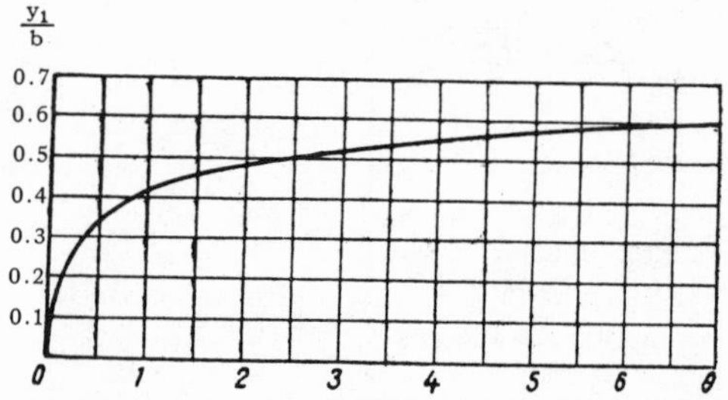


Fig. 12. The magnitude of the ordinate of the inner boundary relative to the mixing zone for nonisothermal gas.

The theoretical curves obtained from this formula are shown in Figs. 9-11. When $M_{exit} \leq 2$, the agreement between the theoretical curves and the experimental data is adequate. When $M_{exit} > 2$, the agreement between the calculated curves and the experimental points is somewhat worse, but the theoretical curves still reflect the general behavior of the experimental points.

4. Determination of the Boundaries and Thickness of the Boundary Layer in the Initial Gas-Dynamic Region of a Jet Issuing from an Underexpanded Nozzle. If we are dealing with a perfect gas, then the boundary of a jet emerging from a nozzle in a similarity regime must be a straight line parallel to the axis. In fact, a turbulent boundary layer makes its appearance. In the case of the initial region of a submerged jet emerging from a nozzle in the similarity regime, the rate of increase of the boundary-layer thickness can be described by the following approximate formula [4]:

$$\frac{db}{dx} = 0.27 \frac{1 + \frac{\rho_H}{\rho_u}}{2}, \tag{1.5}$$

where b is the thickness of the boundary layer, $\rho_H$ is the density of the surrounding medium, and $\rho_u$ is the density of gas in the constant-velocity core.

G. N. Abramovich [4] has obtained curves for the determination of the boundary layer of a jet emerging from a nozzle under similarity conditions as a function of $\theta$ (here, $\theta = T_0^*/T_H$, where $T_0^*$ is the retardation temperature in the receiver and $T_H$ the temperature of the surrounding stationary air). One of such curves for a submerged jet is shown in Fig. 12.

If it is assumed that pressure variations are small in the turbulent boundary layer of the initial region of a jet emerging from an underexpanded nozzle, i.e., that $p \approx p_H$, then the width of the jet can be calculated from formula (1.5) written as

$$\frac{db}{ds} = 0.27 \frac{1 + \frac{\rho_H}{\rho_b}}{2}, \tag{1.6}$$

where b is the thickness of the boundary layer of the initial region of a jet emerging from an underexpanded nozzle (this thickness has been measured in a direction perpendicular to the curvilinear boundary of the jet calculated by the method of characteristics), s is the length of the theoretical boundary from the nozzle orifice to the cross section under consideration, $\rho_H$ is the density of the surrounding medium, and $\rho_b$ is the gas density on the theoretical boundary calculated by the method of characteristics.

Since

$$\frac{\rho_H}{\rho_b} = \frac{\theta}{1+\frac{k-1}{2}M^2},$$

then (1.6) can be rewritten as

$$\frac{db}{ds} = 0.135\left[1+\frac{\theta}{1+\frac{k-1}{2}M_b^2}\right], \tag{1.7}$$

where $M_b$ is the Mach number on the boundary

$$M_b = \left\{\frac{2}{k-1}\left[\left(\frac{p_0}{p_H}\right)^{\frac{k-1}{k}} - 1\right]\right\}^{\frac{1}{2}}. \tag{1.8}$$

Since

$$\frac{p_0}{p_H} = n\frac{p_0}{p_{exit}} = n\left[1+\frac{k-1}{2}M_{exit}^2\right]^{\frac{k}{k-1}}, \tag{1.9}$$

a substitution of (1.9) into (1.8) yields

$$M_b = \left\{\frac{2}{k-1}\left[n^{\frac{k-1}{k}}\left(1+\frac{k-1}{2}M_{exit}^2\right) - 1\right]\right\}^{\frac{1}{2}}. \tag{1.10}$$

After some transformations, formula (1.6) becomes

$$\frac{b}{s} = 0.135\left[1+\frac{\theta}{n^{\frac{k-1}{k}}\left(1+\frac{k-1}{2}M_{exit}^2\right)}\right]. \tag{1.11}$$

The rate of increase of the thickness of the boundary layer in the initial region of a jet emerging from an underexpanded nozzle depends only on the operating regime of the nozzle. If the regime is kept fixed, then the dependence of b on s is linear.

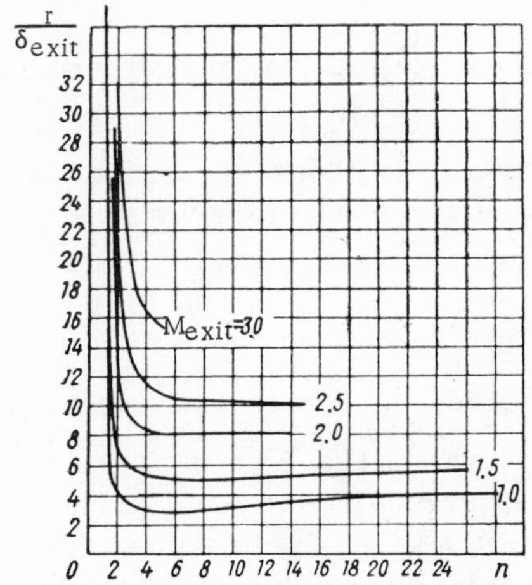


Fig. 13. The dependence of the arc radius for the theoretical jet boundary on the degree of nonsimilarity n for several values of the Mach number $M_{exit}$.

In order to determine the theoretical boundary of the jet, i.e., the boundary for perfect gas emerging from an axially symmetric nozzle with underexpansion, we can make use of the approximate method proposed in [9]. As was mentioned above, the essence of this method is that the jet boundary in the gas-dynamic region obtained by the method of characteristics can be approxi-

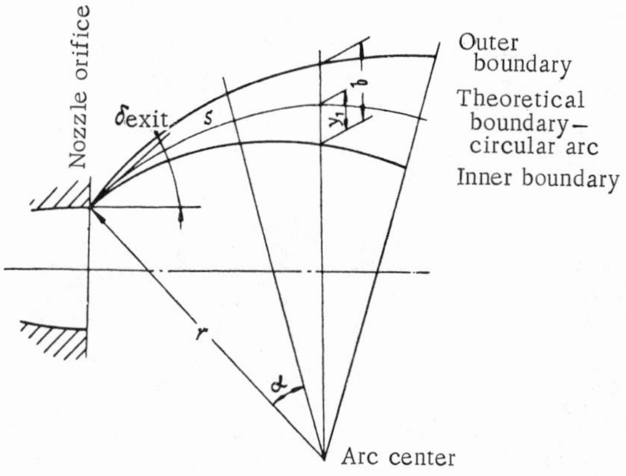


Fig. 14. Schematic diagram illustrating the determination of the jet boundary.

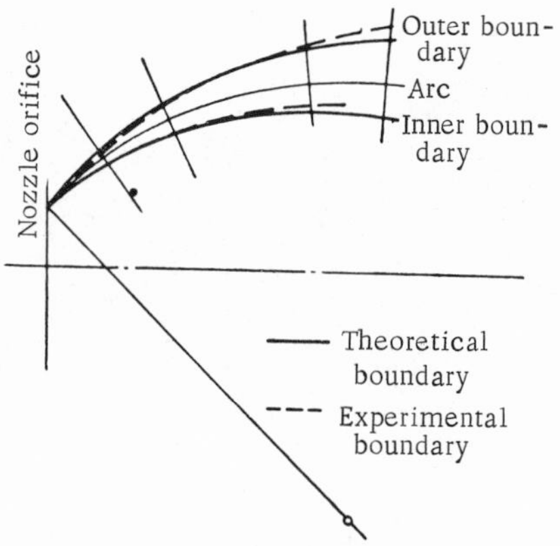


Fig. 15. The boundary layer of a jet emerging from a nozzle; $M_{exit}$ = 1, n=15, $\theta$ = 1.

mated by a circular arc passing through the nozzle and a point at which the diameter of the boundary obtained by the method of characteristics is a maximum. The center of this arc lies on the normal to the jet boundary drawn from the nozzle orifice. The dependence of the arc radius on the operating regime of the jet taken from Love's paper [9] are shown in Fig. 13. The following notation has been used:

r is the arc radius;

$\delta_{exit}$ the angle of inclination of the boundary at the nozzle orifice calculated by the Prandtl–Meyer theory [7, 9].

A schematic diagram illustrating the method used for the determination of the boundary of a jet emerging from an axially symmetric underexpanded nozzle is shown in Fig. 14. Knowing the operating regime of the nozzle, we can use the graph of Fig. 13 to find r and then use Fig. 14 to determine $\delta_{exit}$. Using these values of r and $\delta_{exit}$, we can construct the circular arc which will represent the theoretical jet-boundary. We can then use formulas (1.11) and Fig. 12 to determine b/s and $y_1/b$, where $y_1$ is the distance between the inner boundary of the boundary layer and the boundary of an ideal jet calculated by the method of characteristics.

As a result of this, for each value of the arc length s, where $s = r\alpha$ ($\alpha$ is the angle measured from the first radial line), we can find the magnitudes of b and $y_1$ and, consequently, we can determine the outer and inner boundaries of the boundary layer of the jet.

A comparison of the experimental and theoretical jet boundaries is shown in Fig. 15. This comparison shows that the agreement between the theoretical curves and experiment is satisfactory.

## II. Quantitative Investigations of Jets Emerging from an Axially Symmetric Nozzle with Underexpansion

1. The Geometry of a Jet Emerging from an Axially Symmetric Underexpanded Nozzle. In the usual free turbulent jets emerging from a nozzle under similarity conditions, the pressure in the jet remains almost constant, i.e., the jet widens only on account of the development of the boundary layer, whereas in a jet emerging from an underexpanded nozzle, pressure is higher than in the surrounding medium. If the degree of nonsimilarity is not high and lies within the limits $0.8 < n < 1.2$, then, as was pointed out above, the influence of the pressure difference on the development of the jet is negligibly small and the jet widens in the first place on account of the increase in the thickness of the boundary layer. In this case, the boundary of the jet is almost linear as in the case of usual turbulent free jets. When the degree of nonsimilarity is high ($n > 1.2$), the pressure in the first barrel is

much higher than that in the surrounding medium, so that the jet widens greatly away from the nozzle orifice; the increase in width on account of the broadening of the boundary layer is secondary in this case. The inner and outer boundaries are highly curved near the nozzle orifice.

A schematic diagram of a submerged jet issuing from an axially symmetric underexpanded nozzle is shown in Fig. 16 for high values of n.

The following notation has been used in Fig. 16: u is the local longitudinal velocity in the jet; $u_m$ is the maximum longitudinal velocity in a given cross section; $u_{ja}$ is the velocity on the jet axis; $R_b$ is the radius of the outer boundary of the jet; $R_m$ is the radius of the line of maximum velocity, while in the transition region $R_m$ denotes the radius of the inner boundary of the boundary layer; and $R_0$ is the radius of the core in which the velocity is a constant and equal to $u_0$.

For convenience, it is advantageous to subdivide the jet into four regions:

1) the initial region whose length is w;

2) the first transition region in which a constant-velocity core still exists;

3) the second transition region in which the axial velocity increases in the direction of the jet, but the maximum velocity in any cross section through the jet does not occur on the axis;

4) the main region in which the axial velocity becomes the maximum velocity in a given cross section.

In the boundary layer, the velocity increases from the outer boundary to the inner one and it can be subdivided into two parts: supersonic and subsonic. Beyond the forward discontinuity the flow velocity is subsonic; the oblique-discontinuity surface makes an appearance beyond the point of intersection of the discontinuities, because gas above point A passes through two oblique discontinuities, whereas below A it passes through one direct discontinuity, so that, consequently, the streams have different velocities. The gas which passes through two oblique discontinuities above point A has a supersonic velocity. Therefore, point A of intersection of the two density discontinuities marks the beginning of an annular zone in which intermixing of the subsonic and supersonic streams takes place. From the shadow photograph shown in Fig. 1, we see that the mixing zone developes rapidly. The tangential velocity discontinuity delineating the separation between the subsonic and supersonic flows becomes rapidly smoothed out. At high values of n, the diameter of the forward discontinuity is sufficiently large and the boundary layer at the end of the first barrel of the jet is strongly developed. Therefore, at the end of the first region, the zone between the outer boundary of the boundary layer and the region in which the supersonic and subsonic streams intermix becomes very narrow. In this zone, the velocity decreases from its value on the inner boundary of the boundary layer in both directions – to its value in the subsonic core and to zero on the outer boundary.

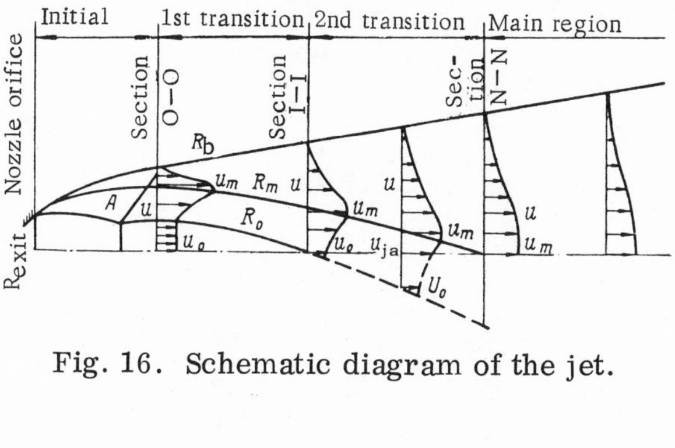


Fig. 16. Schematic diagram of the jet.

After the initial region, the jet in general will have a curvilinear boundary, but its curvature is small.

2. Basic Assumptions. The following assumptions were adopted for the derivation of the equations to be used for the calculation of the velocities in a jet emerging from an axially symmetric underexpanded nozzle:

1) for $n>2$, it was assumed that the static pressure in the jet after the first barrel is equal to the pressure $p_H$ in the surrounding medium;

2) the velocity of flow behind the central forward discontinuity is constant and equal to the axial velocity;

3) the constant-velocity core at the end of the initial region has the same diameter as the zone of the central forward discontinuity, while the velocity is equal to the velocity behind the forward discontinuity;

4) after the initial region, the inner boundary coincides with the line of maximum velocity;

5) the transverse velocity distributions in the zone situated between the outer boundary of the jet and the maximum-velocity line, and the zone lying between the maximum-velocity line and the constant-velocity core can be described by Schlichting's formulas,

$$\frac{u-u_0}{u_m-u_0}=(1-\xi^{1.5})^2, \tag{2.1}$$

where

$$\xi=\frac{R_m-R}{R_m-R_0} \quad \text{for } R_0 \leqslant R \leqslant R_m \tag{2.2}$$

and

$$\frac{u}{u_m}=(1-\xi^{1.5})^2 \tag{2.3}$$

where

$$\xi=\frac{R-R_m}{R_b-R_m} \tag{2.4}$$

for $R_m \leq R \leq R_b$.

6) in the boundary layer of the jet, i.e., in the zone situated between the jet outer boundary and the maximum-velocity line, the variation in the temperature of the retarded stream can be described by

$$\frac{T_0^*-T^*}{T_0^*-T_H}=1-\eta, \tag{2.5}$$

where

$$\eta=\frac{R-R_b}{R_m-R_b}, \tag{2.6}$$

$T_0^*$ is the temperature of the retarded stream in the receiver, $T_H$ is the temperature of the retarded stream in the surrounding medium, and $T^*$ is the local temperature of the retarded stream in the jet.

From Eqs. (2.4) and (2.6) we have

$$\eta=1-\xi. \tag{2.7}$$

With the exception of the outer boundary layer ($R > R_m$), the temperature in the jet is everywhere the same and equal to $T_0^*$.

We can make the following remarks concerning these assumptions. As shown by experiments, the static pressure beyond the initial region of the jet deviates slightly from that in the surrounding medium for all operating regimes of the nozzle except the regime $n \approx 2$, but this deviation does not exceed 20%; pressure oscillations along the jet axis are larger than those along any other line parallel to the axis, but they are quickly damped out; for degrees of non-similarity lying in the range $0.8 \leq n \leq 1.2$, flow in the jet is almost indistinguishable from similarity flow. Therefore, the first assumption will not introduce large errors.

The final cross section of the initial region of the jet is situated close to the position of the central forward discontinuity, so that prior to the section 0–0 the zone of intermixing of the supersonic and subsonic flows which begin at the point A has not yet developed. The thickness of the mixing zone in the cross section 0–0 is very small by comparison with the diameter of the constant-velocity core, so that the difference between the constant-velocity core and the diameter of the central discontinuity can be neglected.

There is no boundary layer in a jet of perfect gas. The results of calculations obtained by the method of characteristics show that the maximum velocity in the initial region occurs on the jet boundary. A boundary layer is formed in a jet of real gas; it is clear that until the second oblique discontinuity, the maximum velocity is to be found on the inner boundary of the boundary layer. The second oblique discontinuity is of variable intensity. Graphs of density distributions obtained by means of an interferometer clearly show that the intensity of the second oblique discontinuity increases as point A is approached, while the boundary to the supersonic part of the jet lies inside the boundary layer. On the basis of these arguments, we can conclude that beyond the initial region, the velocity maximum lies on the inner boundary of the boundary layer.

It is known from experiment that in both the initial and main regions of the jet the longitudinal velocity profile across the jet is well approximated by Schlichting's formula. As has already been pointed out, the zone between the constant-velocity core and the boundary layer of the jet is relatively narrow, so that the approximation of the true velocity profile by Schlichting's formula should not give rise to a large error.

The transition region of the jet is similar to the initial region of the usual free turbulent jet where the temperature of the retarded stream is constant in the boundary layer. There is no reason for not accepting this assumption in the case under consideration.

3. The First Transition Region. In order to determine the maximum velocity in any cross section of the jet, we will make use of the equation of conservation of momentum (between the nozzle orifice and an arbitrary cross section of the jet) which can be written as

$$\pi R_{\text{exit}}^2[\rho_{\text{exit}}\, u_{\text{exit}}^2 + p_{\text{exit}}] = 2\pi \int_0^{R_b} \rho u^2 R\,dR + 2\pi \int_0^{R_b} pR\,dR - \pi (R_b^2 - R_{\text{exit}}^2) p_H, \tag{2.8}$$

where $\rho$ is the local density in the jet, $\rho_{\text{exit}}$ is the air density at the nozzle orifice, u is the local velocity, and $u_{\text{exit}}$ is the velocity at the nozzle orifice.

On the basis of the first assumption, we can conclude that beyond the initial region the local pressure p is equal to the pressure of the surrounding medium $p_H$, i.e., $p = p_H$.

Equation (2.8) can then be simplified to

$$R_{\text{exit}}^2 (\rho_{\text{exit}}\, u_{\text{exit}}^2 + p_{\text{exit}} - p_H) = 2 \int_0^{R_b} \rho u^2 R\,dR. \tag{2.9}$$

Let $\bar{R}$ denote a dimensionless radius, so that

$$\bar{R}=\frac{R}{R_{exit}}, \qquad \bar{R}_b=\frac{R_b}{R_{exit}}, \qquad \bar{R}_m=\frac{R_m}{R_{exit}}, \qquad \bar{R}_0=\frac{R_0}{R_{exit}}.$$

Equation (2.9) can be rewritten as

$$\rho_{exit}u^2_{exit}+p_{exit}-p_H=2\int_0^{\bar{R}_b}\rho u^2\bar{R}d\bar{R}$$

or

$$\frac{p_{exit}u^2_{exit}}{gJc_p\left(\frac{k-1}{k}\right)T_{exit}}+p_{exit}-p_H=2\int_0^{\bar{R}_b}\frac{p_H u^2}{gJc_p\left(\frac{k-1}{k}\right)T}\bar{R}d\bar{R},$$

where J is the mechanical equivalent of heat (J = 427 kg/kcal), and g is the acceleration due to gravity.

After some transformation, we obtain

$$\frac{k}{4}\left[nM^2_{exit}+\frac{n-1}{k}\right]=\int_0^{\bar{R}_b}\frac{u^2}{2gJc_p\left(T^*-\frac{u^2}{2gJc_p}\right)\left(\frac{k-1}{k}\right)}\bar{R}d\bar{R}, \tag{2.10}$$

where

$$n=\frac{p_{exit}}{p_H}.$$

Since the first initial region contains a central core with constant velocity $u_0$ and radius $R_0$, Eq. (2.10) will take the form

$$\frac{k}{4}\left[nM^2_{exit}+\frac{n-1}{k}-\bar{R}_0^2M_0^2\right]=\int_{\bar{R}_0}^{\bar{R}_m}\frac{u^2}{2gJc_p\left(T^*-\frac{u^2}{2gJc_p}\right)\left(\frac{k-1}{k}\right)}\bar{R}d\bar{R}+\int_{\bar{R}_m}^{\bar{R}_b}\frac{u^2}{2gJc_p\left(T^*-\frac{u^2}{2gJc_p}\right)\left(\frac{k-1}{k}\right)}\bar{R}d\bar{R}, \tag{2.11}$$

where $M_0$ is the Mach number in the constant-velocity core and on the basis of the second assumption it is equal to the Mach number beyond the forward discontinuity, namely, $M_C$. Substituting (2.2), (2.4), (2.5), (2.6) into (2.11), we obtain

$$\frac{k-1}{4}\left[nM^2_{exit}+\frac{n-1}{k}-\bar{R}_0^2M_0^2\right]=\int_0^1\frac{u^2}{2gJc_pT^*_0\left(1-\frac{u^2}{2gJc_pT^*_0}\right)}[\bar{R}_m-\xi(\bar{R}_m-\bar{R}_0)](\bar{R}_m-\bar{R}_0)d\xi+$$

$$+\int_0^1\frac{u^2}{2gJc_pT_H\left[1+\eta\left(\frac{T^*_0}{T_H}-1\right)-\frac{u^2}{2gJc_pT_H}\right]}[\bar{R}_m+\xi(\bar{R}_b-\bar{R}_m)](\bar{R}_b-\bar{R}_m)d\xi$$

or

$$\frac{k-1}{4}\left[nM_{\text{exit}}^2+\frac{n-1}{k}-\overline{R}_0^2M_0^2\right]=\int_0^1\left\{-1+\frac{1}{1-\frac{u^2}{2gJc_pT_0^*}}\right\}[\overline{R}_m-\xi(\overline{R}_m-\overline{R}_0)](\overline{R}_m-\overline{R}_0)\,d\xi+$$

$$+\int_0^1\left\{-1+\frac{1}{1-\frac{u^2}{\frac{2gJc_pT_0^*}{\theta}[1+\eta(\theta-1)]}}\right\}[\overline{R}_m+\xi(\overline{R}_b-\overline{R}_m)](\overline{R}_b-\overline{R}_m)\,d\xi, \qquad (2.12)$$

where $\theta=T_0^*/T_H$; $\eta=1-\xi$. Using the abbreviations

$$A=-1+\frac{1}{1-\frac{u^2}{2gJc_pT_0^*}}, \qquad (2.13)$$

$$B=-1+\frac{1}{1-\frac{u^2}{\frac{2gJc_pT_0^*}{\theta}[1+\eta(\theta-1)]}} \qquad (2.14)$$

and substituting (2.13) and (2.14) into (2.12), we obtain

$$\frac{k-1}{4}\left[nM_{\text{exit}}^2+\frac{n-1}{k}-\overline{R}_0^2M_0^2\right]=\overline{R}_m(\overline{R}_m-\overline{R}_0)\int_0^1 A\,d\xi-$$

$$-(\overline{R}_m-\overline{R}_0)^2\int_0^1 A\xi\,d\xi+\overline{R}_m(\overline{R}_b-\overline{R}_m)\int_0^1 B\,d\xi+(\overline{R}_b-\overline{R}_m)^2\int_0^1 B\xi\,d\xi. \qquad (2.15)$$

The expressions for A and B are very complicated and, therefore, the evaluation of the integrals in (2.15) is difficult. In order to carry out the evaluations, we expand the functions A and B in Taylor's series. Formula (2.13) can be written as

$$A=\sum_{i=1}^{\infty}\frac{u^{2i}}{(2gJc_pT_0^*)^i}. \qquad (2.16)$$

Since $u^2/2gJc_pT_0^*$ is always less than unity, this series will be convergent.

Let us now put expression (2.14) into the form

$$B=\sum_{i=1}^{\infty}\frac{\theta u^{2i}}{\{2gJc_pT_0^*[1+(1-\xi)(\theta-1)]\}^i}, \qquad (2.17)$$

where

$$\frac{1}{1+(1-\xi)(\theta-1)}=\sum_{j=1}^{\infty}[(1-\xi)(\theta-1)]^j. \qquad (2.18)$$

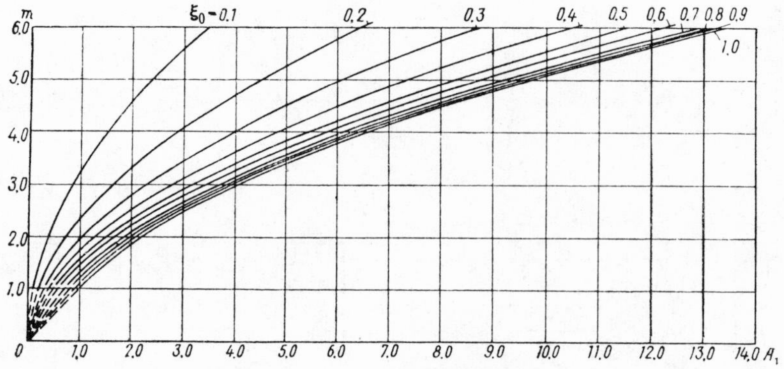


Fig. 17. Auxiliary function.

Since $0 \leq \xi \leq 1$, the series (2.18) will only converge when $\theta < 2$. The series (2.18) is a component of series (2.17) and therefore series (2.17) will only converge when $\theta < 2$.

The value of function A is found by the substitution of expression (2.1) into Eq. (2.16). The integrals appearing in Eq. (2.15) can then be written as

$$\int_0^1 A d\xi = \frac{k-1}{k+1}\lambda_0^2 (A_1)_{\xi_0=1} + \left(\frac{k-1}{k+1}\lambda_0^2\right)^2 (A_2)_{\xi_0=1} + \left(\frac{k-1}{k+1}\lambda_0^2\right)^3 (A_3)_{\xi_0=1}, \tag{2.19}$$

$$\int_0^1 A\xi d\xi = \frac{k-1}{k+1}\lambda_0^2 (A_4)_{\xi_0=1} + \left(\frac{k-1}{k+1}\lambda_0^2\right)^2 (A_5)_{\xi_0=1} + \left(\frac{k-1}{k+1}\lambda_0^2\right)^3 (A_6)_{\xi_0=1}. \tag{2.20}$$

The values of the coefficients $A_1$, $A_2$, $A_3$, $A_4$, $A_5$, and $A_6$ are given in Figs. 17-22 as functions of $m = u_m/u_0$ and $\xi_0$.

Here $\xi$ is the upper limit of the integrals $\int AD\xi$ and $\int A\xi d\xi$, while $\lambda_0$ is the velocity coefficient in the constant-velocity core

$$\lambda_0 = \frac{u_0}{a_{cr}}, \qquad a_{cr} = \sqrt{\frac{2(k-1)}{k+1} gJc_p T_0^*}.$$

The integrals $\int_0^1 B d\xi$ and $\int_0^1 B\xi d\xi$ can be evaluated by the substitution of Eqs. (2.3) and (2.18) into (2.17)

$$\int_0^1 B d\xi = \frac{k-1}{k+1}\lambda_0^2 B_1 + \left(\frac{k-1}{k+1}\lambda_0^2\right)^2 B_2 + \left(\frac{k-1}{k+1}\lambda_0^2\right)^3 B_3, \tag{2.21}$$

$$\int_0^1 B\xi d\xi = \frac{k-1}{k+1}\lambda_0^2 B_4 + \left(\frac{k-1}{k+1}\lambda_0^2\right)^2 B_5 + \left(\frac{k-1}{k+1}\lambda_0^2\right)^3 B_6. \tag{2.22}$$

The values of the coefficients $B_1$, $B_2$, $B_3$, $B_4$, $B_5$, and $B_6$ are shown in Figs. 23-28 as functions of m and $\theta$. Substituting (2.19), (2.20), (2.21), and (2.22) into (2.15), we obtain the equation of conversation of momentum in the first transition region of the jet as

$$\frac{k-1}{4}\left[nM_{exit}^2 + \frac{n-1}{k} - \overline{R}_0^2 M_0^2\right] = \overline{R}_m(\overline{R}_m - \overline{R}_0)\left[\frac{k-1}{k+1}\lambda_0^2 (A_1)_{\xi_0=1} + \left(\frac{k-1}{k+1}\lambda_0^2\right)^2 (A_2)_{\xi_0=1} +\right.$$

$$\left. + \left(\frac{k-1}{k+1}\lambda_0^2\right)^3 (A_3)_{\xi_0=1}\right] - (\overline{R}_m - \overline{R}_0)^2\left[\frac{k-1}{k+1}\lambda_0^2 (A_4)_{\xi_0=1} +\right.$$

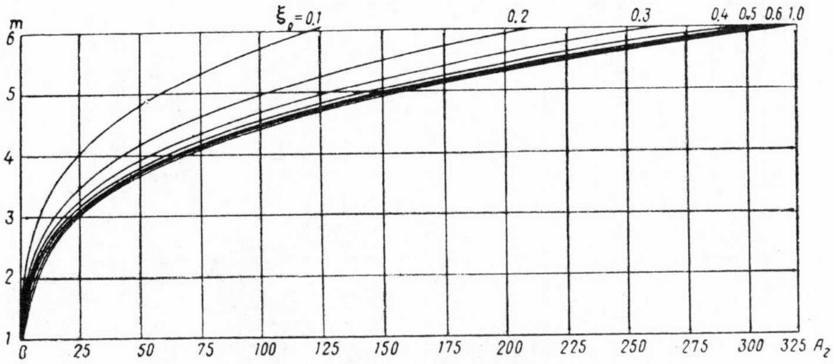


Fig. 18. Auxiliary function.

$$+\left(\frac{k-1}{k+1}\lambda_0^2\right)^2(A_5)_{\zeta_0=1}+\left(\frac{k-1}{k+1}\lambda_0^2\right)^3(A_6)_{\zeta_0=1}\Big]+\overline{R}_m(\overline{R}_b-\overline{R}_m)\times$$
$$\times\left[\frac{k-1}{k+1}\lambda_0^2B_1+\left(\frac{k-1}{k+1}\lambda_0^2\right)^2B_2+\left(\frac{k-1}{k+1}\lambda_0^2\right)B_3\right]+$$
$$+(\overline{R}_b-\overline{R}_m)^2\left[\frac{k-1}{k+1}\lambda_0^2B_4+\left(\frac{k-1}{k+1}\lambda_0^2\right)^2B_5+\left(\frac{k-1}{k+1}\lambda_0^2\right)^3B_6.\right. \qquad (2.23)$$

In Eq. (2.23), the values of $\theta$ and $\lambda_0$ depend on the operating regime of the nozzle. The value of $\theta$ is known for a given operating regime. The value of $\lambda_0$ can be determined from the formula $\lambda_0=\lambda_c$, where $\lambda_c$, the velocity coefficient behind the forward density discontinuity, is determined from the gas-dynamic calculation of the region of the first barrel.

The value of $M_0$ is given by

$$M_0=\frac{\lambda_0}{\sqrt{\frac{k+1}{2}-\frac{k-1}{2}\lambda_0^2}}.$$

Formula (2.23), therefore, contains only four unknowns: m, $\overline{R}_m$, $\overline{R}_0$, and $\overline{R}_b$. As was mentioned above, the pressure in the jet beyond the initial region is almost equal to the pressure of the surrounding medium $p_H$. This means that, starting with the first transition region, the widening of the jet occurs only through the increase in the thickness of the boundary layer. Let us assume that the widening of the boundary layer in the first transition region follows the same law as that holding for the initial region of a usual free turbulent jet emerging from a

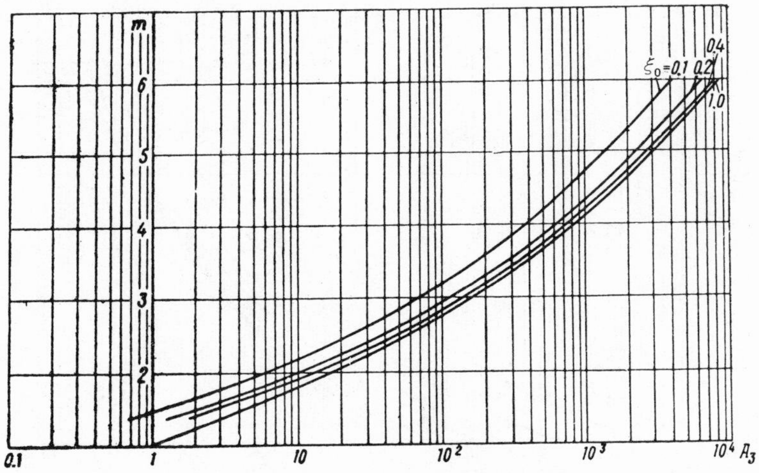


Fig. 19. Auxiliary function.

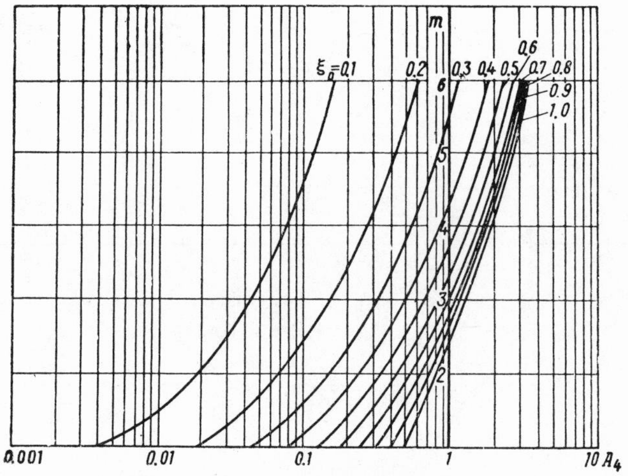


Fig. 20. Auxiliary function.

nozzle in the similarity regime. We can now write down the expression governing the increase in the thickness of the boundary layer of a submerged jet as

$$\frac{d(R_b - R_m)}{dx} = 0.22\,\frac{1+\frac{\rho_H}{\rho_m}}{2}, \tag{2.24}$$

where $\rho_m$ is the density on the maximum-velocity line, and $\rho_H$ is the density on the outer boundary of the jet.

It is known from turbulence theory that the instantaneous velocities at any point of the jet can be decomposed into time-averaged and fluctuation components

$$u = \bar{u} + u', \quad v = \bar{v} + v',$$

where u is the longitudinal, i.e., the main velocity component, and v is the transverse velocity component.

The rate at which the thickness of the boundary layer increases is proportional to the fluctuation component of transverse velocity v'. On the basis of experiments reported in [4],

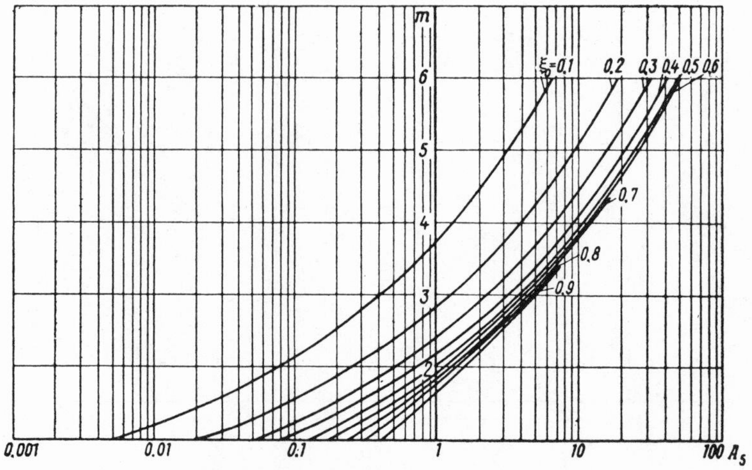


Fig. 21. Auxiliary function.

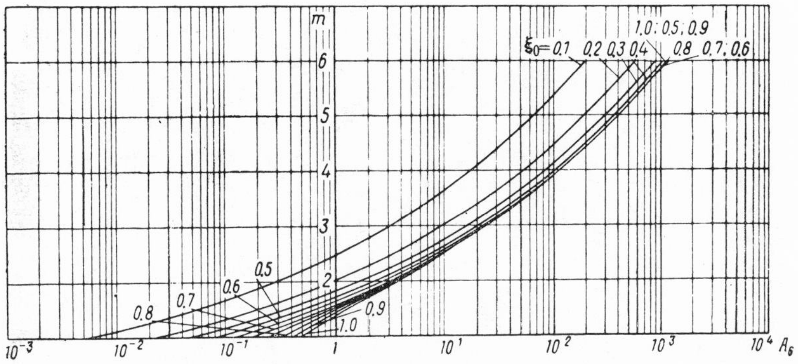


Fig. 22. Auxiliary function.

we know that the distribution of the dimensionless rms fluctuation component of transverse velocity, $\sqrt{v'^2}/\bar{u}_m$, and of the average velocity gradient

$$\frac{\partial\left(\frac{\bar{u}}{\bar{u}_m}\right)}{\partial\left(\frac{y}{b}\right)} \tag{2.25}$$

across the jet are similar to each other. Therefore, the mixing length will also be approximately constant across the jet: $l/b = \text{const}$. In the zone situated between the outer jet boundary $R_b$ and the maximum-velocity line $R_m$ and in the zone situated between the maximum-velocity line $R_m$ and the boundary of the constant-velocity core $R_0$, the dimensionless velocity profiles are similar. Since the zone situated between the radii $R_m$ and $R_0$ lies immediately next to the zone situated between the radii $R_b$ and $R_m$, we have grounds for assuming that the mixing lengths in the two zones will be equal. On the basis of the similarity of the velocity profiles in these zones and the equality of the mixing lengths, we can conclude that the fluctuation components of the transverse velocity will be the same and, consequently, the increase in the width of both zones will be subject to the same laws, which can be written as

$$\frac{d(R_m - R_0)}{dx} = \frac{d(R_b - R_m)}{dx}. \tag{2.26}$$

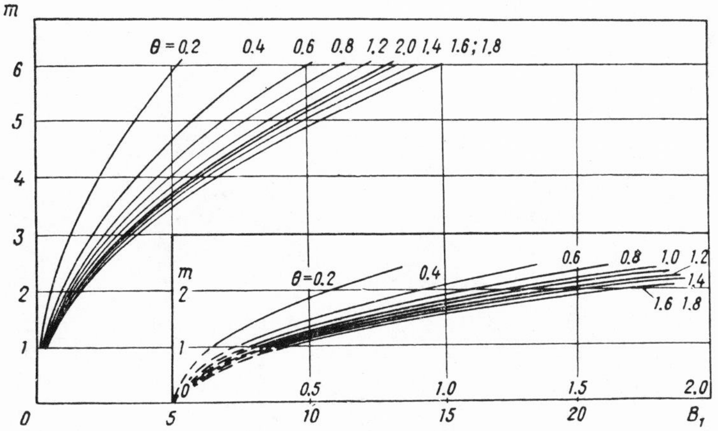


Fig. 23. Auxiliary function.

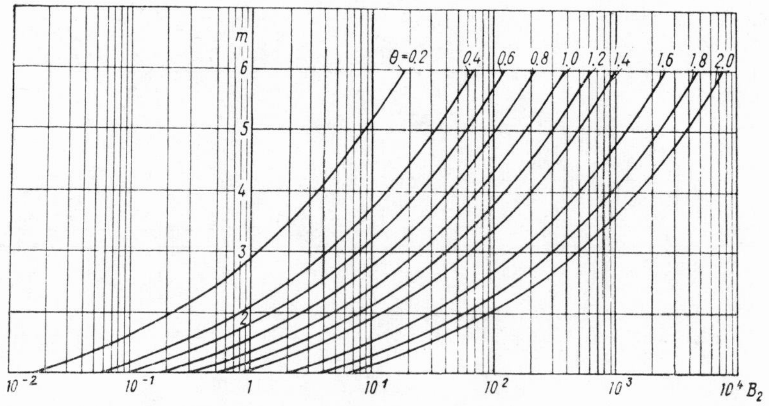


Fig. 24. Auxiliary function.

Moreover, it is known from experiment that the outer boundary of the jet remains linear and then we can write down the following equation for it

$$\frac{dR_b}{dx} = c_b \frac{1 + \frac{\rho_H}{\rho_m}}{2}, \tag{2.27}$$

where $c_b$ is an experimentally determined coefficient which for an air jet issuing from an axially symmetric underexpanded nozzle is equal to 0.117.

Taking into account equalities (2.24), (2.26), and (2.27), we find after some transformation the following equations for determining the various boundaries:

$$\frac{dR_0}{dx} = -0.22\left(\frac{1 + \frac{\rho_H}{\rho_m}}{2}\right); \tag{2.28}$$

$$\frac{dR_m}{dx} = -0.103\left(\frac{1 + \frac{\rho_H}{\rho_m}}{2}\right); \tag{2.29}$$

$$\frac{dR_b}{dx} = 0.117\left(\frac{1 + \frac{\rho_H}{\rho_m}}{2}\right). \tag{2.30}$$

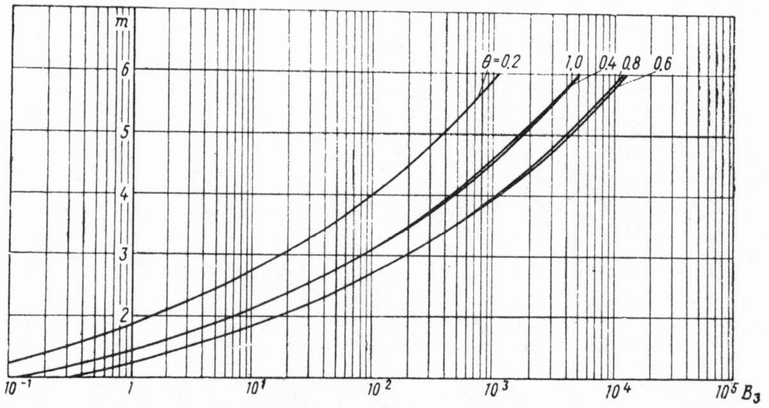


Fig. 25. Auxiliary function.

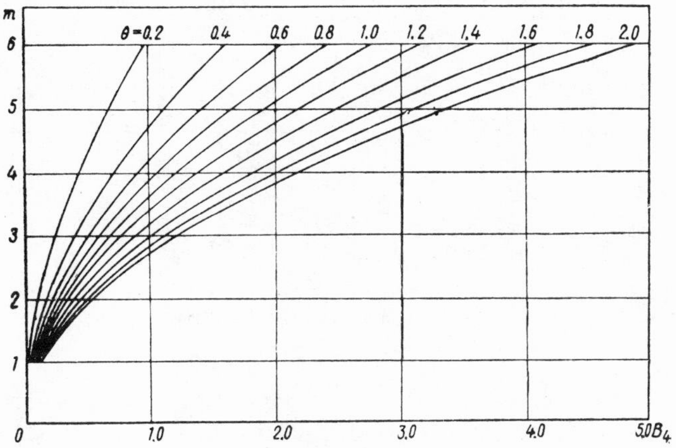


Fig. 26. Auxiliary function.

In these equations $\rho_H/\rho_m$ is a function of the parameters $\lambda_0$, $\theta$, and m and can be written as

$$\frac{\rho_H}{\rho_m}=\frac{p_H/T_H}{\dfrac{p_H}{T_0^*-\dfrac{u_m^2}{2gJc_p}}}=\theta\left(1-\frac{k-1}{k+1}\lambda_0^2m^2\right). \tag{2.31}$$

Substituting Eq. (2.31) into (2.28), (2.29), and (2.30) and integrating, we obtain

$$R_0=-0.323\psi+R_{00}; \tag{2.32}$$

$$R_m=-0,103\psi+R_{m0}; \tag{2.33}$$

$$R_b=0.117\psi+R_{b0}, \tag{2.34}$$

where

$$\psi=\int_{x_0}^{x}\frac{1}{2}\left[1+\theta\left(1-\frac{k-1}{k+1}\lambda_0^2m^2\right)\right]dx, \tag{2.35}$$

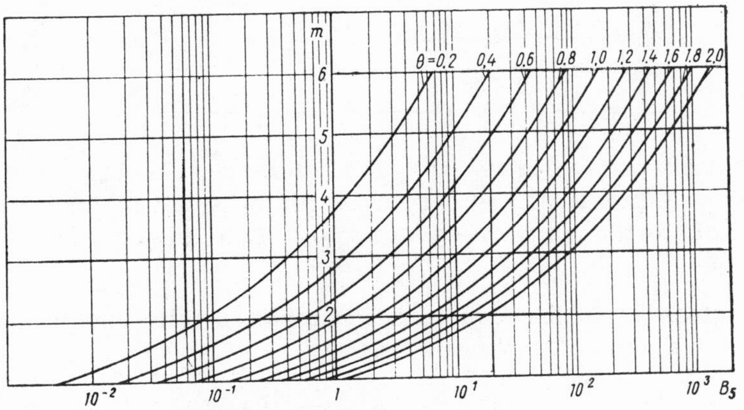


Fig. 27. Auxiliary function.

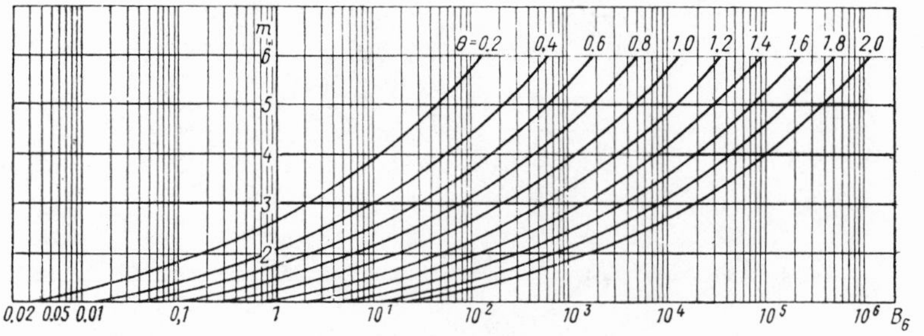


Fig. 28. Auxiliary function.

$R_{m0}$, $R_{00}$, and $R_{b0}$ are the values of the radii in the section O–O of the first transition region of the jet; and $x_0$ is the distance from the nozzle orifice to the section O–O, $x_0 = \omega$.

After substituting expressions (2.32), (2.33), and (2.34) into (2.23) and performing the necessary transformations, we have

$$\frac{k-1}{4}\left[nM^2_{\text{exit}}+\frac{n-1}{k}\right]=a\psi^2+b\psi+c, \tag{2.36}$$

where

$$a=-0.0227\,(a_1+b_1)-0.0484\,(a_2-b_2)+0.0261\,\frac{(k-1)\,\lambda_0^2}{\frac{k+1}{2}-\frac{k-1}{2}\lambda_0^2},$$

$$b=(0.117R_{m0}+0.103R_{00})\,a_1-0.44\,(R_{m0}-R_{00})\,a_2+(0.323R_{m0}-0.103R\quad)\,b_1+$$

$$+0.44(R_{b0}-R_{m0})\,b_2-0.1615\,\frac{(k-1)\,\lambda_0^2R_{00}}{\frac{k+1}{2}-\frac{k-1}{2}\lambda_0^2},$$

$$c=R_{m0}\,(R_{m0}-R_{00})\,a_1-(R_{m0}-R_{00})^2a_2+R_{m0}\,(R_{b0}-R_{m0})\,b_1+$$

$$+(R_{b0}-R_{m0})^2\,b_2+\frac{k-1}{4}\,\frac{\lambda_0^2R^2_{C0}}{\frac{k+1}{2}-\frac{k-1}{2}\lambda_0^2},$$

$$a_1=\frac{k-1}{k+1}\lambda_0^2\,(A_1)_{\xi_0}+\left(\frac{k-1}{k+1}\lambda_0^2\right)^2(A_2)_{\xi_0}+\left(\frac{k-1}{k+1}\lambda_0^2\right)^3(A_3)_{\xi_0},$$

$$a_2=\frac{k-1}{k+1}\lambda_0^2\,(A_4)_{\xi_0}+\left(\frac{k-1}{k+1}\lambda_0^2\right)^2(A_5)_{\xi_0}+\left(\frac{k-1}{k+1}\lambda_0^2\right)^3(A_6)_{\xi_0},$$

$$b_1=\frac{k-1}{k+1}\lambda_0^2\,B_1+\left(\frac{k-1}{k+1}\lambda_0^2\right)^2B_2+\left(\frac{k-1}{k+1}\lambda_0^2\right)^3B_3,$$

$$b_2=\frac{k-1}{k+1}\lambda_0^2B_4+\left(\frac{k-1}{k+1}\lambda_0^2\right)^2B_5+\left(\frac{k-1}{k+1}\lambda_0^2\right)^3B_6.$$

For the first transition region we have $\xi_0 = 1$, while the value of $\psi$ corresponds to a definite value of m. From expression (2.36) we can obtain two solutions for $\psi$ for each value of m. However, the value of $\psi$ in the initial cross section 0-0 of the first transition region is equal to zero.

It can be seen from (2.34) that $\psi$ increases continuously along the jet. Therefore, we will choose the smallest of the two possible values of $\psi$.

Substituting the value of $\psi$ obtained from Eq. (2.36) into Eqs. (2.32), (2.33), and (2.34), we can calculate the values of $R_0$, $R_m$, and $R_b$ corresponding to the given value of m. For $m = m_1$, we have

$$R_0 = 0 \tag{2.37}$$

($m_1$ is the value of m in the end section I–I of the first transition section).

Next, we must determine the value of x corresponding to the given value of m, where m is an unknown function of x. It is very difficult to obtain an exact evaluation of integral (2.35), so that an approximate method must be used.

With this aim, we subdivide the first transition region into several intervals for each of which Eq. (2.35) becomes

$$\psi_i = \int_{x_0}^{x_{i-1}} \frac{1}{2}\left[1+\theta\left(1-\frac{k-1}{k+1}\lambda_0^2 m^2\right)\right]dx + \int_{x_{i-1}}^{x_i} \frac{1}{2}\left[1+\theta\left(1-\frac{k-1}{k+1}\lambda_0^2 m^2\right)\right]dx = \psi_{i-1} + \int_{x_{i-1}}^{x_i} \frac{1}{2}\left[1+\theta\left(1-\frac{k-1}{k+1}\lambda_0^2 m^2\right)\right]dx. \tag{2.38}$$

Here i is an index which depends on the number of intervals chosen.

Assuming that the length of each interval is small, we find that the increase in the parameter m in each interval must also be small. This allows us to replace m in the integrand of (2.38) by its average value $(m_i + m_{i-1})/2$. As a result of this, Eq. (2.38) assumes the simpler form

$$\psi_i = \psi_{i-1} + \frac{1}{2}\left\{1+\theta\left[1-\frac{k-1}{k+1}\left(\lambda_0\frac{m_i+m_{i-1}}{2}\right)^2\right]\right\}(x_i - x_{i-1})$$

or

$$x_i = \frac{2(\psi_i - \psi_{i-1})}{1+\theta\left[1-\frac{k-1}{k+1}\left(\lambda_0\frac{m_i+m_{i-1}}{2}\right)^2\right]} + x_{i-1}. \tag{2.39}$$

Thus, we can calculate the parameters of the jet in the first transition region from formulas (2.28)-(2.35), (2.39), (2.1), (2.2), and (2.3).

4. The Second Transition Region of the Jet. In the second transition region, the velocity profile becomes more flattened. The velocity on the jet axis increases, while at the end of the second transition region the maximum velocity becomes equal to the axial velocity. The results obtained for the first region can be used for calculating the parameters of the second region. We can use an approximate method for the calculation of the variable velocity along the jet axis. We will assume that the flow in the zone lying between the axis and the maximum-velocity line in the second region is produced by a fictitious plane-parallel stream which has an infinitely wide core with a constant velocity $u_0$ (see Fig. 16). According to this assumption, the boundary of constant velocity $u_0$ can be extended as shown in Fig. 16 and the following relation holds between the rates of increase of the thicknesses of the zones $(R_b - R_m)$ and $(R_m - R_0)$:

$$\frac{d(R_b - R_m)}{dx} = \frac{d(R_m - R_0)}{dx}.$$

Consequently, as in the first transition region, the following relations hold:

$$R_b = 0.117\psi + R_{b1}, \tag{2.40}$$

$$R_m = -0.103\psi + R_{m1}, \tag{2.41}$$

$$R_0 = -0.323\,\psi, \tag{2.42}$$

where the subscript 1 is used to label the parameters in the initial section of the second transition region of the jet (i.e., the section I–I). Let us write down the equation of conservation of momentum for this section,

$$\rho_{exit} u_{exit}^2 + p_{exit} - p_H = 2\int_0^{\bar{R}_m} \rho u^2 \bar{R} d\bar{R} + 2\int_{\bar{R}_m}^{\bar{R}_b} \rho u^2 \bar{R} d\bar{R}, \tag{2.43}$$

which, after Eqs. (2.2) and (2.4) have been substituted into it, becomes

$$\rho_{exit} u_{exit}^2 + p_{exit} - p_H = 2\int_0^{\xi_0} \rho u^2 [\bar{R}_m - \xi(\bar{R}_m - \bar{R}_0)](\bar{R}_m - \bar{R}_0)\, d\xi + 2\int_0^1 \rho u^2 [\bar{R}_m + \xi(\bar{R}_b - \bar{R}_m)](\bar{R}_b - \bar{R}_m)\, d\xi, \tag{2.44}$$

where $\xi_0$ is the dimensionless ordinate of the point in the fictitious jet situated on the jet axis.

In Eq. (2.44), the first integral has an variable upper limit $\xi_0$.

It is known from formula (2.2) that

$$\xi_0 = \frac{1}{1 - \frac{R_0}{R_m}}. \tag{2.45}$$

The magnitude of $\xi_0$ varies from zero to unity. In the initial cross section of the second transition region (in section I–I), we have $R_0 = 0$ and $\xi_0 = 1$. In the end section of this region (in section N-N), we have $R_m = 0$ and, consequently, $\xi_0 = 0$.

As the result of some transformations, Eq. (2.44) becomes

$$\frac{k-1}{4}\left(nM_{exit}^2 + \frac{n-1}{k}\right) = \bar{R}_m(\bar{R}_m - \bar{R}_0)\left[\frac{k-1}{k+1}\lambda_0^2 A_1(m,\xi_0) + \left(\frac{k-1}{k+1}\lambda_0^2\right)^2 A_2(m,\xi_0) + \left(\frac{k-1}{k+1}\lambda_0^2\right)^3 A_3(m,\xi_0)\right] -$$
$$-(\bar{R}_m - \bar{R}_0)^2\left[\frac{k-1}{k+1}\lambda_0^2 A_4(m,\xi_0) + \left(\frac{k-1}{k+1}\lambda_0^2\right)^2 A_5(m,\xi_0) +\right.$$
$$\left. + \left(\frac{k-1}{k+1}\lambda_0^2\right)^3 A_6(m,\xi_0)\right] + \bar{R}_m(\bar{R}_b - \bar{R}_m)\left[\frac{k-1}{k+1}\lambda_0^2 B_1(\theta,m) + \left(\frac{k-1}{k+1}\lambda_0^2\right)^2 B_2(\theta,m) + \left(\frac{k-1}{k+1}\lambda_0^2\right)^3 B_3(\theta,m)\right] +$$
$$+(\bar{R}_b - \bar{R}_m)^2\left[\frac{k-1}{k+1}\lambda_0^2 B_4(\theta,m) + \left(\frac{k-1}{k+1}\lambda_0^2\right)^2 B_5(\theta,m) + \left(\frac{k-1}{k+1}\lambda_0^2\right)^3 B_6(\theta,m)\right]. \tag{2.46}$$

Formulas (2.46) and (2.23) have the same form, with the exception that in (2.46) $\xi_0$ varies between zero and unity, whereas $\xi_0 = 1$ in Eq. (2.23).

The values of the coefficients $A_1$, $A_2$, $A_3$, $A_4$, $A_5$, and $A_6$ are given in Figs. 17-22 as functions of the parameters m and $\xi_0$.

The coefficients $B_1$, $B_2$, $B_3$, $B_4$, $B_5$ have the same values as in the first region of the jet and are given in Figs. 23-28.

Substituting Eqs. (2.41) and (2.42) into (2.45), we obtain

$$\psi=\frac{\overline{R}_{m1}(1-\xi_0)}{0.22\xi_0+0.103}. \tag{2.47}$$

From the system of equations (2.40), (2.41), (2.42), and (2.47), we find that

$$\begin{aligned}\frac{k-1}{4}\left(nM^2_{\text{exit}}+\frac{n-1}{k}\right)=&[-0.0227(a_1+b_1)-0.0484(a_2-b_2)]\psi^2+\\&+[0.117\overline{R}_{m1}a_1-0.4\overline{R}_{m1}a_2+(0.323\overline{R}_{m1}-0.103\overline{R}_{b1})b_1+\\&+0.44(\overline{R}_{b1}+\overline{R}_{m1})b_2]\psi+\overline{R}^2_{m1}(a_1-a_2)+\overline{R}_{m1}(\overline{R}_{b1}-\overline{R}_{m1})b_1+(\overline{R}_{b1}-\overline{R}_{m1})^2b_2,\end{aligned} \tag{2.48}$$

where the coefficients $a_1$, $a_2$, $b_1$, $b_2$ are given by

$$\left.\begin{aligned}a_1&=\frac{k-1}{k+1}\lambda_0^2A_1(m_1\xi_0)+\left(\frac{k-1}{k+1}\lambda_0^2\right)^2A_2(m_1\xi_0)+\left(\frac{k-1}{k+1}\lambda_0^2\right)^3A_3(m_1\xi_0),\\a_2&=\frac{k-1}{k+1}\lambda_0^2A_4(m_1\xi_0)+\left(\frac{k-1}{k+1}\lambda_0^2\right)^2A_5(m_1\xi_0)+\left(\frac{k-1}{k+1}\lambda_0^2\right)^3A_6(m_1\xi_0),\\b_1&=\frac{k-1}{k+1}\lambda_0^2B_1(m_1\theta)+\left(\frac{k-1}{k+1}\lambda_0^2\right)^2B_2(m_1\theta)+\left(\frac{k-1}{k+1}\lambda_0^2\right)^3B_3(\theta_1m),\\b_2&=\frac{k-1}{k+1}\lambda_0^2B_4(m_1\theta)+\left(\frac{k-1}{k+1}\lambda_0^2\right)^2B_5(m_1\theta)+\left(\frac{k-1}{k+1}\lambda_0^2\right)^3B_6(m_1\theta).\end{aligned}\right\} \tag{2.49}$$

Having found from Eq. (2.47) the value of $\psi$ for each value of $\xi_0$ and substituting it into formula (2.48), we can find the value of m corresponding to the given $\xi_0$. With this value of m, we can then determine the corresponding value of x from the formula

$$x_i=\frac{2(\psi_i-\psi_{i-1})}{1+\theta\left[1-\frac{k-1}{k+1}\left(\lambda_0\frac{m_i+m_{i-1}}{2}\right)^2\right]}+x_{i-1},$$

where $x_i$ is the distance from the nozzle orifice to the cross section I-I.

Substituting the known values of m and $\xi_0$ into Eq. (2.1), we can determine the velocities $u_m$ and $u_{0c}$ in each cross section of the second transition region of the jet.

5. The Main Region of the Jet. In the main region of the jet, the maximum velocity lies on the jet axis. In this region, the assumption that the pressure in the jet is a constant is close to reality. The flow pattern in the transition region affects the flow in the main region. In the jet region under consideration, the boundary is curvilinear and at a sufficiently great distance from the nozzle orifice the boundary becomes linear with an inclination of 0.22. In the initial part of the main region, the inclination of the jet boundary varies from a value, equal to the inclination of the boundary in section N-N, to 0.22. According to the theory of a free turbulent jet, the jet boundary is given by the formula

$$\frac{dR_b}{dx}=c_0\left[\frac{1+\frac{\rho_H}{\rho_m}}{2}\right],$$

which after some transformation becomes

$$\frac{dR_b}{dx}=c_0\left[1+\theta\left(1-\frac{k-1}{k+1}\lambda_0^2m^2\right)\right]. \tag{2.50}$$

For the initial part of the main region of the jet, we can find the value of the coefficient $c_0$ as the arithmetic mean of the experimental values of the coefficients for the transition and main regions,

$$c_0 = \frac{0.117 + 0.22}{2} = 0.1685.$$

The equation of conservation of momentum in the main region can be written as

$$\rho_{exit} u^2_{exit} + p_{exit} - p_{н} = 2 \int_0^{\bar{R}_b} \rho u^2 \bar{R} d\bar{R}. \qquad (2.51)$$

After a number of transformations, this equation becomes

$$f = \frac{k}{4}\left(nM^2_{exit} + \frac{n-1}{k}\right). \qquad (2.52)$$

Differentiating Eq. (2.51), we obtain

$$dR_b = \frac{-\sqrt{\frac{f}{b_2}}}{2b_2} \frac{db_2}{dm} dm. \qquad (2.53)$$

Substituting expression (2.53) into (2.50), we can obtain the following formula for the determination of x:

$$x_i = \int_{m_i}^{m_n} \frac{\sqrt{\frac{f}{b_2}} \frac{db_2}{dm}}{0.337 b_2 \left[1 + \theta\left(1 - \frac{k-1}{k+1} \lambda_0^2 m^2\right)\right]} dm + x_n, \qquad (2.54)$$

where $x_n$ is the distance between the nozzle orifice and the section N–N,

$$\frac{db_2}{dm} = \frac{k-1}{k+1}\lambda_0^2 \frac{dB_4}{dm} + \left(\frac{k-1}{k+1}\lambda_0^2\right)^2 \frac{dB_5}{dm} + \left(\frac{k-1}{k+1}\lambda_0^2\right)^3 \frac{dB_6}{dm};$$

$$\frac{dB_4}{dm} = 2\theta\,(0.1665 - 0.1782\theta + 0.1114\theta^2 - 0.0235\theta^3)\, m;$$

$$\frac{dB_5}{dm} = 4\theta^2\,(0.2053 - 0.5459\theta + 0.9231\theta^2 - 0.7242\theta^3 + 0.3553\theta^4 - 0.1017\theta^5 + 0.0129\theta^6)\, m^3;$$

$$\frac{dB_6}{dm} = 6\theta^3(0.7248 - 3.02\theta + 7.1316\theta^2 - 10.1438\theta^3 +$$
$$+ 9.9588\theta^4 - 6.8196\theta^5 + 3.3392\theta^6 - 1.0794\theta^7 + 0.21\theta^8 - 0.0186\theta^9)\, m^5.$$

For a jet emerging from a nozzle with $\theta = 1$, we have

$$\frac{dB_4}{dm} = 0.1524m; \quad \frac{dB_5}{dm} = 0.4992m^3; \quad \frac{dB_6}{dm} = 1.698m^5.$$

It is very difficult to evaluate the integral on the right-hand side of (2.54) analytically, so that a graphical method is recommended for the solution of

$$\varphi(m) = \frac{\frac{db_2}{dm}}{b_2^{3/2}\left[1 + \theta\left(1 - \frac{k-1}{k+1}\lambda_0^2 m^2\right)\right]}. \qquad (2.55)$$

On the basis of (2.54), we can write

$$x_i = \frac{\sqrt{f}}{0.337} F + x_n,$$

where F is the area underneath the curve $\varphi$(m) between the ordinates $m = m_1$ and $m = m_n$.

## Literature Cited


1. L. P. Volkova and M. Ya. Yudelich, "Collision losses in stepped tubes at supersonic pressure ratios," Izv. Akad. Nauk SSSR, Otd. Tekhn. Nauk, No. 4 (1958).
2. G. N. Abramovich, Turbulent Free Jets of Liquids and Gases, Gosenergoizdat (1948).
3. G. N. Abramovich, "Turbulent jets in a moving medium," Izv. Akad. Nauk SSSR, Otd. Tekhn. Nauk, No. 6 (1957).
4. G. N. Abramovich, Theory of Turbulent Jets, Fizmatgiz 1960.
5. N. E. Kochin, I. A. Kibel', and N. V. Roze, Theoretical Hydromechanics, Vol. II, Gostekhteoretizdat (1954).
6. R. Sauer, Compressible Fluid Flow [Russian translation] (1954).
7. A. Ferri, Aerodynamics of Supersonic Flows [Russian translation], Gostekhteoretizdat (1952).
8. T. C. Adamson and J. A. Nicholls, "On the structure of jets from highly underexpanded nozzles into still air," J. Aerospace Sci., Vol. 26, No. 1 (1959), p. 16.
9. E. S. Love et. al., "Experimental and Theoretical studies of axisymmetric free jets," NASA Tech. Rep. R-6 (1959).
10. C. K. Thornhill and P. L. Owen, "The flow in an axially symmetrical jet from a nearly sonic jet into a vacuum," Brit. ARS Rand M, No. 2616 (1962).
11. Pai Shih-yi, Theory of Jets, Fizmatgiz (1960).
12. C. J. Wang, and J. B. Peterson, "Spreading of supersonic jets from axially symmetric nozzles," Jet Propulsion, Vol. 28, No. 5 (1958), p. 321.
13. A. Ferri, "The linearized characteristics method and its application to practical nonlinear supersonic problems," NASA Rep. 1102 (1952).
14. J. Winckler, "The Mach interferometer applied to study an axially symmetric supersonic air jet," Rev. Sci. Instr., Vol. 19, No. 5 (1948), p. 307.

# TURBULENT SUBMERGED JETS OF REAL GASES †

G. N. Abramovich, V. I. Bakulev,
I. S. Makarov, and B. G. Khudenko

The experimental investigations of axially symmetric jets of liquid nitrogen at supercritical pressures were carried out by means of special apparatus, a schematic drawing of which is shown in Fig. 1. The principal part of the apparatus is the high-pressure chamber 1. Its operative section was constructed in two ways. The first variant incorporated a viewing port and was used for visual observations and optical measurements by means of an IAB-451 instrument, while the second variant was used for the measurement of velocity-head and temperature profiles across the jet. The working part of the chamber had an internal diameter of 116 mm.

The present investigation concerned jets of liquid nitrogen (critical pressure $p_* = 34.6$ atm, critical temperature $T_* = 126°K$) issuing into the pressure chamber from a shaped nozzle 2 into gaseous nitrogen. Liquid nitrogen was at a temperature of 80-90°K, heated nitrogen at a temperature of 250-420°K. The pressure in the pressure chamber $p_1$ was kept approximately constant at 40 atm. [Liquid nitrogen was ejected by compressed air from a reservoir with a volume of 0.4 $m^3$. Two systems were used for the nitrogen feed. Cold nitrogen was fed directly to the interchangeable nozzle of the apparatus through the butterfly valve 3. Nozzles with diameters of 5.0, 3.0, and 1.12 mm were used during the experiments. In the other system, the cold nitrogen passed through the butterfly valve 4 into the heat exchanger 5 which was heated by combustion chamber 6 and then the heated nitrogen was supplied to the assembly. An adjustable nozzle 7 was used to maintain constant pressure in the assembly.

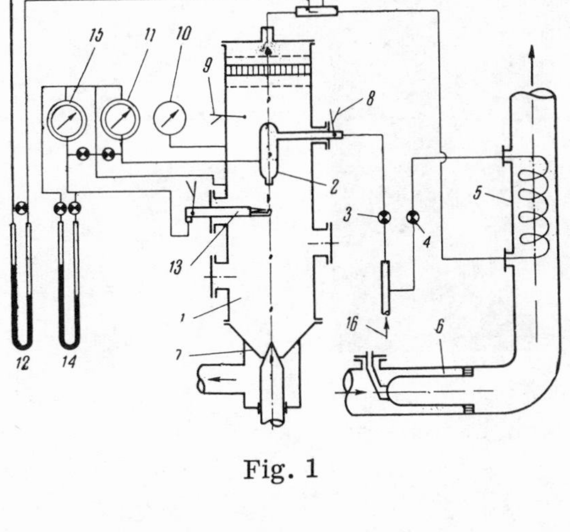


Fig. 1

The following quantities were measured during the experiments: $T_0$, the temperature of the cold nitrogen by means of thermocouple 8 situated at the entry to the nozzle, $T_2$, the temperature of the heated nitrogen by means of thermocouple 9 at the entry into the working part of the pressure vessel, $P_2$, the pressure in this section of the pressure vessel by means of manometer 10, $\Delta p_3$, the pressure drop in the section between the nozzle and the working part of the pressure

† The Russian text of this article was published in Izvestiya Akad. Nauk SSSR, Mekhanika Zhidkosti i gaza, No. 1, 1966, pp. 154-158.

vessel by means of the differential manometer 11, $h_M$, the velocity head at one point of the hot-nitrogen line by means of the differential manometer 12. The velocity head and temperature across the jet were measured by means of a Pitot tube combined with a thermocouple 13, at several fixed points along the jet. The output of this thermocouple was measured by a PP-1 potentiometer. The output of the velocity-head tube was fed to two differential manometers: a mercury manometer 14 used for measuring small pressure drops and a low-sensitivity manometer 15 used for the measurement of high pressure drops.

The width of the jet mixing zone was measured by means of the IAB-451 instrument with the first variant of the working part of the pressure chamber. Figure 2 shows shadow photographs of a cold nitrogen jet and a gas jet with a very small temperature difference (an almost isothermal jet). The outer boundary of the jet is clearly visible in these photographs. The in-

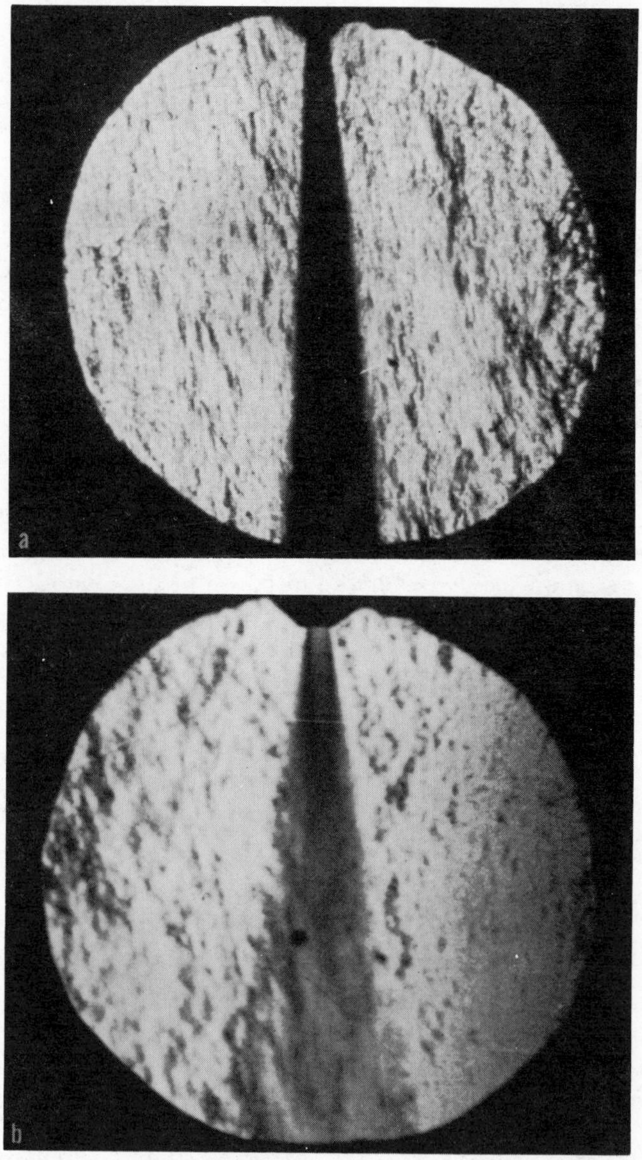


Fig. 2. Shadow photographs of (a) a cold nitrogen jet ($T_0 = 80°K$, $T_2 = 363°K$) and (b) of an isothermal jet.

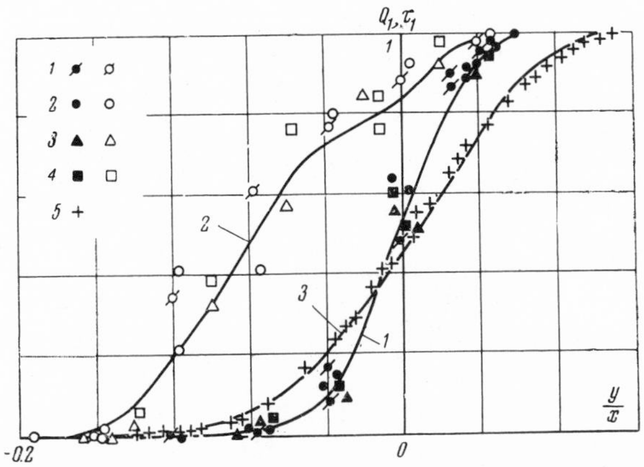


Fig. 3. The velocity-head and temperature profiles in the initial region of the jet. The experimental points (open symbols for $\tau_1$, filled in symbols for $Q_1$) were obtained for the following values of the parameters ($x/r_0$, $T_2$°K, $\theta_2$, $r_0$ mm): 1) 10, 417, 20.8, 2.5, 2) 16.7, 360, 18.8, 1.5, 3) 16.7, 378, 16, 1.5, 4) 16.7, 410, 6.9, 1.5, 5) – – 1.25; the theoretical curves are 1) $Q_1$, $a = 0.0905$, 2) $\tau_1$, $a = 0.093$, 3) $Q_1$, $a = 0.1$.

ner boundary of the cold nitrogen jet is not visible because of the large density change in the jet boundary layer.

The second variant of the pressure chamber was used for the measurement of the velocity head and temperature in several transverse sections of the jet when the emission velocity $u_0$ of the jet was varied in the interval 20-50 m/sec. The variations of Reynolds number across the nozzle exit were included in the range $R = (1.7\text{-}5.8) \cdot 10^5$. The velocity of the parallel flow did not exceed 0.3 m/sec, so that the jet could be considered to be submerged in all cases. The experiments were carried out for two temperatures of the heated nitrogen: $T_2 = (250\text{-}300)$°K and $T_2 = (370\text{-}420)$°K.

In the case of the initial region, the experimental data were processed with the help of the relations

$$Q_1 = \frac{\langle \rho u \rangle \langle u \rangle}{\rho_0 u_0^2} = f\left(\frac{y}{x}\right), \quad \tau_1 = \frac{\langle \Delta T \rangle}{\Delta T_0} = \frac{\langle T \rangle - T_2}{T_0 - T_2} = f\left(\frac{y}{x}\right)$$

and in the case of the main region with the help of the relations

$$Q_2 = \frac{\langle \rho u \rangle \langle u \rangle}{\rho_3 u_3^2} = f\left(\frac{y}{x}\right) \text{ and } \tau_2 = \frac{\langle \Delta T \rangle}{\Delta T_3} = \frac{\langle T \rangle - T_2}{T_3 - T_2} = f\left(\frac{y}{x}\right).$$

Here x, y are the coordinates of the measurement point, $\rho_0 u_0^2$ is the velocity head at the nozzle exit, $\rho_3 u_3^2$ the velocity head on the jet axis, $\langle \rho u \rangle$ $\langle u \rangle$ the averaged velocity head at the point of measurement, $\langle T \rangle$ the average temperature at the point of measurement, $\rho_0$ the nitrogen density at the nozzle exit, and $\rho_2$ the density of the surrounding medium.

The variation of the velocity head along the jet axis has been described as follows:

$$Q_3 = \frac{\rho_3 u_3^2}{\rho_0 u_0^2} = f\left(\frac{x}{r_0}\right),$$

where $r_0$ is the radius of the nozzle.

The velocity-head and temperature profiles in the initial region are shown in Fig. 3. The same figure also shows for comparison purposes the velocity-head profile for an isothermal air jet obtained with other apparatus.

It can be seen from a comparison of the experimental data for the initial region of the jet that the boundaries of a low-temperature nitrogen jet in this region are linear as in the case of the isothermal jet. The width of the boundary layer of the cold nitrogen jet is less than that of the isothermal jet and, consequently, the cold-nitrogen jet has the higher range. The opening angle of the jet is independent of the pressure drop $\Delta p_3$ at the nozzle (emission velocity $u_0$). The profiles in the initial region of the low-temperature jet were found to be affine and fuller than those of the isothermal jet.

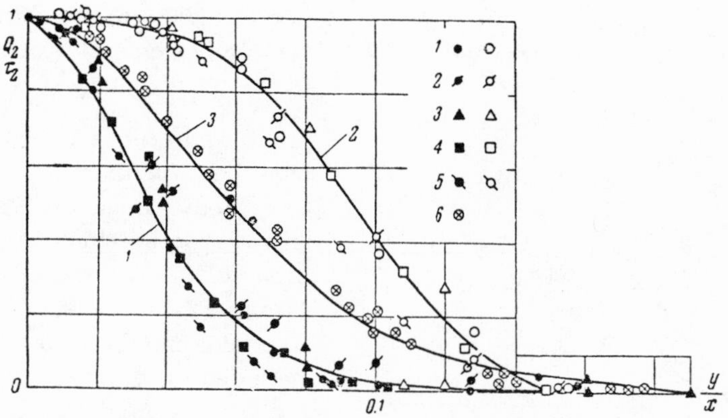


Fig. 4. The velocity-head and temperature profiles in the main region of the jet. The experimental points (open symbols for $\tau_1$, filled in symbols for $Q_1$) were obtained for the following values of the parameters ($x/r_0$, $T_2$°K, $\theta_2$, $r_0$ mm): 1) 49.4, 250, 8.09, 1.5, 2) 49.4, 230, 7.37, 1.5, 3) 44.6, 282, 7.84, 0.56, 4) 34.7, 287, 10.4, 1.5, 5) 34.7, 404, 15.1, 1.5, 6) – – 1, 1.5; the theoretical curves are: 1) $Q_2$, $a = 0.07$, 2)) $\tau_2$, $a = 0.0665$, 3) $Q_2$, $a = 0.08$.

On the basis of experimental data (Figs. 2, 3), we can say that at supercritical pressures the liquid nitrogen jet qualitatively behaves in the same manner as the usual gas jet [1]. In other words, in the case of a liquid nitrogen jet (temperature below the critical temperature) propagating in a medium consisting of gaseous nitrogen (temperature above the critical temperature), mixing in the nonisothermal boundary layer at supercritical pressures occurs without the formation of droplets.

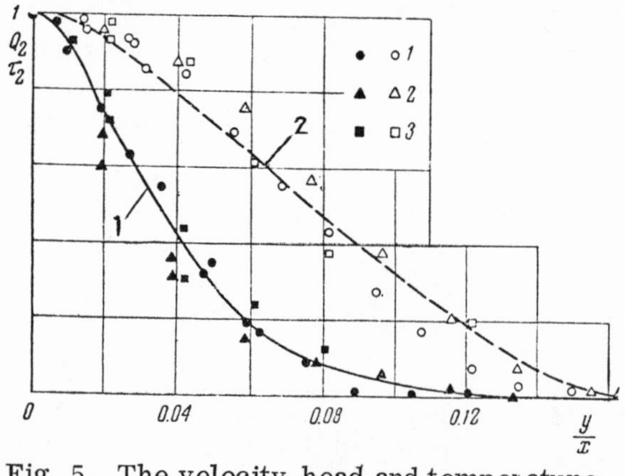


Fig. 5. The velocity-head and temperature profiles in the main region of the jet. The experimental points (open symbols for $\tau_2$, filled in symbols for $Q_2$) were obtained for the following values of the parameters ($x/r_0$, $T_2$°K, $\theta_2$, r mm): 1) 132, 389, 1.97, 0.56, 2) 92.8, 408, 3.2, 0.56, 3) 66.7, 200, 2.71, 1.5; the theoretical curves are: 1) $Q_2$, $a = 0.067$, 2) $\tau_2$, $a = 0.064$.

The figures showing the experimental velocity-head and temperature profiles for the initial region of the jet also show the corresponding theoretical profiles calculated from the equations given in [2].

The theoretical profiles were fitted to the experimental points with the help of the experimental constant $a$. The turbulent Prandtl number was chosen such that the values of the coefficient $a$ for the dynamic and thermal profiles were as close as possible to each other. It was assumed for the isothermal jet that $a = 0.1$. In the case of the cold nitrogen jet with Prandtl number $P = 0.87$, the value of the coefficient $a$ for the velocity-head profile ($a = 0.0905$) was only a little different from its value for the temperature profile ($a = 0.093$). With these values of the coefficients, the theoretical profiles were in satisfactory agreement with the experimental points.

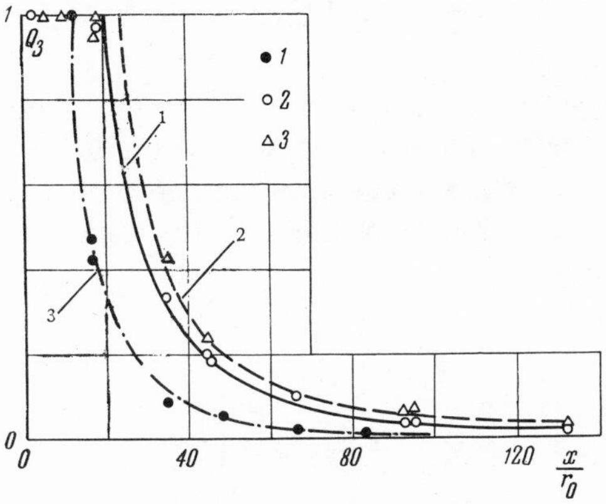


Fig. 6. Variation of the velocity head along the jet. The experimental points are: 1) $\rho_2/\rho_0 = 1$, $T_2 = 280°K$, 2) 0.061, 280°K, 3) 0.039, 400°K; the theoretical curves are: 1) $\rho_2/\rho_0 = 0.061$, $a = 0.072$, 2) 0.039, 0.072, 3) 1, 0.083.

The values of the experimental coefficient $a$ obtained above indicate that its magnitude does not remain constant, but varies somewhat with a sufficiently large change in the relative density $\theta_2 = \rho_0/\rho_2$, which in our case changed from $\theta_2 = 1$ for the isothermal jet to $\theta_2 = 20$ for the cold nitrogen jet.

The velocity-head and temperature profiles obtained for the main region of the jet are shown in Figs. 4 and 5. The velocity-head profile for an isothermal jet is given in Fig. 4 for comparison purposes.

As can be seen from these data, the velocity-head profiles for the main region of the jet are not affine.

According to the experimental data, the main region of the cold nitrogen jet can be roughly subdivided into two subregions: the first region has a density ratio $\theta_2 = 15$–$8$ (at the beginning of the main region; see Fig. 4) and the second has a density ratio $\theta_2 = 4$–$2$ (at a greater distance from the nozzle; see Fig. 5). The profiles for the first regions are fuller by comparison with those for the second region. This can be seen most clearly from the temperature profiles.

The relative width of the main region of the cold nitrogen jet is less than that of the isothermal jet.

On the basis of the experiments performed, we can say that the profiles change along the jet and at a sufficiently large distance from the nozzle they approach the profiles for an isothermal jet. The relative width increases with distance away from the nozzle and also approaches its value for an isothermal jet.

Thus, the experimental data confirm the assumption normally made for theoretical calculations that the profiles vary with position along a jet of real gas [2, 3].

The velocity-head and temperature profiles for the main region of an axially symmetric cold nitrogen jet were calculated on the basis of [3]. The comparison of the theoretical profiles with the experimental ones has been made with the help of the experimental coefficient a in the same manner as was done for the initial region. For a jet with Prandtl number $P = 0.87$, the values of the coefficient $a$ for dynamic profiles ($a = 0.07$–$0.067$) and for thermal profiles ($a = 0.0665$–$0.064$) are found to be approximately the same. The theoretical profiles obtained with the given value of $a$ are in satisfactory agreement with experimental data. The value of $a$ chosen for the isothermal jet was $a = 0.08$. As in the initial region, the coefficient $a$ is not a constant but varies within relatively narrow limits when there is a significant change in the initial density ratio. This variation in the value of the coefficient $a$ as a function of the initial temperature ratio $T_0/T_2$ can be explained if it is assumed that the approximate theory given in [2, 3] does not take account of all factors influencing the deformation of profiles and the position of the jet boundary.

The variation of the relative velocity-head along the main region of a cold nitrogen jet is shown in Fig. 6 for several temperatures of the surrounding medium, $T_2$, together with the relative velocity head in isothermal jets. As can be seen from this figure, the range of the cold-nitrogen jet is greater than that of the isothermal jet. The smaller the temperature ratio

$T_0/T_2$, the smaller the opening angle of the jet and, therefore, the greater the range of the jet. The opening angle is independent of the emission velocity $u_0$.

The comparison of the experimental data with the results of theoretical calculations carried out on the basis of [3] shows that the values of the experimental coefficient $a$ for the velocity head along the jet axis are little different from the values of the corresponding coefficient obtained from measurements across the jet. The theoretical variation of the velocity head along the jet axis is in satisfactory agreement with experimental data.

## Literature Cited

1. G. N. Abramovich, Theory of Turbulent Jets, Fizmatgiz, 1960.
2. V. I. Bakulev, "The calculation of turbulent submerged jets of real gases," Inzh. Zh., Vol. 1, No. 3 (1961).
3. V. I. Bakulev, "The calculation of the main region of a turbulent axially symmetric jet of real gas," Inzh.-Fiz. Zh., Vol. 7, No. 10 (1964).